Analysis of Changes
NEC-2008

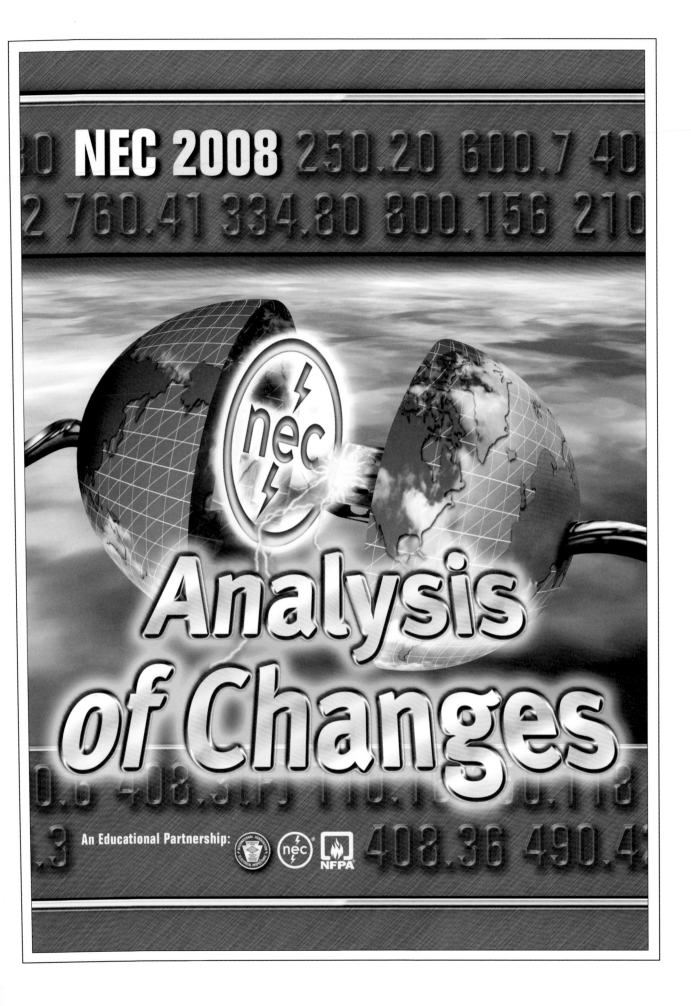

Copyright © 1978, 1980, 1983, 1986, 1989, 1992, 1995, 1998, 2001, 2004, 2007 by
International Association of Electrical Inspectors
901 Waterfall Way, Suite 602
Richardson, TX 75080-7702

ISBN: 1-890659-45-2

Library of Congress Control Number: 2007931156

Notice to the Reader

This book has not been processed in accordance with NFPA Regulations Governing Committee Projects. Therefore, the text and commentary in it shall not be considered the official position of the NFPA or any of its committees and shall not be considered to be, nor relied upon as a formal interpretation of the meaning or intent of any specific provision or provisions of the 2008 edition of NFPA 70, *National Electrical Code.*[1]

Publishers do not warrant or guarantee any of the products described herein or perform any independent analysis in connection with any of the product information contained herein. Publisher does not assume, and expressly disclaims, any obligation to obtain and include information referenced in this work.

The reader is expressly warned to consider carefully and adopt all safety precautions that might be indicated by the activities described herein and to avoid all potential hazards. By following the instructions contained herein, the reader willingly assumes all risks in connection with such instructions.

THE PUBLISHERS MAKE NO REPRESENTATIONS OR WARRANTIES OF ANY KIND, INCLUDING, BUT NOT LIMITED TO, THE IMPLIED WARRANTIES OF FITNESS FOR PARTICULAR PURPOSE, MERCHANTABILITY OR NON-INFRINGEMENT, NOR ARE ANY SUCH REPRESENTATIONS IMPLIED WITH RESPECT TO SUCH MATERIAL. THE PUBLISHERS SHALL NOT BE LIABLE FOR ANY SPECIAL, INCIDENTAL, CONSEQUENTIAL OR EXEMPLARY DAMAGES RESULTING, IN WHOLE OR IN PART, FROM THE READER'S USES OF OR RELIANCE UPON THIS MATERIAL.

[1] *National Electrical Code* and *NEC* are registered trademarks of the National Fire Protection Association, Inc., Quincy, MA 02269

This book conveys the information related to each change as of July 3, 2007, but does not reflect any subsequent appeal or action taken by the NFPA Standards Council.

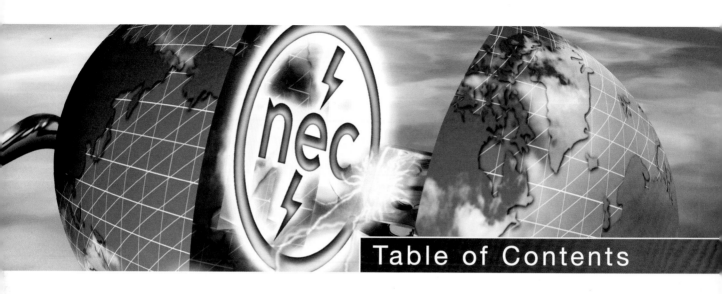

Table of Contents

Chapter 4: Equipment for General Use, Articles 400 – 480

Chapter 5: Special Occupancies, Articles 500 – 590

Preface

This book has been prepared with the objective of providing coverage of major changes in the 2008 *National Electrical Code*. Great care has been taken to select changes that provide the best, most complete information and greatest benefit. There were 3,688 proposals and 2349 public comments processed by the twenty code-making panels but this book does not include every proposal and public comment that was accepted nor does it include any that was rejected.

Significant effort has been made to include references to proposals and public comments as part of the coverage of each change covered in the *Analysis of Changes*. The objective is to make it easier to follow the progress of proposed changes and to understand how the change developed and was finally accepted. Proposals and public comments were selected based on the industry impact of the final accepted change. Those that are exactly the same or that made the same type of recommendation have not all been included because several of the covered changes had multiple proposals or comments associated with them. In those cases, the selection was made to provide the reader with sufficient information to show action on the change from start to final acceptance. Readers are encouraged to review the substantiation included with proposals and comments associated with changes to get a more complete understanding of what the submitter intended to accomplish and why the action was proposed. It also helps to understand how the proposed change reaches its final form by following actions and statements made by the *NEC* committees. Users of the 2008 *National Electrical Code* are encouraged to obtain either the electronic form or the printed hard copy of the *NEC Report on Proposals* and the *NEC Report on Comments*. These valuable resources include a more detailed record of each change and provide actual panel actions and statements to help clarify the changes that were accepted.

The *NEC* is continually being revised due to its inherent dynamics, and the focus in recent code cycles has been on making the *Code* more user-friendly. Developing it into a set of safety rules involving a technically complex industry and having that document in a form where it can be adopted by a legislative body to become law is challenging. No compilation of this number of actions would be possible in the short time frame involved in the *NEC* change process without the help of many people. The IAEI code panel representatives who participated by providing useful information that enabled this document to be developed are to be commended for their contribution to the overall work. Individual members of the IAEI staff who worked long hours and through many difficulties should also be recognized: Michael J. Johnston, director of education, codes and standards, contributing developer and technical editor; Michael Weitzel, codes and standards specialist and contributor; John Watson, creative director; Laura Hildreth, research editor; and Kathryn Ingley, managing editor. Their talents combined with their professional training and experience has enabled IAEI to develop and produce progressively superior training material that aids IAEI in achieving its objectives. It is also important to recognize industry contributions of product photos and text review. From all who helped make this document possible, it is hoped that readers will find it to be an important source of practical information regarding changes in the *NEC* and that it is presented in a manner that it is both enjoyable to use and easy to understand.

Article 100

Revisions to sections where the term _neutral_ is used

NEC, Various pages

Proposal 5-36, various proposals to revise sections where the term _neutral_ is used
ROP, p. 26

Comment 5-18
Log 1501
ROC, p. 16

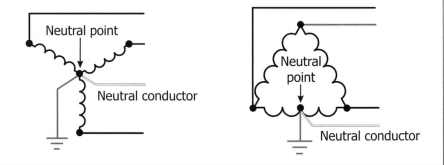

Neutral Conductor and Neutral Point

Neutral point of an electrical system

Neutral conductor

The terms _neutral conductor_ and _neutral point_ have been defined in Article 100. Rules throughout the _NEC_ have been revised and clarified as to when the word "neutral" refers to the neutral conductor of a system or circuit, or when the term refers to the neutral point of system.

Neutral point

Neutral conductor

Neutral point

Neutral conductor

Analysis and Effect

The Technical Correlating Committee assigned a task group with the objective of reviewing the possibilities of defining the term _neutral_ as a result of Comment 1-147 on Proposal 1-122 at the 2004 May meeting, National Electrical Code Committee Report on Proposals. The work of this task group revealed that two definitions were necessary to address how _neutral_ is used in various requirements throughout the _NEC_. In some cases, the word refers to a _neutral conductor_; in other cases, it refers to the _neutral point_ of a system. The two new definitions were the result of the task group's efforts as adjusted by CMP-5 during the Report on Proposals meeting in January 2006. A fine print note was added after the definition of neutral point to provide users with descriptive information.

The two new definitions provide needed clarity where _neutral_ is used in the _NEC_. These definitions help to differentiate between two separate entities that were previously referred to with the one word. The definition of _neutral conductor_ indicates that the conductor is intended to carry current under normal operation. It is important to note that neutral conductors are still allowed to be excluded from the correction factor requirements where the conductor carries only the unbalanced current from the other conductors of the same circuit, as provided in 310.15(B)(4)(a). Another important point to consider is that neutral conductors of power systems are typically the grounded conductor of such systems, but not all grounded conductors are neutral conductors.

Neutral point relates to a common connection point for a neutral conductor connection at the source or system windings. Common electrical power systems with a neutral point include, but are not limited to, a single-phase, three-wire, 120/240-volt systems, or a 208Y/120-volt three-phase, four-wire, wye-connected systems. A three-phase, three-wire, delta-connected system is an example of a system that does not include a neutral point.

Change at a Glance

Two new terms—_neutral conductor_ and _neutral point_—have been added to Article 100; where _neutral_ is used, one of the above terms will replace it.

Code Language
Article 100, Code-Wide

Neutral Conductor. The conductor connected to the neutral point of a system that is intended to carry current under normal conditions.

Neutral Point. The common point on a wye-connection in a polyphase system or midpoint on a single-phase, 3-wire system, or midpoint of a single-phase portion of a 3-phase delta system, or a midpoint of a 3-wire, direct-current system

FPN: At the neutral point of the system, the vectorial sum of the nominal voltages from all other phases within the system that utilize the neutral, with respect to the neutral point, is zero potential.

Various *Code* rules in which neutral was previously used have been changed to read either *neutral conductor* or *neutral point*, depending on what entity is covered in that particular requirement.

Summary of Change

New definitions of the terms *neutral conductor* and *neutral point* have been added to Article 100.

Article 100, Entire Code

New definitions, revised definitions, deleted definition and revised rules throughout the entire *NEC*

NEC, Various pages

Proposal 5-1, 5-2, 5-6, 5-8, 5-9, 5-12, 5-14, 5-16, 5-18, 5-38
Log 160, 1512, 1513, 1515, 1517, 1516,1514, 2933, 3554, 1518
ROP, p. 9, 15, 16, 17, 18, 19, 28

Comment 5-1, 5-3, 5-4, 5-5, 5-6, 5-8, 5-9
Log 990, 1671, 1853, 1221, 2079, 1223, 30
ROC, p. 1, 11, 12, 13

Analysis and Effect

A task group was assembled from an action of the Technical Correlating Committee directives to explore several significant issues identified in Proposal 5-1 and Comment 5-1 in the 2005 *NEC* cycle regarding *grounding* and *bonding* terminology used in the *Code*. As part of the assigned task, the group was responsible for developing proposals for *NEC*-2008 to establish consistent use of all defined terms related to grounding and bonding used in Article 250 and throughout the *NEC*. The following represents the basic scope of the assigned Task Group on Grounding and Bonding.

• To explore issues identified by Proposal 5-1 and Comment 5-1 in the 2005 *NEC* cycle.

• To consider developing proposals for *NEC*-2008 to establish consistent use of the terms grounding and bonding as discussed in the identified proposals and comments during the 2005 *NEC* development process.

• To consider other codes and standards, such as the Canadian Electrical Code (CEC), Part 1 and International Electrotechnical Commission (IEC) 60364 in an effort to harmonize the use of the terms *grounding* and *bonding*

• To consider the interrelationship of the *NEC* with product standards and the National Electrical Safety Code (NESC)

The work of the Task Group on Grounding and Bonding involved several members from Code-Making Panel 5 as well as representatives of various other code-making panels and members of the NEC Technical Correlating Committee. The research and development work of this task group was extensive and took over a year, resulting in several proposals to revise certain definitions of terms related to grounding and bonding in Article 100. The definition of *effectively grounded* was deleted because the term is subjective and there are no specific parameters to use in determining whether or not something is effectively grounded. Instances where it was used in previous editions of the *Code* have been revised to remove the word "effectively" from the phrase. The word *grounded*, by definition, means connected to the earth, which could be made solidly through a resistor or other impedance device. The connection to the earth is not always effective and varies based on geographical location, or seasonal conditions, and so forth. The word "*effective*" is used in the performance rules in Section 250.4 that relate to the effectiveness of the ground-fault current path necessary to facilitate overcurrent device operation, which is appropriate and measurable. The use of the word "effective" in this section remains unchanged.

The task group also performed a global *NEC* analysis to address how each of the

Change at a Glance

Grounding and bonding terms have been redefined and simplified for accuracy. Appropriate code-wide usage has been ensured.

grounding or bonding terms were used in Article 250 and to make proposals for necessary revisions as required. The task group also had the responsibility to address specifically how each term was currently being used throughout the rest of the *NEC*. Where revisions were necessary, the task group developed and submitted proposals to each NEC Technical Committee. In many cases, revisions included specific prescriptive direction in order to clarify for users what is meant by a rule that includes the words "shall be grounded." The changes in this instance often resulted in changing the term *shall be grounded* to *shall be connected to an equipment grounded conductor* where that was the original intention of the requirement. As a result of these changes, simplified and more accurately defined terms related to grounding and bonding are now in Article 100. Where these grounding and bonding terms are used, revisions have been made in the *Code* rules to correlate with their definitions and provide users with clear requirements.

Summary of Change

Definitions of several terms related to grounding and bonding have been revised. The definition *effectively grounded* was deleted, and a new definition of *ungrounded* has been added. Throughout the entire *NEC*, revisions have been made to numerous *Code* rules where grounding and bonding terms are used.

Code Language
Global

Revisions to the following definitions of grounding and bonding terms.

Bonded (Bonding) – Revised
Ground – Revised
Grounded (Grounding) – Revised
Grounded Effectively – Deleted
Grounding Conductor, Equipment (EGC) – Revised
Grounding Electrode – Revised
Grounding Electrode Conductor – Revised
Ungrounded – New

Note: See the actual definition in Article 100 for each revision. Each revised definition will be covered in this text under Article 100.

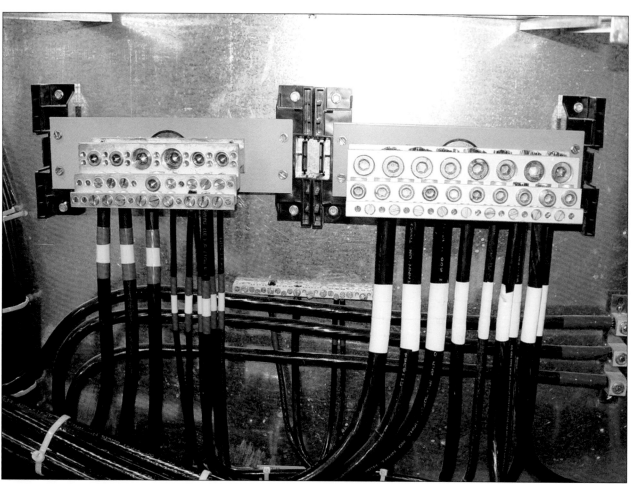

90.3

ii

90.3

Code Arrangement

NEC, p. 23

Proposal 1-6
Log 839
ROP, p. 3

Comment
None

Analysis and Effect

This slight revision adds clarity and improves usability. Section 90.3 is essential to users in that it provides important information about the *NEC* structure, and how the requirements contained within the nine chapters of the *Code* relate to each other and how they are to be applied. Previously, this section simply indicated that chapter 9 consisted of tables, and did not provide any indication of applicability of these tables. The revision clarifies that the information in chapter 9 tables has mandatory application when referenced from other rules in the *NEC*. For example, Section 344.22 requires that the number of conductors in rigid metal conduit shall not exceed the fill percentages specified in table 1, chapter 9. Although this concept was widely understood by many in the industry, the additional text provides clear direction for users about the applicability of those chapter 9 tables and related rules throughout the *Code*.

Chapter 9 includes text and notes to tables that have mandatory application as well. For example, the notes following table 1 provide mandatory requirements that must be applied to installations and systems relating to conduit and tubing fill percentages. The fine print notes that directly follow table 1 apply to this table, but are explanatory in nature as provided in 90.5(C). Although this is only a slight revision, it should provide additional clarity for seasoned users while at the same time providing clearer direction for new users and those learning the essentials of correctly using and applying the *NEC*.

Change at a Glance

- Chapter 9 applies when *NEC* rules refer to its requirements and tables.

Code Language

90.3

Code Arrangement

This *Code* is divided into the introduction and nine chapters, as shown in Figure 90.3. Chapters 1, 2, 3, and 4 apply generally; Chapters 5, 6, and 7 apply to special occupancies, special equipment, or other special conditions. These latter chapters supplement or modify the general rules. Chapters 1 through 4 apply except as amended by Chapters 5, 6, and 7 for the particular conditions.

Chapter 8 covers communications systems and is not subject to the requirements of Chapters 1 through 7 except where the requirements are specifically referenced in Chapter 8.

Chapter 9 consists of tables that are applicable as referenced.

Annexes are not part of the requirements of this *Code* but are included for informational purposes only.

Summary of Change:

The words "applicable as referenced" have been added to the fourth sentence applying to chapter 9.

Chapter

Selected
Changes

Article 100

100
Definitions

Article 100
NEC, Various pages

___

Proposal
None

___

Comment
None

___

Change at a Glance

Technical definitions are the responsibility of the appropriate code committee; general definitions are the responsibility of Panel 1.

Chapter 1 General

> **ARTICLE 100**
> **Definitions**
>
> **Scope.** This article contains only those definitions essential to the proper application of this *Code*. It is not intended to include commonly defined general terms or commonly defined technical terms from related codes and standards. In general, only those terms that are used in two or more articles are defined in Article 100. Other definitions are included in the article in which they are used but may be referenced in Article 100.
>
> Part I of this article contains definitions intended to apply wherever the terms are used throughout this *Code*. Part II contains definitions applicable only to the parts of articles specifically covering installations and equipment operating at over 600 volts, nominal.
>
> **I. General**
>
> **Accessible (as applied to equipment).** Admitting close approach; not guarded by locked doors, elevation, or other effective means.
>
> **Accessible (as applied to wiring methods).** Capable of being removed or exposed without damaging the building structure or finish or not permanently closed in by the structure or finish of the building.
>
> can include varying amounts of combustible gases, depending on the askarel type.
>
> **Attachment Plug (Plug Cap) (Plug).** A device that, by insertion in a receptacle, establishes a connection between the conductors of the attached flexible cord and the conductors connected permanently to the receptacle.
>
> **Authority Having Jurisdiction (AHJ).** The organization, office, or individual responsible for approving equipment, materials, an installation, or a procedure.
>
> > FPN: The phrase "authority having jurisdiction" is used in NFPA documents in a broad manner, since jurisdictions and approval agencies vary, as do their responsibilities. Where public safety is primary, the AHJ may be a federal, state, local, or other regional department or individual such as a fire chief; fire marshal; chief of a fire prevention bureau, labor department, or health department; building official;
>
> **Bonded (Bonding).** Connected to establish electrical continuity and conductivity.
>
> ...or departmental official may be the AHJ.
>
> **Device.** A unit of an electrical system that carries or controls electrical energy as its principal function.
>
> **Bathroom.** An area including a basin with one or more of

Copyright©IAEI 2007

Analysis and Effect

This change in procedure is the result of a TCC assigned Task Group on Definitions in Article 100. This change should have a positive effect on distribution of workloads for the code-making panels and allow for more effective correlation by the TCC. Additionally, this change should result in more accurately defined terms in Article 100 and provide for more consistent correlation of terms throughout the *NEC*. Key terms in the *Code* should mean what they imply, and they should be used consistently with their definitions. This change also promotes consistency with how terms in other NFPA standards are handled where multiple technical committees are assigned to one standard.

The definitions of terms in the .2 section of each article are not impacted by this change in procedure and will continue to be the responsibility of the code-making panel responsible for that particular article. As an example of how this change was implemented, the terms related to grounding and bonding including, but not limited to, *ground, grounded, grounding electrode, grounding electrode conductor, bonded (bonding), bonding jumper, bonding jumper equipment, bonding jumper main, equipment grounding conductor, effectively grounded, solidly grounded, grounded conductor,* etc., will be under the scope of CMP-5. CMP-5 will be responsible for the technical meaning of all terms related to grounding and bonding and any proposed revisions, while Article 100 will contain these definitions.

Code Language
100
Definitions

Applies to various definitions contained in Article 100.

Summary of Change

The 2008 *NEC* development process shifted responsibility for any technical definitions that fall under the scope of certain *NEC* Technical Committees. Traditionally all of the definitions in Article 100 were the responsibility of Code-Making Panel 1. Action by the NEC Technical Correlating Committee (TCC) results in each code-making panel being responsible for definitions of terms that are under their responsibility, but these definitions will continue to be located in Article 100. Definitions that are general in nature will continue to be assigned to Code-Making Panel 1.

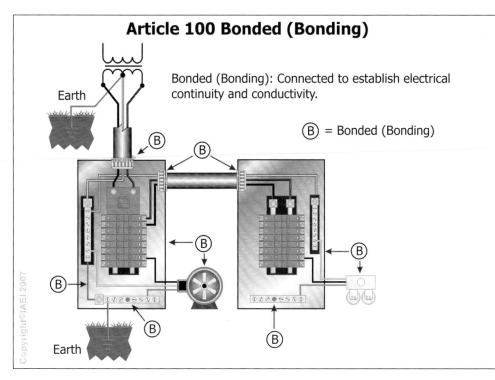

Article 100 Bonded (Bonding)

Earth

Bonded (Bonding): Connected to establish electrical continuity and conductivity.

Ⓑ = Bonded (Bonding)

Earth

Copyright©IAEI 2007

Proposal 5-2
Log 1512
ROP, p. 9

Comment
None

Analysis and Effect

This revision is the result of the work of the TCC Task Group on Grounding and Bonding to keep terms related to grounding and bonding in their simplest form. There must be both *continuity* and *conductivity* between conductive parts that are bonded together. This definition for bonding has been rewritten to apply generally throughout the *NEC*. Specific performance criteria to be accomplished by bonding are clearly provided in Section 250.4 and Part V of Article 250. The purpose of bonding is to connect two or more conductive objects together to: (1) ensure the electrical continuity of the fault-current path, and (2) provide the capacity and ability to conduct safely any fault current likely to be imposed, and (3) minimize potential differences (voltage) between conductive components. *Bonding* is to convey that normally non-current-carrying conductive materials likely to become energized must be *electrically connected together* and to the supply source in a manner that establishes an effective fault-current path. "Normally non-current-carrying conductive materials likely to become energized" include: (1) conductive materials enclosing electrical conductors or equipment, or (2) forming part of such equipment, or (3) other electrically conductive materials and equipment that may present a shock hazard. Specific bonding is required solely to minimize the difference of potential (voltage) between conductive components such as for health care facilities, swimming pools, agricultural buildings, etc.

Code Language
100
Definitions

Bonded (Bonding). Connected to establish electrical continuity and conductivity.

Summary of Change

The definition was simplified to clearly indicate what bonding (bonded) means.

Change at a Glance

Bonding connections ensure continuity and conductivity.

100

Definitions

Branch-Circuit Overcurrent Device
NEC, p. 26

Proposal 10-1a
Log 1259
ROP, p. 10

Comment 10-1
Log 1416
ROC, p. 5

Change at a Glance

Branch-circuit overcurrent devices provide full-range protection for services, feeders, branch circuits and equipment.

Analysis and Effect

Supplementary overcurrent device was introduced in *NEC*-2005 yet there was no definition for *branch-circuit overcurrent device*, which is used throughout the *NEC*. A branch-circuit overcurrent device provides protection for the conductors, and it also provides protection for the entire circuit. Action by CMP-10 incorporated the words "service, feeder, and" into the definition to illustrate that branch-circuit overcurrent devices could be utilized to protect branch circuits, and that these devices could provide overcurrent protection for service and feeder circuits as well. The phrase "circuit conductors" in the original proposal was replaced with the word "circuits" to provide clarification that conductors and equipment were not the only elements of a circuit that could be protected by overcurrent devices. This change clarifies that such devices can protect the entire branch circuit, not just conductors. This definition also provides users with a means to clearly distinguish branch-circuit overcurrent devices that are full-range overcurrent protective devices from supplementary overcurrent devices that are not full-range. Full-range overcurrent protective devices provide protection for services, feeders, branch circuits and equipment, as compared to the limitations of supplementary overcurrent devices that provide only limited protection for specific applications and utilization equipment. This revision promotes more appropriate and consistent application of overcurrent protective devices within the limitations of their intended use.

Code Language

100
Definitions

Branch-Circuit Overcurrent Device. A device capable of providing protection for service, feeder, and branch circuits and equipment over the full range of overcurrents between its rated current and its interrupting rating. Branch-circuit overcurrent protective devices are provided with interrupting ratings appropriate for the intended use but no less than 5,000 amperes.

Summary of Change

A new definition of the term *branch-circuit overcurrent device* has been added to Article 100. The new definition of branch-circuit overcurrent device describes its function and protection applications while providing a clear differentiation between supplementary overcurrent devices that have more limited application.

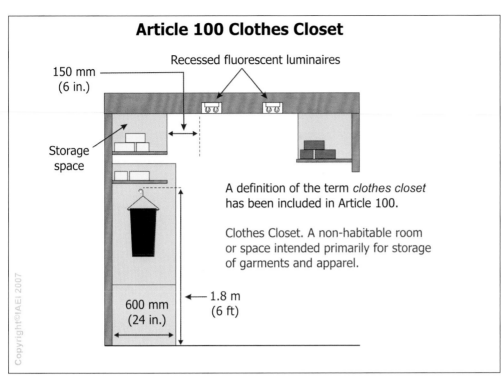

Article 100 Clothes Closet

150 mm (6 in.)

Recessed fluorescent luminaires

Storage space

A definition of the term *clothes closet* has been included in Article 100.

Clothes Closet. A non-habitable room or space intended primarily for storage of garments and apparel.

600 mm (24 in.)

1.8 m (6 ft)

Copyright©IAEI 2007

100

Definitions

Clothes Closet
NEC, p. 26

Proposal 1-20
Log 358
ROP, p. 11

Comment 1-22
Log 2099
ROC, p. 7

Analysis and Effect

The term *clothes closet* is used in the *NEC* and has various requirements that apply to electrical installations within clothes closets such as those provided in 240.24(D), 410.8, and 550.11(A). Without a definition of what constitutes a clothes closet, applying the requirements to such spaces or rooms is subject to inconsistency. If the area in question meets the criteria provided in the new definition, then the rules addressing clothes closets apply. If the area in question does not meet the criteria of the proposed definition, then all other *Code* rules still apply. Some users often desire relief from the clothes closet rules in the *NEC*, but do not want to adhere to the other rules that would apply if the area in question is determined not to be a clothes closet. The word "space" has been added to cover common applications encountered in the field, such as where the closet is in an area or space and not a room. The new definition should provide needed clarity and also promote more uniform and consistent application of *NEC* requirements where clothes closets are involved.

> ### Change at a Glance
>
> A clothes closet is a non-habitable space intended for storage of apparel.

Code Language
100
Definitions

Clothes Closet. A non-habitable room or space intended primarily for storage of garments and apparel.

Summary of Change

A new definition of the term *clothes closet* has been added to Article 100.

This new definition provides users with the basic criteria for what constitutes a clothes closet in order to clarify and distinguish between rules applying to clothes closets and those that have application to areas other than clothes closets.

1

100

Definitions

Device
NEC, p. 27

Proposal 9-7
Log 86
ROP, p. 13

Comment
None

Change at a Glance

Devices carry and control electric energy, but can also utilize a minimal amount of electric energy.

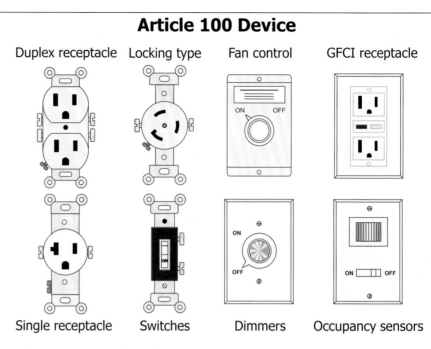

Article 100 Device

Duplex receptacle   Locking type   Fan control   GFCI receptacle

Single receptacle   Switches   Dimmers   Occupancy sensors

Copyright©IAEI 2007

A device is a unit of an electrical system that carries or controls electrical energy as its principal function.

Analysis and Effect

Action by CMP-9 results in revisions to the existing definition of the term *device*. The functional concept of a device has been retained as that is a true description of how a device is intended to operate. The revision clarifies that a device carries or controls electric energy as its principle function, but it could also utilize minimal amounts of electrical energy in normal operation. The effect of this change addresses devices that carry and control electric energy, but can also utilize electric energy. Examples of devices that can utilize minimal energy levels include illuminated snap switches and receptacles, GFCI receptacles with LED function indication, receptacle-type surge protection devices, motion sensors, occupancy sensors, and so forth. The revision allows for the definition to apply to all devices from a functional perspective without excluding what constitutes a device because it also may utilize minimal amounts of electrical energy as a normal function of the device design and operation.

Code Language
100
Definitions

Device. A unit of an electrical system that carries or controls electric energy as its principal function.

Summary of Change

The definition of *device* in Article 100 has been revised to clarify device function and operation. The revision to this definition clarifies that devices carry and control electrical energy as a principle function, but some devices could also utilize small amounts of energy during normal operating conditions.

Ground simply means "the earth."

100

Definitions

Ground
NEC, p. 28

Proposal 5-8
Log 1515
ROP, p. 16

Comment 5-4
Log 1853
ROC, p. 12

Analysis and Effect

This revision is the result of the work of the TCC assigned Task Group on Grounding and Bonding. It was determined that keeping terms related to grounding and bonding in their simplest form enhances clarity and usability for *Code* users. Where any requirements in the *NEC* use *ground*, the earth is the intended meaning in their application. For this reason, the present definition of *ground* has been rewritten to simply describe the conductive body, earth. The purpose of *ground* is to serve as a common electrical potential reference for an electrical system or equipment. The intent of *ground* is to describe the earth for premises wiring systems. The phrase "some conducting body that serves in place of the earth" in the present definition has been deleted because the task group concluded that it leaves *Code* users wondering what that conducting body serving as a substitute for the earth really is. Vehicles such as airplanes and automobiles typically have a metal frame that is used as a reference for the onboard electrical wiring, and this reference is often referred to as *ground;* but in actuality it is not the earth. It also should be noted that these types of installations are not covered by the rules of the *NEC* as indicated in Section 90.2(B). Where the *NEC* refers to *ground* it implies a connection to the earth and not something that serves in place of the earth. The work of this task group also included verification of how the word *ground* is used to ensure consistency with the revised definition and revised those rules accordingly for consistency. Terms such as *ground-fault protection* and *ground-fault circuit interrupter* are not impacted by this revision.

Code Language
100
Definitions

Ground. The earth.

Summary of Change

This revision to the existing definition of the term *ground* has been revised and simplified for clarity.

Change at a Glance

Ground simply means "the earth."

100

Definitions

Grounded (Grounding)
NEC, p. 28

Proposal 5-9, 5-13
Log 1517, 357
ROP, p. 17 and 18

Comment
None

Change at a Glance

Grounded (grounding) means connected to the earth either directly or through a conductive body.

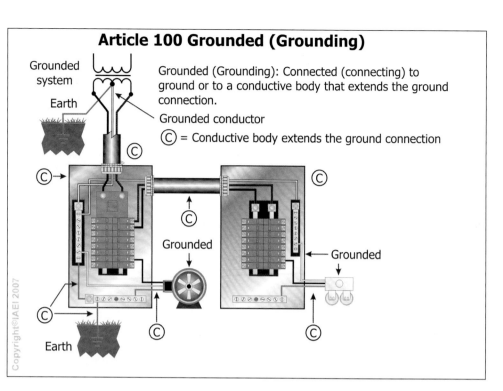

Article 100 Grounded (Grounding)

Grounded system

Earth

Grounded (Grounding): Connected (connecting) to ground or to a conductive body that extends the ground connection.

Grounded conductor

ⓒ = Conductive body extends the ground connection

ⓒ Grounded

ⓒ Grounded

ⓒ

Earth

Copyright©IAEI 2007

Analysis and Effect

The definition for *grounded* has been revised to improve clarity and usability and to accurately describe its purpose and function. *Grounding* has been added with the word *grounded* to describe the action of connecting a system or a conductive part to *ground* (earth). The phrase "… that extends the ground connection" was added to emphasize that the conductive body actually extends the *ground* connection such as the items in 250.118 for the purpose of grounding in premises wiring. An equipment grounding conductor is an example of a conductive body that is an extension of the *ground* (earth) connection. Because *ground* is defined as "the earth," it is implied, by definition, that *grounded (grounding)* is "a connection to ground (earth)." The phrase "some conducting body that serves in place of the earth" in the present definition of *grounded* has been deleted because it does not define what a conducting body serving as a substitute for the earth really is. Where the *NEC* refers to *ground* it implies a connection to the earth and not something that serves in place of the earth or as an earth substitute, such as a vehicle or airplane frame. Where an item is *grounded* it is connected to the earth either directly through a grounding electrode and grounding electrode conductor, or it is connected to the earth through the equipment grounding conductor. The equipment grounding conductor extends the ground (earth) connection.

Code Language

100

Definitions

Grounded (Grounding). Connected (connecting) to ground or to a conductive body that extends the ground connection.

Summary of Change

The definition of *grounded* has been revised to include the term *grounding* and to clarify the meaning of the terms where used in a number of *NEC* rules.

100

Definitions

Grounding Electrode
NEC, p. 28

Proposal 5-14
Log 1514
ROP, p. 18

Comment
None

Analysis and Effect

A new definition of the term *grounding electrode* was included in *NEC*-2005 to establish consistency where the term is used. Establishing a common and simple definition for *grounding electrode* helps users understand what grounding electrodes are and what they are supposed to accomplish. The term d*evice* has been removed because d*evice* is defined in Article 100. *Device* as used in the 2005 definition created conflicts and does not accurately or completely describe what a *grounding electrode* is. *Grounding electrode* has been generalized under this revision as a "conductive object," which is inclusive of all the *grounding electrodes* identified in 250.52(A) that are permitted to be used as electrodes. The concept of establishing and maintaining a *Direct connection* to the earth has also been incorporated in the revised definition. This is an important concept and characteristic of any *grounding electrode*. The *grounding electrode* establishes and maintains a direct connection to earth. While the definition is still general in nature, it is should be understood by *Code* users that only the electrodes identified in Section 250.52(A) are required or permitted to be used.

Code Language
100
Definitions

Grounding Electrode. A conducting object through which a direct connection to earth is established.

Summary of Change

The definition of *grounding electrode* has been revised to clarify what a *grounding electrode* is and how it functions.

Change at a Glance

Grounding electrodes are conductive objects that must establish a direct connection to the earth.

1

100

Definitions

Grounding Conductor,
Equipment (EGC)
NEC, p. 28

Proposal 5-6
Log 1513
ROP, p. 15

Comment 5-3
Log 1671
ROC, p. 11

Change at a Glance

The revised definition and
fine print notes clarify that
the equipment grounding
conductor performs grounding and bonding functions,
in addition to serving as an
effective ground-fault current path.

Analysis and Effect

Action by CMP-5 on Proposal 5-6 resulted in improved clarity and usability of this term code-wide.
This change resulted from efforts of the TCC-assigned
Task Group on Grounding and Bonding to clarify
and simplify grounding and bonding terms in Article
100, and, where necessary, to revise *Code* requirements where the terms are used. The revised definition of *equipment grounding conductor* incorporates
the concept of connecting non-current-carrying metal
parts together, which is bonding, as defined. Fine
Print Note No. 1 recognizes the bonding functions
that are inherent to the functionality of an equipment
grounding conductor; and FPN No. 2 provides users a reference to 250.118, where the list of suitable
equipment grounding conductors is provided. The
equipment grounding conductor has three major
roles in the grounding and bonding scheme
for electrical installations. The EGC provides a
grounding connection to earth for equipment,
thus performing a grounding function. It also
connects the non-current-carrying metal parts
of equipment together and to the system
grounded conductor, the grounding electrode
conductor, or both, which is bonding. During ground-fault conditions, the equipment
grounding conductor provides the effective
ground-fault current path to facilitate overcurrent device operation.

Code Language

100

Definitions

Grounding Conductor, Equipment
(EGC). The conductive path installed
to connect normally non-current-carrying metal parts of equipment together
and to the system grounded conductor or to the grounding electrode conductor, or both.

FPN No. 1: It is recognized that the equipment grounding conductor also performs
bonding.

FPN No. 2: See 250.118 for a list of acceptable equipment grounding conductors.

Summary of Change

The acronym EGC has been
included according to *NEC
Style Manual* requirements;
the definition has been
revised, and two new fine
print notes have been added.

28

Analysis of Changes *NEC-2008*

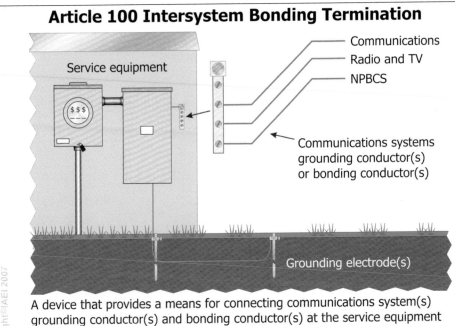

Article 100 Intersystem Bonding Termination

Service equipment

Communications
Radio and TV
NPBCS

Communications systems
grounding conductor(s)
or bonding conductor(s)

Grounding electrode(s)

Copyright©AEI 2007

A device that provides a means for connecting communications system(s)
grounding conductor(s) and bonding conductor(s) at the service equipment
or at the disconnecting means for buildings or structures supplied by a feeder
or branch circuit.

100
Definitions

**Intersystem Bonding
Termination**
NEC, p. 28

Proposal 5-20
Log 1885
ROP, p. 20

Comment 5-11
Log 1670
ROC, p. 13

Analysis and Effect

This new definition was submitted as a companion proposal to other proposed rules that include this term. *Intersystem bonding termination* is included in new rules that now appear in several articles of the *NEC* including Articles 250, 770, 800, 820, and 830, and so forth. Based on the general requirements in Section 2.2.2.1 of the *NEC Style Manual*, defined terms that appear in two or more articles of the *Code* are required to be located in Article 100. This definition is necessary because the term is introduced in new requirements that have been added in Article 250 and chapters 7 and 8. The definition clearly describes a common grounding and bonding termination point that is now required to be provided at the service equipment or discon-necting means for other buildings or structures supplied by feeders or branch circuits. By including a definition of this term in the *NEC*, users and enforcement officials will be able to apply the requirements that use the term in a more uniform and consistent fashion.

Change at a Glance

Intersystem bonding termination describes a common grounding and bonding termination point now required in Article 250 and chapters 7 and 8.

Code Language

100
Definitions

Intersystem Bonding Termination.
A device that provides a means for connecting communications system(s) grounding conductor(s) and bonding conductor(s) at the service equipment or at the disconnecting means for buildings or structures supplied by a feeder or branch circuit.

Summary of Change

The definition of *intersystem bonding termination* has been added to Article 100 as a result of the new term being used in new requirements added to 250.94 as well as to the articles in chapters 7 and 8.

1

100

Definitions

Kitchen
NEC, p. 29

Proposal 1-36
Log 356
ROP, p. 21

Comment 2-5
Log 5
ROC, p. 13

Change at a Glance

A sink and permanent facilities for food preparation and cooking are required for an area to qualify as a *kitchen*.

Analysis and Effect

Action by CMP-1 on Proposal 1-36 along with affirmation by CMP-2 on Comment 2-5 results in a new definition of the term *kitchen*. In general, Section 2.2.2.1 of the *NEC Style Manual* requires that Article 100 contain definitions of terms that appear in two or more other articles of the *NEC*. *Kitchen* is used in various articles throughout the *NEC*. In the 2005 *NEC* development process CMP-2 accepted a definition of *kitchen* as used in Section 210.8(B)(2) as it relates to the application in that particular requirement. Defined terms should have consistent application where they are used in any requirement of the *Code*. The new definition establishes a common definition of *kitchen*, and it includes information about what constitutes a *kitchen*. The new definition provides clarity and improves usability in the *NEC* and should result in more uniform application of rules that apply to those areas or rooms that qualify as *kitchens* by definition.

Code Language
100
Definitions

Kitchen. An area with a sink and permanent facilities for food preparation and cooking.

Summary of Change

A new definition of the term *kitchen* has been added to Article 100. This definition provides a more consistent meaning throughout the *NEC* where the term is used.

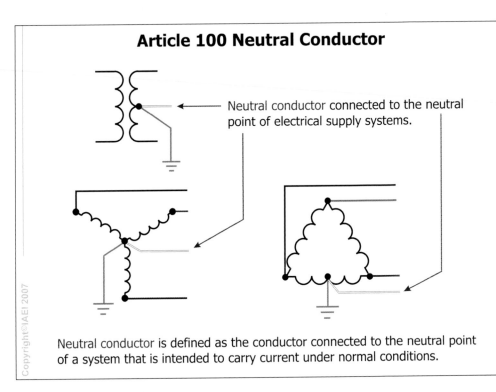

Article 100 Neutral Conductor

Neutral conductor connected to the neutral point of electrical supply systems.

Neutral conductor is defined as the conductor connected to the neutral point of a system that is intended to carry current under normal conditions.

Copyright©IAEI 2007

100

Definitions

Neutral Conductor
NEC, p. 29

Proposal 5-36
Log 1554
ROP, p. 26

Comment 5-18
Log 1501
ROC, p. 16

Analysis and Effect

Proposal 1-122 and associated comments in the 2005 *NEC* development process that introduced a new definition of the term *neutral conductor* were all held for further study. The *NEC* Technical Correlating Committee assigned a specific task group to examine the necessity of such a definition in the *Code*. A definition of *neutral conductor* was developed as a result of work by the *NEC* TCC Task Group. This definition of *neutral conductor* and the associated new definition for *neutral point* were determined necessary so that the appropriate conductor can be identified whenever these terms are used in particular requirements such as in 310.15(B)(4), 250.26, and 250.36. These new definitions are derived from the IEC definition of *neutral conductor* and the IEEE Standard C57.12.80-2002 definition of *neutral point*. Both definitions were crafted into *NEC* language and style, and were expanded as needed to cover the various cases relevant to the terms' usage throughout the *Code*.

According to the new definition, a *neutral conductor* exists even where it does not function as a *neutral conductor*. In other words, where the return conductor is not shared by two or more circuits in the system, as would be apparent in multiwire branch circuits, it is considered a neutral conductor as long as it is connected to the *neutral point* of the system.

This change should result in commonly defined terms used in the *NEC*. This change also promotes more uniform and consistent application of the requirements applying to neutral conductors and provides clarity as to what the *neutral point* of a system (source) is, so as to differentiate the connection point from the *neutral conductor* (wire or bus) that connects to it. In addition to clarifying what constitutes a *neutral conductor*, the revised text also differentiates between the *neutral conductor* and the *equipment grounding conductor*, which are in fact both ultimately connected to the *neutral point* of a system. The differentiation is that under some normal conditions, the *neutral conductor* is expected to be current-carrying, while under normal conditions the *equipment grounding conductor* is never intended to function as a normal current-carrying conductor.

Change at a Glance

Neutral conductors are defined and differentiated between the neutral points of electrical systems.

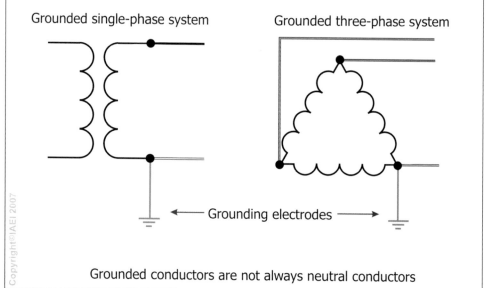

Article 100 Grounded Conductors (Not Neutrals)

Grounded single-phase system

Grounded three-phase system

← Grounding electrodes →

Copyright©IAEI 2007

Grounded conductors are not always neutral conductors

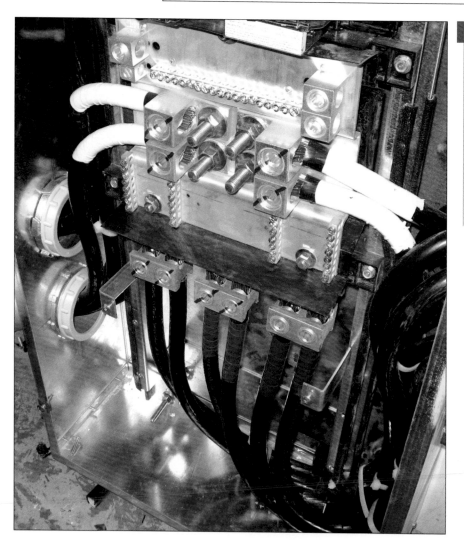

Code Language
100
Definitions

Neutral Conductor. The conductor connected to the neutral point of a system that is intended to carry current under normal conditions.

Summary of Change

A definition of the term *neutral conductor* has been developed and added to Article 100.

Analysis of Changes *NEC*-2008

Article 100 Neutral Point

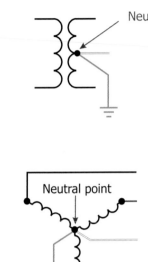

Neutral point of an electrical system

Neutral point is defined as the common point on a wye-connection in a polyphase system, or midpoint on a single-phase, 3-wire system, or mid-point of a single-phase portion of a 3-phase delta system, or a midpoint of a 3-wire direct-current system.

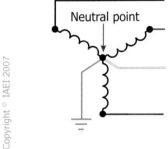

Neutral point

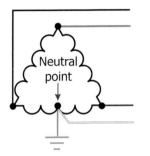

Neutral point

Copyright © IAEI 2007

100

Definitions

Neutral Point
NEC, p. 29

Proposal 5-36
Log 1554
ROP, p. 26

Comment 5-18
Log 1501
ROC, p. 16

Analysis and Effect

A definition of *neutral point* was developed as a result of work by the *NEC* TCC Task Group on the definition of *neutral conductor*. The new definition of *neutral point* and the associated new definition for *neutral conductor* were determined necessary so that the appropriate conductor can be identified whenever these terms are used in particular *Code* requirement such as in 310.15(B)(4), 250.26, and 250.36. These definitions are derived from the IEC definition of *neutral conductor*, and the IEEE Standard C57.12.80-2002 definition of *neutral point*. Both definitions were crafted into *NEC* language and style, and were expanded as needed to cover the various cases relevant to the terms' usage throughout the *Code*.

The *neutral point* of a system or source is the point where neutral conductors connect. The new definition includes various system configurations that normally include a *neutral point* to which neutral conductors are connected. A new fine print note is included to explain in mathematical terms the relationship between the ungrounded phase conductors and the common *neutral point* of a system.

This change should result in commonly used terms being explained through definitions. This change also promotes more uniform and consistent application of the requirements applying to *neutral conductors* and clarifies what the *neutral point* of a system (source) is, so as to differentiate the connection point from the *neutral conductor* (wire or bus) that connects to it.

Code Language
100
Definitions

Neutral Point. The common point on a wye-connection in a polyphase system or midpoint on a single-phase, 3-wire system, or midpoint of a single-phase portion of a 3-phase delta system, or a midpoint of a 3-wire, direct-current system.

FPN: At the neutral point of the system, the vectorial sum of the nominal voltages from all other phases within the system that utilize the neutral, with respect to the neutral point, is zero potential.

Summary of Change

A definition of the term *neutral point* has been developed and added to Article 100. This new definition provides a clear differentiation between a neutral conductor and the point on an electrical system where the neutral conductor is connected.

Change at a Glance

The *neutral point* of a system or source is the point where neutral conductors connect.

1

100

Definitions

Qualified Person
NEC, p. 30

Proposal 1-45
Log 2589
ROP, p. 27

Comment
None

Change at a Glance

Qualified persons must have skills, knowledge and training to recognize and avoid electrical hazards.

Analysis and Effect

Section 110.16 addresses the general requirements for arc-flash warnings for qualified persons on equipment. *Qualified person* was supplemented in *NEC*-2005 with an FPN that references NFPA 70E-2004 where electrical safety training requirements can be found. Qualified persons should be trained to identify and understand the relationship between electrical hazards and possible injury or death. Employees that are qualified by receiving such safety training are better equipped to make decisions involving their safety and the safety others. The changes to this definition correlate between the requirements for *qualified persons* provided in NFPA 70E-2004 Section 110.6(D). The revised definition clarifies that being trained includes understanding not only what the hazards are but also how to avoid them. Working on equipment while it is in an electrically safe work condition is always the best approach, but this is not feasible in all situations. When de-energizing is determined to be infeasible or introduces additional or increased hazards, qualified persons are required to be trained in the appropriate level of personal protective equipment, any applicable safety procedures, and necessary work practices. See NFPA 70E-2004 for what constitutes a *qualified person* as defined.

Code Language
100
Definitions

Qualified Person. One who has skills and knowledge related to the construction and operation of the electrical equipment and installations and has received safety training to recognize and avoid the hazards involved.

FPN: Refer to NFPA 70E®-2004, *Standard for Electrical Safety in the Workplace*, for electrical safety training requirements.

Summary of Change

The definition of the term *Qualified Person* has been revised to clarify the general characteristics of training referred to in the definition. The words "to recognize and avoid the" have been added to clarify what the safety training is expected to accomplish.

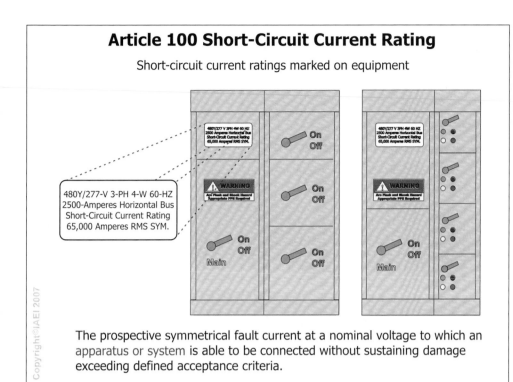

Article 100 Short-Circuit Current Rating

Short-circuit current ratings marked on equipment

480Y/277-V 3-PH 4-W 60-HZ
2500-Amperes Horizontal Bus
Short-Circuit Current Rating
65,000 Amperes RMS SYM.

The prospective symmetrical fault current at a nominal voltage to which an apparatus or system is able to be connected without sustaining damage exceeding defined acceptance criteria.

Copyright©IAEI 2007

100

Definitions

Short-Circuit Current Rating
NEC, p. 31

Proposal 10-2
Log 1743
ROP, p. 28

Comment
None

Analysis and Effect

Section 2.2.2.1 of the *NEC Style Manual*, in general, requires that Article 100 contain definitions of terms that are used in more than one article. The term *short-circuit current rating* is used in various requirements throughout the *NEC*. The new definition provides users with a general understanding what the term means as applied to equipment. Many product standards such as UL 67 for Panelboards, UL 891 for Dead-Front Switchboards, and UL 508A for Industrial Control Panels require a *short-circuit current rating* to be identified and marked on the product. Section 110.10 is a general requirement that clearly calls for short-circuit current ratings of components to be selected and coordinated in electrical systems to permit circuit protective devices to clear a fault without causing extensive damage. Installers and enforcement authorities will be able to apply such requirements that use this term consistently and correctly with a definition that promotes common understanding of the term. Where a *Code* requirement calls for *short-circuit current rating*, the equipment referred to in the requirement should be identified with such information to ensure proper application.

Change at a Glance

The term *short-circuit current rating* used multiple times in the *NEC* has been clarified by definition

Code Language
100
Definitions

Short-Circuit Current Rating. The prospective symmetrical fault current at a nominal voltage to which an apparatus or system is able to be connected without sustaining damage exceeding defined acceptance criteria.

Summary of Change

A new definition of the term *short-circuit current rating* has been clarified and added to Article 100.

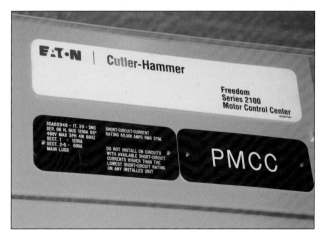

100

Definitions

Surge Arrester and Surge Protective Devices (SPDs)
NEC, p. 31

Proposal 5-340
Log 2601
ROP, p. 250

Comment
None

Change at a Glance

Surge protective devices replace the term *transient voltage surge protector.*

Analysis and Effect

The terms *surge arrester* and *transient voltage surge suppressors* (TVSS) are used in multiple articles of the *NEC*. Therefore, in accordance with Section 2.2.2.1 of the *NEC Style Manual*, these two definitions have been relocated to Article 100. The definition of *surge arrester* has not been revised, but the definition of *transient voltage surge suppressor (TVSS)* has been extensively revised. The term *transient voltage surge suppressor (TVSS)* has also been changed to the term *surge protective devices (SPDs)*. The revisions to this definition are the result of efforts by Underwriters Laboratories (UL) to correlate the *NEC* coverage of these protective devices with the reorganization and revisions to UL Standard 1449, *Surge Protective Devices (SPDs)*. The performance description for surge protective devices remains the same in the definition and it has been expanded to provide useful information about four specific types of surge protective devices. An important differentiation is made between Type 1 and Type 2 permanently connected surge protection devices intended for use on electrical systems not exceeding 600 volts. Type 1 devices are suitable for use on the line side of the service disconnect overcurrent device(s), and Type 2 devices are intended for use on the load side of a service disconnect overcurrent device(s). Types 3 and 4 surge protective devices (SPDs) are also provided in the definition and apply to point of utilization SPDs and component SPDs. Where *transient voltage surge suppressor (TVSS)* was used in the *NEC* in the past, it will be replaced with *surge protective devices (SPDs)* as a result of this change. Revisions to Article 285 will be covered in chapter 2 of this text.

Surge Arrester. A protective device for limiting surge voltages by discharging or bypassing surge current; it also prevents continued flow of follow current while remaining capable of repeating these functions.

Surge-Protective Device (SPD). A protective device for limiting transient voltages by diverting or limiting surge current; it also prevents continued flow of follow current while remaining capable of repeating these functions and is designated as follows:

Type 1: Permanently connected SPDs intended for installation between the secondary of the service transformer and the line side of the service disconnect overcurrent device.

Type 2: Permanently connected SPDs intended for installation on the load side of the service disconnect overcurrent device, including SPDs located at the branch panel.

Type 3: Point of utilization SPDs.

Type 4: Component SPDs, including discrete components, as well as assemblies.

FPN No. 1 For further information on Type 1, Type 2, Type 3, and Type 4 SPDs, see UL 1449, *Standard for Surge Protective Devices.*

Summary of Change

The definition of *surge arrester* has been relocated from 280.2 to Article 100. The definition of *transient voltage surge suppressor (TVSS)* has been relocated from 285.2 to Article 100 and revised. The term *transient voltage surge suppressor (TVSS)* has been changed to *surge protective devices (SPDs).*

100

Definitions

Ungrounded
NEC, p. 32

Proposal 5-38
Log 1518
ROP, p. 28

Comment
None

Change at a Glance

Ungrounded means, "not connected to the earth."

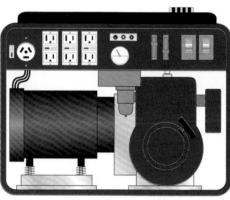

Article 100 Ungrounded

Ungrounded. Not connected to ground or to a conductive body that extends the ground connection.

Frames of portable generators are typically ungrounded

Typical portable generator

Copyright © IAEI 2007

Analysis and Effect

This change was the result of work by the NEC TCC assigned Task Group on Grounding and Bonding. The new definition of this term differentiates clearly between *grounded (grounding)* and the term *ungrounded*. An entity is either grounded (connected to the earth) or it is not. Both terms are now clearly defined. This is a companion to the revisions to *grounded (grounding)* and other changes throughout the *NEC* relative to this task group's recommended revisions to requirements that use terms related to grounding and bonding concepts.

An *ungrounded* system is one that is not intentionally connected to ground either solidly or through any resistor or impedance device. Examples of *ungrounded* systems are covered by Sections 250.21 and 250.22. An *ungrounded* conductor is a circuit conductor that is not intentionally connected to ground. Examples of *ungrounded* conductors are line (phase) circuit conductors that are not intentionally grounded. The phrase "… that extends the ground connection" is included to emphasize that the conductive body actually extends the ground connection such as the items in 250.118 for the purpose of "grounding" in premises wiring. Since *ground* is defined as "the earth, it should be clear to *Code* users with this new definition that when something is *ungrounded*, it is not connected to the earth.

Code Language
100
Definitions

Ungrounded. Not connected to ground or to a conductive body that extends the ground connection.

Summary of Change

A new definition of the word *ungrounded* has been added to Article 100.

Deteriorating Agents
NEC, p. 34

Proposal 1-61
Log 1981
ROP, p. 32

Comment 1-41, 1-42
Log 300, 1512
ROC, p. 18, 19

REVISION

Analysis and Effect

The changes in this section clarify the specific types of identified enclosures that are required to be protected from permanent damage from the weather during building construction. Equipment that is not identified for outdoor use or with a type designation indicating such suitability must be protected from damage where exposed to weather while the building is under construction. Enclosures that are suitable for wet locations by specific identification or type designation would not be required to be protected from the weather, but should be protected from permanent damage that may occur from other reasons during the construction process. Although fine print notes are explanatory material and not enforceable as indicated in 90.5(C), they often provide users and *Code* enforcement with needed information to accurately apply the rules they supplement. The new FPN No. 3 enhances usability by providing an appropriate reference to new Table 110.20 that provide users with necessary information about the designations for equipment enclosure types and the suitable uses for such enclosures.

> ### Change at a Glance
> Identifies enclosure types and electrical equipment that must be protected against damage from the weather during building construction.

Code Language
110.11

Deteriorating Agents
Unless identified for use....where exposed to excessive temperatures.

Equipment not identified for outdoor use and equipment identified only for indoor use, such as "dry locations," "indoor use only," "damp locations," or enclosure Types 1, 2, 5, 12, 12K and/or 13, shall be protected against permanent damage from the weather during building construction.

FPN No. 3: See Table 110.20 for appropriate enclosure-type designations.

Summary of Change

The last sentence of this section has been revised and clarified to be more specific as to the equipment covered by requirements in 110.11. A new fine print note (FPN) No. 3 has been added to provide a reference to a new Table 110.20 that includes enclosure type designations.

1

110.12(A)

Unused Openings
NEC, p. 34

Proposal 1-71
Log 2677
ROP, p. 34

Comment 1-50
Log 834
ROC, p. 21

Change at a Glance

"Cable or raceway" has been deleted to extend the requirements to all unused openings.

Analysis and Effect

The revisions provide clarity and usability from a practical application standpoint. These changes address concerns expressed in public Comments 1-198, 1-200, 1-201, 1-202, and 1-203, and Proposals 1-160, 1-161 that were submitted during the 2005 *NEC* development process, but held for further study. Action by CMP-1 on Proposal 1-71 resulted in the removal of the words "cables or raceways" to broaden the requirements of this section. By removing the various types of equipment listed in the existing rule, it now has application to any openings in apparatus that qualifies as electrical equipment as defined in Article 100. The openings referred to in this requirement are not limited to just raceway or cable openings, and the rule applies to any opening other than those necessary for normal operation of the equipment or those needed for installation of such equipment. This revision excludes operational openings in equipment, such as ventilation openings and mounting holes, from the requirement to be closed.

The rule has also been expanded slightly to address openings in equipment that are inherent to design and product listing requirements. These revisions should result in more complete coverage of equipment openings that are intended to be closed, if unused; and clearly distinguish such openings from those that are intended to remain open or that are necessary for installation or proper operation of the equipment.

There were no changes to the last sentence of the section that includes specific details of the types of plugs, plates, or other accessories manufactured for closing unused openings in electrical equipment.

Code Language
100.12(A)
Unused Openings

Unused openings, other than those intended for the operation of equipment, those intended for mounting purposes, or those permitted as part of the design for listed equipment, shall be closed to afford protection substantially equivalent to the wall of the equipment. Where metallic plugs or plates are used with nonmetallic enclosures, they shall be recessed at least 6 mm (¼ in.) from the outer surface of the enclosure.

Summary of Change

This section has been revised to remove the list of various types of equipment that are covered and to generalize the requirements to all unused openings, other than those necessary for operation of the equipment.

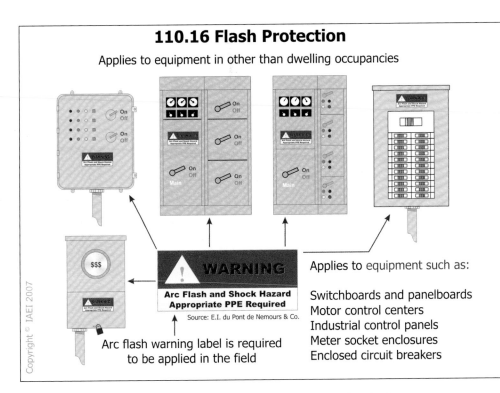

110.16 Flash Protection

Applies to equipment in other than dwelling occupancies

Applies to equipment such as:

Switchboards and panelboards
Motor control centers
Industrial control panels
Meter socket enclosures
Enclosed circuit breakers

WARNING

**Arc Flash and Shock Hazard
Appropriate PPE Required**

Source: E.I. du Pont de Nemours & Co.

Arc flash warning label is required
to be applied in the field

Copyright © IAEI 2007

110.16

Flash Protection
NEC, p. 35

Proposal 1-84
Log 2338
ROP, p. 37

Comment 1-55
Log 836
ROC, p. 22

Analysis and Effect

Section 110.16 has been revised to provide additional clarity for *Code* users and to allow for more appropriate and consistent application to field installations that qualify for the warning labels required by this section. This revision generalizes the requirement by providing examples of equipment that would qualify for the field-applied arc-flash warning labels. The previous requirements were limited only to the types of equipment actually identified in the rule. By including the words "Electrical equipment such as" the concept of applicability is expanded to other similar equipment that are likely to require examination, adjustment, servicing, or maintenance while energized. This revision clarifies that the requirement can also apply to other items such as a large enclosed circuit breaker, fusible switch, and similar equipment not specifically included in the previous text in this section. The fine print notes to this rule have not been affected by these changes; they still provide appropriate references to other applicable standards with relative information about safe work practices and guidelines for designing safety signs and labels for equipment.

Change at a Glance

The warning label requirement applies to more types of equipment than those listed.

Code Language
110.16
Flash Protection

Electrical equipment, such as switchboards, panelboards, industrial control panels, meter socket enclosures, and motor control centers, that are in other than dwelling occupancies, and are likely to require examination, adjustment, servicing, or maintenance while energized shall be field marked to warn qualified persons of potential electric arc flash hazards. The marking shall be located so as to be clearly visible to qualified persons before examination, adjustment, servicing, or maintenance of the equipment.

Summary of Change

Section has been revised to clarify the limits of applicability of the requirements contained in this rule. The words "Electrical equipment such as" have been added to the first sentence in this rule.

1

110.20

Enclosure Types
NEC, p. 36

Proposal 1-95
Log 1980
ROP, p. 41

Comment 1-64, 1-114
Log 976, 70
ROC, p. 24, 291

110.20 Enclosure Types

For Outdoor Use										
Provides a degree of protection against the following environmental conditions	Enclosure Type Number									
	3	3R	3S	3X	3RX	3SX	4	4X	6	6P
Incidental contact with the enclosed equipment	X	X	X	X	X	X	X	X	X	X
Rain, snow, and sleet	X	X	X	X	X	X	X	X	X	X
Sleet*	-	-	X	-	-	X	-	-	-	-
Windblown dust	X	-	X	X	-	X	X	X	X	X
Hose-down	-	-	-	-	-	-	X	X	X	X
corrosive agents	-	-	-	X	X	X	-	X	-	X
Temporary submersion	-	-	-	-	-	-	-	-	X	X
Prolonged submersion	-	-	-	-	-	-	-	-	-	X

For Indoor Use										
Provides a degree of protection against the following environmental conditions	Enclosure Type Number									
	1	2	4	4X	5	6	6P	12	12K	13
Incidental contact with the enclosed equipment	X	X	X	X	X	X	X	X	X	X
Falling dirt	X	X	X	X	X	X	X	X	X	X
Falling liquids and light splashing	-	X	X	X	X	X	X	X	X	X
Circulating dust, lint, fibers, and flyings	-	-	X	X	-	X	X	X	X	X
Settling airborne dust, lint, fibers and flyings	-	-	X	X	X	X	X	X	X	X
Hose-down and splashing water	-	-	X	X	-	X	X	-	-	-
Oil and coolant seepage	-	-	-	-	-	-	-	X	X	X
Oil or coolant spraying and splashing	-	-	-	-	-	-	-	-	-	X
Corrosive agents	-	-	-	X	-	-	X	-	-	-
Temporary submersion	-	-	-	-	-	X	X	-	-	-
Prolonged submersion	-	-	-	-	-	-	X	-	-	-

*Mechanism shall be operable when ice covered.

Reproduction of Table 110.20 (in part)

Typical enclosures

Type 1

Type 3R

Table 430.91 has been relocated to section 110.20.
Enclosure type designations apply to electrical enclosures beyond those for motor controller enclosures and those enclosures shall be marked.

Analysis and Effect

This new Section 110.20 and Table 110.20 are the result of actions on Proposals 1-152 and 1-157 and associated public Comments 1-229, 1-230, 1-231, and 1-233 from the 2004 Reports on Proposal and Reports on Comments that were held for further study during the 2005 NEC development process. This change creates a new Section 110.20 and relocates existing Table 430.91 to become Table 110.20. The information within the relocated table essentially remains the same. It is appropriate for this table that includes enclosure type designations and information about their use to be located in Article 110 where general requirements to all electrical installations are included. Electrical enclosures in addition to the enclosures used for motor applications as covered by Article 430 are also required to be suitable for the environment in which they are installed. The effect of this change provides consistency between the UL General Information for Electrical Equipment Directory (UL White Book) category (AALZ) and the *NEC*, which applies generally to all electrical equipment, not just equipment associated with motor installations covered by Article 430. Relocating requirements of 430.91 and Table 430.91 into a general application area (Article 110) of the *Code* and specifically indicating the types of equipment to which the requirements apply will add clarity for users. The equipment types in the list are required by current industry product standards to use a Type number marking.

Change at a Glance

Table 430.91, covering electrical enclosure types, has been relocated to Article 110 to allow for general application.

Copyright©AEI 2007

Code Language

110.20
Enclosure Types

Enclosures (other than surrounding fences or walls) of switchboards, panelboards, industrial control panels, motor control centers, meter sockets, and motor controllers, rated not over 600 volts nominal and intended for such locations, shall be marked with an enclosure-type number as shown in Table 110.20.

Table 110.20 shall be used for selecting these enclosures for use in specific locations other than hazardous (classified) locations. The enclosures are not intended to protect against conditions such as condensation, icing, corrosion, or contamination that may occur within the enclosure or enter via the conduit or unsealed openings.

Summary of Change

A new section 110.20 and associated Table 110.20 have been added to Article 110.

110.22

Identification of Disconnecting Means
NEC, p. 37

___

Proposal 1-98
Log 1978
ROP, p. 43

___

Comment 1-69, 1-70
Log 269, 350
ROC, p. 25

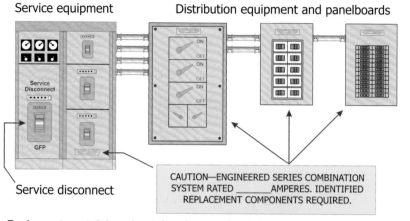

110.22 Identification of Disconnecting Means

Service equipment

Distribution equipment and panelboards

Service Disconnect

GFP

Service disconnect

CAUTION—ENGINEERED SERIES COMBINATION SYSTEM RATED _____ AMPERES. IDENTIFIED REPLACEMENT COMPONENTS REQUIRED.

Copyright© IAEI 2007

Equipment containing circuit breakers or fuses applied in engineered series combination ratings in accordance with 240.86(A) shall be field marked. The marking is required to be readily visible, located as directed by the engineer, and shall include the specific text shown on the above label example.

Note that Section 240.86(A) applies to existing installations only.

Analysis and Effect

Section 240.86 was revised in the 2005 *NEC* development process to include an alternate method of applying a series rated combination of overcurrent devices that is selected under engineering supervision for existing installations. It is important to understand this alternative provided in 240.86(A) applies to existing installations only, and provides a method to allow older existing electrical equipment to remain where the overcurrent protection is coordinated and selected for the design and application by a licensed professional engineer engaged in the design and maintenance of electrical systems and installations.

The primary differences between 240.86(A) and the requirements in 240.86(B) are that the series combinations covered by the requirements in 240.86(B) are listed and tested devices for use in series rated combinations. The alternative in 240.86(A) allows for a selected engineered design consisting of coordinated overcurrent protection that provides the required protection for equipment in such applications that meets the general requirements of Section 110.10. The revision to Section 110.22 incorporates a field-applied labeling requirement for existing equipment that is applied in an engineered series rated combination covered by 240.86(A). The new requirements for series rated combination systems labeling parallel the current field-marking rules

> ### Change at a Glance
> New label requirements for equipment where an engineered series rated combination is selected under engineering supervision.

for listed and tested series rated combinations. The key element of the label is that it includes the wording "engineered series rated combination" and the specific equipment requiring the labels will be as directed by the engineer responsible for the design using the provisions of 240.86(A) for existing installations.

Summary of Change

Section 110.22 has been revised and restructured into three subdivisions to include a new requirement for field-applied caution labels to indicate the equipment has been applied with a series rating combination selected under engineering supervision. A new FPN has been added to provide a reference to Section 240.86(A) for correlation.

Code Language
110.22
Identification of Disconnecting Means

(A) General. Each disconnecting means shall be legibly marked to indicate its purpose unless located and arranged so the purpose is evident. The marking shall be of sufficient durability to withstand the environment involved.

(B) Engineered Series Combination Systems. Where circuit breakers or fuses are applied in compliance with series combination ratings selected under engineering supervision and marked on the equipment as directed by the engineer, the equipment enclosure(s) shall be legibly marked in the field to indicate the equipment has been applied with a series combination rating. The marking shall be readily visible and state the following:

CAUTION — ENGINEERED SERIES COMBINATION SYSTEM RATED _____ AMPERES. IDENTIFIED REPLACEMENT COMPONENTS REQUIRED.

FPN: See 240.86(A) for engineered series combination systems.

(C) Tested Series Combination Systems. Where circuit breakers or fuses are applied in compliance with the series combination ratings marked on the equipment by the manufacturer, the equipment enclosure(s) shall be legibly marked in the field to indicate the equipment has been applied with a series combination rating. The marking shall be readily visible and state the following:

CAUTION — SERIES COMBINATION SYSTEM RATED _____ AMPERES. IDENTIFIED REPLACEMENT COMPONENTS REQUIRED.

FPN: See 240.86(B) for tested series combination systems.

1

110.26 (C)(2)

Entrance to and Egress from Working Space
NEC, p. 38

Proposal 1-123, 1-127
Log 1198, 3487
ROP, p. 50, 51

Comment 1-87, 1-92
Log 986, 2330
ROC, p. 31, 32

Change at a Glance

Equipment size and rating determine necessity for two entrances.

110.26(C)(2) Large Equipment

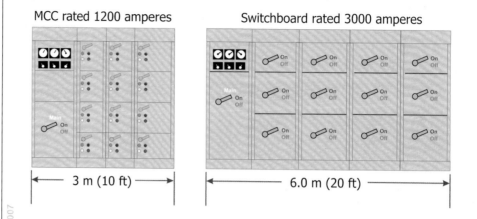

Large equipment rated at 1200 amperes or more and over 1.8 m (6 ft) in width requires access and egress from the working space at both ends of the equipment.

Analysis and Effect

Action by CMP-1 restores the dimension 1.8 m (6 ft) that applies to equipment rated at 1200 amperes or more that constitutes large equipment covered by this section. The requirement for physical size was removed during the 2005 *NEC* development process, which presented some challenges for meeting the requirements for two entrances and egress paths from some types of equipment where it was not practical or, in some cases, not possible. For example, a 1200-ampere panelboard that is 900 mm (3 ft) in width would be required to meet the two-entrance requirement as provided in *NEC*-2005. By restoring the requirement for physical size, building and engineering designs are less impacted by a requirement that is not necessary in all cases.

This *Code* rule, in addition to many others, has to include minimum dimensions and energy levels that serve as a starting point for users regarding applicability. It should be understood that large equipment with lower ampacity ratings, such as 800-ampere or 1000-ampere rated switchboards, and so forth, in larger sizes, present similar challenges and safety concerns relative to whether two entrances or exits are provided.

Code Language [C](2)

Large Equipment

For equipment rated 1200 amperes or more and over 1.8 m (6 ft) wide that contains overcurrent devices, switching devices, or control devices, there shall be one entrance to and egress from the required working space not less than 610 mm (24 in.) wide and 2.0 m (6 1/2 ft) high at each end of the working space.

Summary of Change

This revision restores the words "and over 1.8 m (6 ft) wide." The provisions dealing with personnel doors have been incorporated into a new 110.26(C)(3) as a result of the panel action on Comment 1-92.

110.26 (C)(3)

Entrance to and Egress from Working Space
NEC, p. 38, 39

Proposal 1-123, 1-127
Log 1198, 3487
ROP, p. 50, 51

Comment 1-87, 1-88, 1-92
Log 986, 987, 2330
ROC, p. 31, 32

REVISION!

Analysis and Effect

Section 110.26(C) provides requirements that address access to and egress from the working spaces required by 110.26(A). These changes provide clarity and improve usability of this section covering entrance and egress door requirements for large equipment working spaces. Previously, the requirements relating to personnel door swing direction and hardware applied only where the entrance to the working space was gained through a door at the boundary of the required working space. The problem with this section in the previous editions of the *Code* was that there was no set dimension from the equipment or required working space that users could refer to for appropriate and consistent application of this requirement. This resulted in the existing requirements for door hardware and door swing direction being applied to doors for rooms, and not to the doors located at and allowing access to the working space for the equipment.

These revisions provide needed clarification as to when doors must open in the direction of egress and when they need to be equipped with appropriate hardware to allow for release under simple pressure. CMP-1 responded favorably to the concepts introduced by Proposal 1-127 that established a minimum distance from the working space that would govern when a personnel door(s) should swing out and be equipped with panic bars or pressure plate hardware. Action by CMP-1 on Comments 1-87 and 1-92 results in a new list item (3) in this section making it more user friendly and, as revised, refers to a specific distance of 7.6 m (25 ft) from the nearest edge of the working space for determining the applicability of this requirement. The result is a requirement that applies to doors that is more easily understood by all users and is much more enforceable in a uniform and consistent fashion. The positive impact in improving safety for personnel is inherent to the revisions of this section as well.

Change at a Glance

Personnel access doors less than 25 ft from the working space are to open outward with simple pressure.

Code Language
110.26(C)(3)
Personnel Doors

Where equipment rated 1200 A or more that contains overcurrent devices, switching devices, or control devices is installed and there is a personnel door(s) intended for entrance to and egress from the working space less than 7.6 m (25 ft) from the nearest edge of the working space, the door(s) shall open in the direction of egress and be equipped with panic bars, pressure plates, or other devices that are normally latched but open under simple pressure.

Summary of Change

A new list item (3) has been created in 110.26(C). The second sentence in 110.26(C)(2) has been relocated to this new item (3) and revised to address specific requirements relating to personnel doors. The remainder of 110.26(C)(2) is unchanged by this renumbering and restructuring resulting from actions on these proposal and comments.

110.26(G)

Locked Electrical Equipment Rooms or Enclosures
NEC, p. 39

Proposal 1-100
Log 2934
ROP, p. 43

Comment 1-71
Log 1672
ROC, p. 26

Change at a Glance

Locked electrical rooms and enclosures are considered accessible to qualified persons.

110.26(G) Locked Electrical Rooms or Enclosures

Locked Electrical Equipment Rooms or Enclosures.

Electrical equipment rooms or enclosures housing electrical apparatus that are controlled by a lock(s) shall be considered accessible to qualified persons.

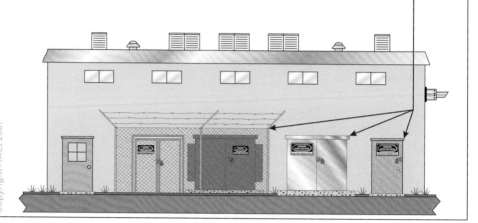

Analysis and Effect

The general requirements in 110.26 are related to working spaces about electrical equipment. The last sentence in this section relates to enclosures and rooms, and access thereto. Action by CMP-1 on Comment 1-71 to Proposal 1-100 results in the removal of the last sentence from 110.26 and relocating it in a new subdivision (G) titled "Locked Electrical Rooms or Enclosures." This revision provides a more logical layout for users and clear direction on the accessibility requirements for equipment located in locked enclosures or rooms. For safety reasons, many electrical rooms and electrical equipment enclosures are required to be kept locked to restrict unqualified persons from being exposed to potential associated hazards. In addition to the relocation of this text, the revision helps clarify that such locked rooms or enclosures, which could be a locked fence area, are considered accessible to qualified persons who have the keys or other means by which the equipment is rendered accessible.

Code Language
110.26(G)

Locked Electrical Equipment Rooms or Enclosures
Electrical equipment rooms or enclosures housing electrical apparatus that are controlled by a lock(s) shall be considered accessible to qualified persons.

Summary of Change
The last sentence of 110.26 has been relocated to a new subdivision (G) in 110.26 covering locked electrical equipment rooms or enclosures.

Analysis of Changes *NEC*-2008

Entrance to Enclosures and Access to Working Space
NEC, p. 41

Proposal 1-147, 1-148
Log 3223, 1197
ROP, p. 55, 56

Comment 1-99
Log 2332
ROC, p. 34

Analysis and Effect

The revisions to this rule provide additional clarification about what enclosures are covered by the requirements for entrance and egress means. It is clear under this revision that the enclosures in 110.31, such as fenced areas, vaults, rooms, closets, and so forth are required to meet the entrance and access requirements of this section. The new language in the second sentence of 110.33(A) clarifies that the entrance requirement applies to the enclosure and not necessarily the working space in all cases since the entrance to the enclosure could contain a door. CMP-1 responded favorable to the concepts introduced by Proposal 1-148 that established a minimum distance from the working space that would govern when the door should swing out and be equipped with panic bars or pressure plate hardware. Action by CMP-1 on Comment 1-99 results in a new list item (3) in this section making it more user friendly and, as revised, this section refers to a specific distance of 7.6 m (25 ft) from the nearest edge of the working space for determining the applicability of this requirement. The 7.6 m (25 ft) distance is reasonable and provides for safe egress from the area. Currently, some jurisdictions are applying the requirement where personnel doors are a considerable distance from the working space, such as in large areas or rooms. The revisions to this section provide clear direction for installers and enforcement officials as to when the requirement for the door to swing away from the working space applies, and also when it must be equipped with simple release hardware as specified in this rule. Personnel doors that are located 7.6 m (25 ft) or more from the working space required by this section will not be required to meet the physical and operational characteristics of this rule as a result of this change. The requirements for personnel door swing, hardware characteristics, distances from required working spaces are also consistent with those rules in 110.26(C) for equipment operating at 600 volts or less.

Change at a Glance

Personnel doors less than 25 feet from the working space are to swing outward with simple pressure.

Code Language
110.33

Entrance to Enclosures and Access to Working Space

(A) Entrance. At least one entrance to enclosures for electrical installations as described in 110.31 not less than 610 mm (24 in.) wide and 2.0 m (6 1/ 2 ft) high shall be provided to give access to the working space about electric equipment.

(3) Personnel Doors. Where there is a personnel door(s) intended for entrance to and egress from the working space less than 7.6 m (25 ft) from the nearest edge of the working space, the door(s) shall open in the direction of egress and be equipped with panic bars, pressure plates, or other devices that are normally latched but open under simple pressure.

(B) Access. Permanent ladders or stairways shall be provided to give safe access to the working space around electrical equipment installed on platforms, balconies, or mezzanine floors or in attic or roof rooms or spaces.

Summary of Change

The words "to enclosures for electrical installations as described in 110.31" have been added to clarify applicability of this rule. The second sentence of 110.33(A) has been relocated as a new item list item (3) covering requirements for personnel doors.

Chapter

Selected
Changes

Article 200

200.2(A) & (B)
200.6(B) Exception
210.4(A) and (B)
210.4(D)
210.5(C)
210.8(A)(2), & (A)(5) & FPN
210.8(B)
210.8(B)(4)
210.8(B)(5) and Exception
210.8(B)(5) Exception 1
210.8(C)
210.12(B)
210.12(B) Exception No. 1
210.12(B) Exception No. 2
210.19(A)(1) Exception No. 2
210.52
210.52(E)
210.52(E)(3)
210.52(G)
210.60(A)
210.62
215.2(A)(1) Exception
215.6

215.10, Exception No. 3
215.12(C)
220.82(B) & (C)
220.82(C)(2)
225.18
225.22, Exception
225.39
230.24(B)
230.44 Exception
230.49 and 230.50
230.53
230.54(A) and (B)
230.71
230.71, 230.82, 230.94
230.79
230.82(3)
230.205(A)
240.15
240.21(B)(1) FPN &
240.21(C)(2) FPN
240.21(C)(2)(4)
240.21(C)(3)
240.21(H)
240.24(B)
240.24(F)

240.86(A)
240.92(B) & Table 240.92(B)
Article 250 and Code-Wide
Revisions
250.4(B)(4)
250.8
250.20(D) and FPN No. 1
250.28(D)
250.30(A)(4)
250.32(B) and Exception
250.35
250.52(A)(3)
250.52(A)(6)
250.64(D)
250.68(A) and Exception No. 2
250.94
250.112(I)
250.118 and FPN
250.119 Exception
250.120(A) FPN
250.122(C)
250.122(F)(2)
250.142(B)(2) Exc. No. 2 (2)
250.146
250.146(A)
250.146(D)
Article 280
280.25, 285.28
Article 285

200.2(A) & (B)

Insulation and Continuity
NEC, p. 45

Proposal 5-90
Log 3389
ROP, p. 187

Comment 5-47
Log 1906
ROC, p. 125

200.2(B) Continuity

The continuity of a grounded conductor shall not depend on a connection to a metallic enclosure, raceway, or cable armor.

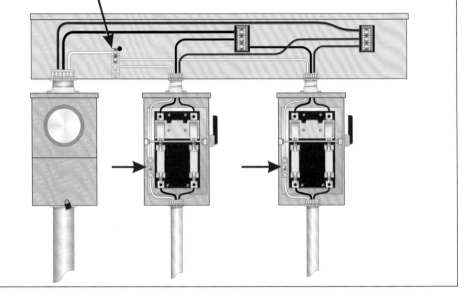

Copyright© IAEI 2007

Analysis and Effect

This section has been restructured into a format consistent with the *NEC Style Manual*, and it incorporates new rules that address continuity requirements for the grounded conductor(s). Substantiation provided with the original proposal 5-90 (Log No. 3389) identified a concern that was not specifically addressed by a clear requirement in previous editions of the *NEC*. The new text in (B) provides users with rules that will prohibit enclosures, raceways, or cable armor from being used to establish and maintain continuity of any grounded conductor. This requirement applies not only to service conductors, but also to grounded conductors of feeders and branch circuits. This change results in clear requirements for grounded conductor terminations and connections that will not depend on other than terminals or connection devices that are intended for this type of connection. Grounded conductor continuity is currently addressed in 300.13(B), which is limited in application to installations of grounded conductors installed with multiwire branch circuits. This section provides requirements for maintaining continuity where devices such as receptacles could be removed. This revision fills a void in the *Code* with a rule that addresses grounded (often, neutral) conductor continuity in a general nature without the limitations of those in 300.13(B).

Change at a Glance

Metallic enclosures, raceways, or cable armor are not permitted to be used for continuity of grounded conductors.

200.2(B) Continuity

The continuity of a grounded conductor shall not depend on a connection to a metallic enclosure, raceway, or cable armor.

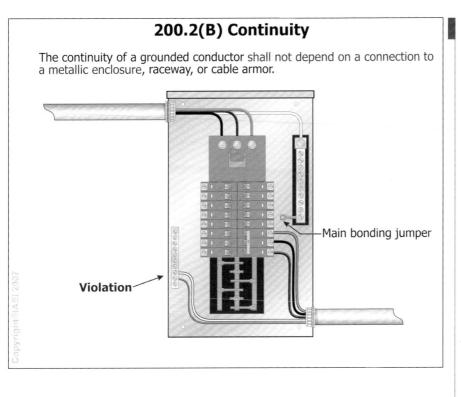

Violation →

—Main bonding jumper

Copyright ©IAEI 2007

Code Language
200.2

General

... in accordance with 200.6. The grounded conductor shall comply with 200.2(A) and (B).

(A) Insulation. The grounded conductor, where insulated, shall have...as described in 250.184(A).

(B) Continuity. The continuity of a grounded conductor shall not depend on a connection to a metallic enclosure, raceway, or cable armor.

Summary of Change

Section 200.2 has been restructured to include subdivisions in accordance with the *NEC Style Manual*. A new (B) has been added to this section addressing continuity of grounded conductors.

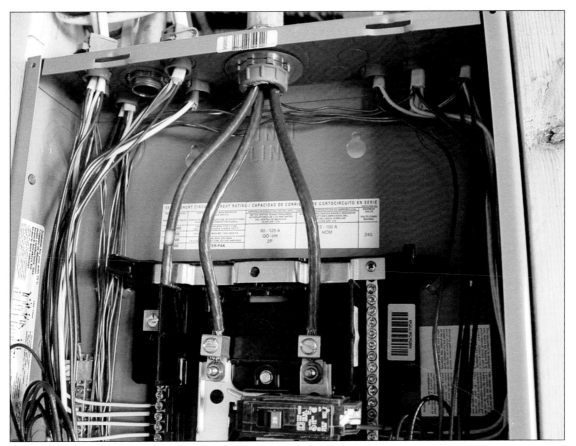

210.4(A) and (B)

Proposal 2-10
Log 2679
ROP, p. 61

Comment 2-6
Log 1344
ROC, p. 37

Change at a Glance

Simultaneously disconnecting all conductors of multiwire branch circuits is now expanded to *all* multiwire branch circuits.

210.4 Multiwire Branch Circuits

210.4 Multiwire branch circuits

(A) General. ....All conductors of a multiwire branch circuit shall originate from the same panelboard or similar distribution equipment

(B) Disconnecting means. Each multiwire branch circuit shall be provided with a means that will simultaneously disconnect all ungrounded conductors at the point where the branch circuit originates.

Copyright©IAEI 2007

Analysis and Effect

The changes to this section provide a clear requirement for the same point of origin for all conductors of multiwire branch circuits. These circuits must originate at the same panelboard or similar distribution equipment. Multiwire branch circuits sharing a common neutral can present unexpected hazards where ungrounded conductors of the multiwire branch circuit are not disconnected simultaneously. The safety concern associated with un-intentional voltage being present on multiwire branch circuits during maintenance is not always fully appreciated. *NEC*-2005 included no requirement to disconnect all ungrounded conductors of multiwire branch circuit in general. Section 210.4(B) of *NEC*-2005 includes a simultaneous disconnecting means requirement for un-grounded conductors of multiwire branch circuits, but only where the multiwire branch circuit supplies more than one device or component on the same mounting strap or yoke. While this use of multiwire branch circuits is common and recognized by the *Code*, because of this revision it is now permitted only where a means is provided to disconnect simultaneously all ungrounded conductors of that circuit. The effect of this revision is that the requirement for disconnecting all conductors of multiwire branch circuits is expanded to all multiwire branch circuits, not just those that supply more than one device mounted on the same yoke or mounting strap.

Code Language

(A)

General

Branch circuits recognized by this article shall be permitted as multiwire circuits. A multiwire circuit shall be permitted to be considered as multiple circuits. All conductors of a multiwire branch circuit shall originate from the same panelboard or similar distribution equipment.

(B)

Disconnecting Means

Each multiwire branch circuit shall be provided with a means that will simultaneously disconnect all ungrounded conductors at the point where the branch circuit originates.

Summary of Change

Information about conductors of multiwire branch circuits originating from the same panelboard or distribution equipment has been relocated to 210.4(A). 210.4(B) now addresses disconnecting means for simultaneously disconnecting all ungrounded conductors of all multiwire branch circuits.

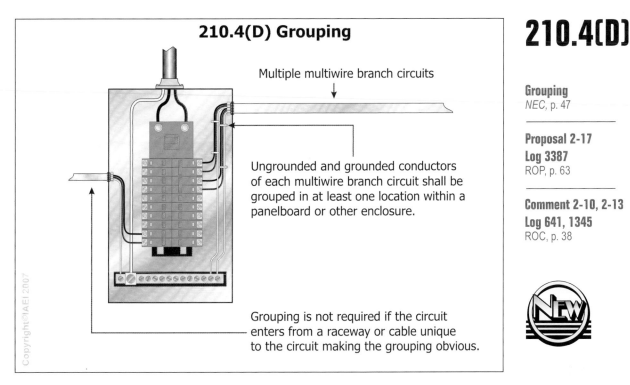

210.4(D) Grouping

Multiple multiwire branch circuits ↓

Ungrounded and grounded conductors of each multiwire branch circuit shall be grouped in at least one location within a panelboard or other enclosure.

Grouping is not required if the circuit enters from a raceway or cable unique to the circuit making the grouping obvious.

Copyright©IAEI 2007

210.4(D)

Grouping
NEC, p. 47

Proposal 2-17
Log 3387
ROP, p. 63

Comment 2-10, 2-13
Log 641, 1345
ROC, p. 38

Analysis and Effect

Action by CMP-2 on proposal 2-17 (Log No. 3387) results in a new requirement for grouping all conductors of multiwire branch circuits within the enclosure where the branch circuit originates, usually a panelboard. This revision continues the recent trends to provide workers with more ready means to identify all conductors of a multiwire branch circuit with their associated grounded (neutral) conductor. Substantiation with the proposal identified the hazards of not de-energizing all ungrounded conductors of multiwire branch circuits, which usually results in current remaining present in the neutral of such circuits. The change requires all conductors of multiwire branch circuits, including the neutral, to be grouped by using wire ties or similar means in at least one location where the circuit enters the panelboard. The new exception relaxes the grouping requirement where the arrangement of entry to the enclosure where the branch circuit originates makes the grouping obvious, such as a single conduit or single cable assembly containing only the multiwire branch-circuit conductors.

Change at a Glance

Multiwire branch circuits must be grouped together with their associated grounded (neutral) conductor at the branch-circuit panelboard unless the grouping is obvious.

Code Language
210.4(D)
Grouping

The ungrounded and grounded conductors of each multiwire branch circuit shall be grouped by wire ties or similar means in at least one location within the panelboard or other point of origination.

Exception: The requirement for grouping shall not apply if the circuit enters from a cable or raceway unique to the circuit that makes the grouping obvious.

Summary of Change

A new subdivision (D) covering grouping of multiwire branch circuits has been added to Section 210.4.

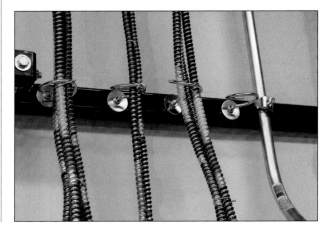

2

210.5(C)

Ungrounded Conductors
NEC, p. 48

Proposal 2-22, 2-23
Log 2221, 2681
ROP, p. 63, 64

Comment 2-15
Log 9
ROC, p. 39

Change at a Glance

Identification of ungrounded conductors by phase and system is required where the premises wiring includes more than one nominal voltage system.

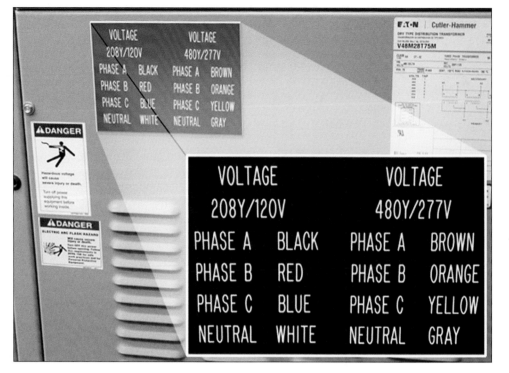

Analysis and Effect

Section 210.4(B) of *NEC*-2002 included a requirement to identify the conductors of multiwire branch circuits by both phase and system. This section was relocated to 210.5(C) in *NEC*-2005 and expanded to apply to all branch circuits, not just multiwire branch circuits. However, during the 2005 *NEC* development process, the requirement for identification by phases in addition to systems was inadvertently omitted without substantiation. This revision restores this requirement and applies it to all branch circuits, not just multiwire branch circuits to be identified by both phase and system. The term *where accessible* imposed the identification requirements to conditions that were not necessarily practical in all cases. Adjustment in wording to specifically require the identification means to be applied "at all termination, connection and splice points" clarifies that the identification means does not have to be applied in conduit bodies or other access points where the conductors are accessible, but pass through such fittings. The change results in ease of circuit and system verification by inspectors and enhanced safety levels for installers and workers by improving the means of identifying branch circuits and the systems from which they are supplied. The revisions in this section also have been expanded to allow readily available documentation to serve as a circuit identification means in addition to the means posted at the equipment where the branch circuit originates.

Code Language
210.5(C)

Ungrounded Conductors
Where the premises wiring system has branch circuits supplied from more than one nominal voltage system, each ungrounded conductor of a branch circuit shall be identified by phase or line and system at all termination, connection and splice points. (The remainder of this section is unchanged)

Summary of Change

This section has been revised to add the words "phase or line and" before the word "system," expanding the identification requirements. The words "where accessible" have been replaced by the words "at all termination, connection and splice points." Other revisions in this section add an allowance for readily available documentation to serve as a branch circuit identification means.

210.8(A)(2) & (A)(5) Exceptions No. 1 and 2 Deleted

All 125-volt, single-phase, 15- and 20-ampere receptacles in dwelling unit garages, accessory buildings, and basements are required to have ground-fault circuit-interrupter protection.

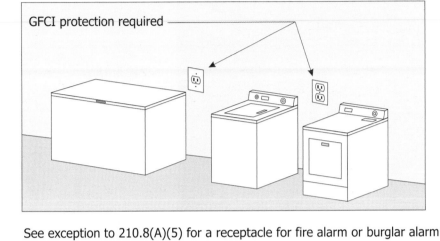

GFCI protection required

See exception to 210.8(A)(5) for a receptacle for fire alarm or burglar alarm system located in basements.

Dwelling Units
NEC, p. 49

Proposal 2-40, 2-41, 2-51
Log 3601, 3602, 3182
ROP, p. 67, 68

Comment 2-34
Log 1997
ROC, p. 43

Analysis and Effect

The exception for receptacles that are not readily accessible has been deleted because the concept of being "readily accessible" is too vague and can lead to inconsistencies in how the requirements are applied. A garage door opener might not be readily accessible to short persons, but very well could be accessible to persons that are taller. The shock protection of this requirement should apply to all persons. Exception No. 2 has been deleted to establish consistency with the GFCI receptacle requirements in 210.8(A)(7) that were expanded in the 2005 *NEC*. The product safety standards for appliances covered by this exception require appliances to be manufactured with insulation dielectric leakage levels that do not exceed 0.5 mA. This level of leakage current is far below the 4–6 mA leakage thresholds of Class A ground-fault circuit interrupters manufactured to UL Standard 943. There clearly is no longer a need for either of these exceptions. Deleting the two exceptions creates consistency between the requirements in 210.8(A)(2) and 210.8(A)(7) and enhances the level of shock protection for persons where leakage levels in appliances could develop and present shock hazards that, under the previous allowances of the exceptions, would otherwise go undetected. Protection by ground-fault circuit interrupters is not related to the location of the receptacle. If cord- and plug-connected utilization equipment (appliances exempted by the previous exceptions) has abnormal or excessive leakage current levels that will trip the GFCI, protection should be provided. Based on the information in the applicable product safety standards, the maximum leakage current for typical cord- and plug-connected equipment (appliances) is .5 mA. The trip range for Class A GFCI protective devices is 4–6 mA. In order for this utilization equipment to trip a GFCI protective device, leakage current levels would have to reach 8 to 12 times that permitted by the product standard, creating safety concerns. The fact that the receptacle is not readily accessible will have no impact on the shock hazard protection for persons coming in contact with the utilization equipment. The new FPN following the exception to (5) provides an appropriate reference to Article 760 for specific requirements that apply to branch circuits supplying fire alarm systems and circuits.

Change at a Glance

The GFCI protection requirements for receptacles in basements, garages, and accessory buildings have been expanded to all 125-volt, single-phase, 15- and 20-ampere receptacles regardless of their accessibility or whether an appliance is easily moved from one location to another.

Code Language
210.8(A)(2)

Garages and Unfinished Basements
Garages, and also accessory buildings that have a floor located at or below grade level not intended as habitable rooms and limited to storage areas, work areas, and areas of similar use.

210.8(A)(5)

Unfinished basements — for purposes of this section, unfinished basements are defined as portions or areas of the basement not intended as habitable rooms and limited to storage areas, work areas, and the like.

Exception to (5): A receptacle supplying only a permanently installed fire alarm or burglar alarm system shall not be required to have ground-fault circuit-interrupter protection.

FPN: See 760.41(B) and 760.121(B) for power supply requirements for fire alarm systems.

Receptacles installed under the exception to 210.8(A)(5) shall not be considered as meeting the requirements of 210.52(G).

Summary of Change

The two existing exceptions to Section 210.8(A)(2) and Exception Nos. 1 and 2 to (A)(5) have been deleted. Additional text added to 210.8(A)(5) indicates that any receptacles installed under the exception to 210.8(A)(5) shall not be considered as meeting the requirements of 210.52(G). A new FPN refers users to 760.41(B) and 760.121(B) for fire alarm system supply circuit requirements.

Other Than Dwelling Units
NEC, p. 49

Proposal 2-70
Log 1443
ROP, p. 72

Comment 2-5, 2-50
Log 5, 1357
ROC, p. 13, 47

REVISION

Analysis and Effect

The changes to this section expand the GFCI protection requirement to all outdoor 15- and 20-ampere, 125-volt receptacles. The addition of the new Exception No. 2 provides for a limited alternative that relaxes the GFCI protection requirement for outdoor applications in industrial establishments only, where the conditions of maintenance and supervision ensure that only qualified personnel are involved. Such qualifying receptacles are limited to use with equipment that meets the restrictions of an assured equipment grounding conductor program as specified in 590.6(B)(2). In addition to promoting consistent application of the GFCI receptacle requirements in outdoor locations and increasing shock protection for users in general, the revision removes the need for determining which receptacles are accessible to the public.

Change at a Glance

Generally, all 125-volt, single-phase, 15- and 20-ampere receptacles outside are required to be protected by ground-fault circuit-interrupter protection.

Code Language

(B)
Other Than Dwelling Units

All 125-volt, single-phase, 15- and 20-ampere receptacles installed in the locations specified in (1) through (5) shall have ground-fault circuit-interrupter protection for personnel:

(1) Bathrooms
(2) Kitchens
(3) Rooftops
(4) Outdoors

Exception No. 1 to (3) and (4): Receptacles that are not readily accessible and are supplied from a dedicated branch circuit for electric snow-melting or deicing equipment shall be permitted to be installed without GFCI protection.

Exception No. 2 to (4): In industrial establishments only, where the conditions of maintenance and supervision ensure that only qualified personnel are involved, an assured equipment grounding conductor program as specified in 590.6(B)(2) shall be permitted for only those receptacle outlets used to supply equipment that would create a greater hazard if power is interrupted or having a design that is not compatible with GFCI protection.

Summary of Change

This revision expands the GFCI requirements to all 125-volt, single-phase, 15- and 20-ampere receptacles installed outdoors. A new exception has been added for industrial establishments that afford controlled conditions indicated in the exception.

210.8(B)(4)

Other Than Dwelling Units
NEC, p. 49

Proposal 2-70
Log 1443
ROP, p. 72

Comment 2-39, 2-41
Log 13, 1358
ROC, p. 44, 45

Change at a Glance

GFCI protection is required on all 15- and 20-ampere outdoor receptacles, unless they are inaccessible or serviced by qualified personnel.

Analysis and Effect

The changes to this section expand the general requirements for GFCI protection requirement to all outdoor 15- and 20-ampere, 125-volt receptacles other than those identified in the exceptions as revised. The addition of Exception No. 2 to item (4) provides for a limited alternative that relaxes the GFCI protection requirement for outdoor applications in industrial establishments only, where the conditions of maintenance and supervision ensure that only qualified personnel are involved. Such qualifying receptacles are limited to use with equipment that meets the restrictions of an assured equipment grounding conductor program as specified in 590.6(B)(2). In addition to promoting consistent application of the GFCI receptacle requirements in outdoor locations and increasing shock protection for users in general, the revision removes the need for determining which receptacles are accessible to the public.

Summary of Change

This revision expands the GFCI requirements to all 15- and 20-ampere receptacles installed outdoors other than those identified in the two exceptions. A new exception has been added for industrial establishments that afford controlled conditions indicated in the exception.

Code Language

(B)

Other Than Dwelling Units
All 125-volt, single-phase, 15- and 20-ampere receptacles installed in the locations specified in (1) through (5) shall have ground-fault circuit-interrupter protection for personnel:
(3) Rooftops
(4) Outdoors

Exception No. 1 to (3) and (4): Receptacles that are not readily accessible and are supplied from a dedicated branch circuit for electric snow-melting or deicing equipment shall be permitted to be installed without GFCI protection.

Exception No. 2 to (4): In industrial establishments only, where the conditions of maintenance and supervision ensure that only qualified personnel are involved, an assured equipment grounding conductor program as specified in 590.6(B)(2) shall be permitted for only those receptacle outlets used to supply equipment that would create a greater hazard if power is interrupted or having a design that is not compatible with GFCI protection.

Other Than Dwelling Units
NEC, p. 50

Proposal 2-81
Log 81
ROP, p. 74

Comment 2-57
Log 796
ROC, p. 48

Analysis and Effect

In *NEC*-2005, the requirement for ground-fault cir-cuit-interrupter protection within 1.8 m (6 ft) of wet bar sinks in dwelling units was expanded to include laundry and utility sinks, as well as to address the apparent elec-trocution and shock hazards present in such wet loca-tions. This revision introduces the same GFCI require-ments for receptacles within 1.8 (6 ft) of sinks in other than dwelling applications. The effect of this expanded GFCI requirement not only increases electrocution and shock protection for persons in these locations but also promotes more consistent application of the *NEC* rules for dwelling units and other than dwelling units where the hazard is the same. Ground-fault circuit-interrupt-er protection will now be required for all 15- and 20-ampere receptacles in the vicinity of sinks regardless of the type of non-dwelling occupancy where the sink is located. The new Exception No. 2 recognizes that recep-tacle GFCI requirements are modified by more specific requirements in Ar-ticle 517 for certain patient care loca-tions other than those covered by the general provisions in 210.8(B)(1).

Change at a Glance

GFCI protection is gener-ally now required for all 125-volt, single-phase, 15- and 20-ampere receptacles installed within 1.8 m (6 ft) of the outside edge of sinks in other than dwellings.

Code Language
210.8(B)(5)

Sinks
—where receptacles are installed within 1.8 m (6 ft) of the outside edge of the sink.

Exception No. 2 to (5): For recep-tacles located in patient care areas of health care facilities other than those covered under 210.8(B)(1), GFCI pro-tection shall not be required.

Summary of Change

A new subdivision (5) has been added to Section 210.8(B) to address GFCI protection requirements at sinks in other than dwelling units. A new Exception No. 2 relaxes this requirement for receptacles located in patient care areas of health care facilities.

210.8(B)(5)
Exception 1

Other Than Dwelling Units
NEC, p. 50

Proposal 2-71
Log 2554
ROP, p. 72

Comment 2-44
Log 571
ROC, p. 46

Analysis and Effect

The revisions to Section 210.8(B)(5) result in GFCI requirements for all 125-volt, single-phase, 15- and 20-ampere receptacles located within 1.8 m (6 ft) of any sink. This new exception relaxes this requirement in industrial laboratories where interruption of power by a ground-fault circuit interrupter would result in greater hazards for personnel. Substantiation with Comment 2-44 indicated that there are certain receptacles in industrial laboratories that require continuity of service for specific processes and sudden interruption of power to these loads could result in increased hazards for personnel. The new exception has application only in industrial laboratories.

Code Language

210.8(B)(5)
Receptacles
Exception No. 1 to (5)
In industrial laboratories, receptacles used to supply equipment where removal of power would introduce a greater hazard shall be permitted to be installed without GFCI protection.

Summary of Change

A new Exception No. 1 has been added to 210.8(B)(5).

Change at a Glance

The new exception relaxes the GFCI requirement for receptacles in industrial laboratories where interruption of receptacle power would introduce greater hazards.

210.8(C)

Boat Hoists
NEC, p. 50

Proposal 2-87
Log 3065
ROP, p. 75

Comment
None

Analysis and Effect

Section 210.8(C) requiring ground-fault circuit-interrupter protection for 125-volt, 15- and 20-ampere branch-circuit outlets supplying boat hoists in dwelling unit applications was new for *NEC*-2005. This GFCI requirement applied to the branch-circuit outlet whether a receptacle was installed or the boat hoist equipment was directly wired to the branch-circuit outlet. The new requirement for this protection was supported by evidence of shock and electrocution at these types of installations provided by the Consumer Product Safety Commission. These findings affirmed the need for GFCI protection for all boat hoist installations in dwelling applications.

Substantiation provided by the Consumer Product Safety Commission (CPSC) has demonstrated that shock and electrocution hazards are present in boat hoist wiring exceeding the limited circuit ratings covered in the previous requirement. The revisions to this rule result in requirements for ground-fault protection for personnel for all branch circuit configurations up to 240 volts that supply boat hoist equipment. The requirements of this section continue to apply only to boat hoist installations installed in dwelling unit locations. This change affords greater levels of shock protection for persons operating boat hoist equipment supplied by a number of voltage and ampacity configurations up to 240 volts.

Code Language
210.8(C)

Boat Hoists

GFCI protection shall be provided for outlets not exceeding 240 volts that supply boat hoists installed in dwelling unit locations.

Summary of Change

This section has been revised to include GFCI protection for all outlets not exceeding 240 volts.

Change at a Glance

Ground-fault circuit-interrupter protection applies to all boat hoist outlets not exceeding 240 volts.

2

210.12(B)

Dwelling Units
NEC, p. 51

Proposal 2-142
Log 3488
ROP, p. 89

Comment 2-95
Log 757
ROC, p. 59

Change at a Glance

Combination-type AFCI-protective devices are now required in all dwelling unit rooms, except for kitchens, bathroom, garages, basements, and rooms or areas not specified in this section.

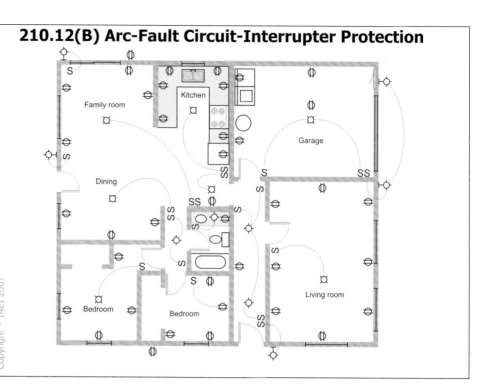

210.12(B) Arc-Fault Circuit-Interrupter Protection

Copyright © IAEI 2007

Analysis and Effect

The change results in evolution from the original substantiation provided by the Consumer Product Safety Commission (CPSC) in the 1999 *NEC* cycle that identified the need for such protection to reduce fires in dwelling units. Arc-fault circuit-interrupter protection (AFCI) was introduced in *NEC*-1999 as a means to reduce the number of residential fires by combining overcurrent protection with the mitigation of arcing effects in damaged branch-circuit wiring. The AFCI provides this protection by recognizing unique electrical characteristics of arcing effects (arc signatures) with subsequent and timely circuit interruption.

Since the introduction of AFCI protection to the *NEC*, there has been a plethora of industry anxiety and speculation, and some resistance. For the previous three *NEC* cycles, CMP-2 reviewed extensive amounts of convincing data and information pertaining to the benefit of AFCI for the protection of dwelling unit bedroom branch circuits, but industry should understand that there is nothing unique or special about the circuits supplying the bedrooms. This was no more than the area of the dwelling selected by CMP-2 to serve as a proving ground for the AFCI technology to evolve, rather than implementing whole-house protection at that time. CMP-2 expanded the AFCI protection requirements to branch-circuit outlets that supply dwelling unit bedrooms in the 2002 *NEC* cycle as a means to enhance safety and to gain experience by putting the application in an easily defined and limited area. Proposals to expand this requirement to the whole house were rejected in the 2005 *NEC* cycle as the technology was evolving. Arc-fault circuit interrupters have since been proving that they are effective in detecting and clearing arcing conditions or events in wiring systems before damage and loss could occur.

Experience has also shown that AFCI-protective devices detect numerous wiring errors; and in addition, they have proactively identified wiring and equipment damage and deficiencies that could have been potential sources of fire where protected only by conventional protection devices. It should be understood by users that the protection afforded by the AFCI is for the branch-circuit wiring as provided in the rule. Some of the benefits of this type of protection are that it can provide a level of protection from arcing effects beyond the outlets at the end of the branch circuit, but that is not its

Analysis of Changes *NEC*-2008

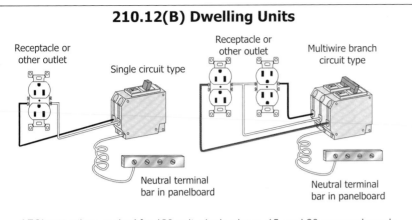

210.12(B) Dwelling Units

Receptacle or other outlet

Single circuit type

Neutral terminal bar in panelboard

Receptacle or other outlet

Multiwire branch circuit type

Neutral terminal bar in panelboard

AFCI protection required for 120-volt, single-phase, 15- and 20-ampere branch circuits installed in dwelling unit family rooms, dining rooms, living rooms, parlors, libraries, dens, bedrooms, sunrooms, recreation rooms, closets, hallways, or similar rooms or areas.

Listed arc-fault circuit interrupter, combination-type, shall be installed to provide protection of the branch circuit."

Code Language
210.12(B)
Dwelling Units

All 120-volt, single phase, 15- and 20-ampere branch circuits supplying outlets installed in dwelling unit family rooms, dining rooms, living rooms, parlors, libraries, dens, bedrooms, sunrooms, recreation rooms, closets, hallways, or similar rooms or areas shall be protected by a listed arc-fault circuit interrupter, combination-type, installed to provide protection of the branch circuit.

Summary of Change

This section has been revised to include a list of rooms and areas where the serving branch circuits are required to be protected by arc-fault circuit-interrupter protection. Essentially the requirements for AFCI protection are expanded to most areas and rooms in dwelling units with the exception of kitchens, bathrooms, garages, basements, and other areas or rooms not specifically identified in this section. The AFCI-protective devices must be listed combination-types. The sentence referencing the effective date of January 1, 2008, has been removed from this section under this revision.

main purpose as some have alleged or anticipated it should be. As the AFCI technology has evolved and improved further, there is no longer a strong basis or logical reasoning for limiting this protection to circuits that supply only outlets serving dwelling unit bedrooms, when the increased protection is needed for other circuits. The objective of the original proposal introduced the requirement in *NEC*-1999. This expansion continues the effort to reduce and minimize fires of electrical origin in dwellings.

The second paragraph has been deleted because the effective date for combination-type ACFI-protective devices is at approximately the same time frame as publication of *NEC*-2008 and is no longer necessary. During the discussions at the Report on Proposals hearings, there were suggestions of extending the effective date. Those proposed extensions were rejected by CMP-2, which affirms the panel's intentions that all AFCI-protective devices be listed combination-types as of January 1, 2008.

210.12(B)
Exception
No. 1

Dwelling Units
NEC, p. 51

Proposal 2-126
Log 596
ROP, p. 85

Comment 2-129
Log 797
ROC, p. 70

Change at a Glance

The 6 ft length restriction is no longer included; Type AC cable is now a recognized metallic wiring method in the exception.

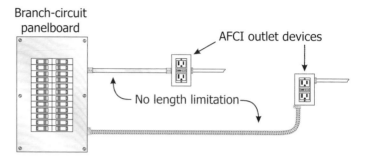

210.12(B) Exception No. 1

AFCI protection is required to be a combination type by January 1, 2008

Branch-circuit panelboard

AFCI outlet devices

No length limitation

Device-type AFCI protection is permitted at first outlet where the branch circuit is installed using RMC, IMC, EMT, or Type AC cable meeting the requirements in 250.118.

Combination-type listed AFCI device is required to be installed at the first outlet to provide protection for the remaining portion of the branch circuit.

Copyright © IAEI 2007

Analysis and Effect

The exception to 210.12(B) in *NEC*-2005 provided an alternative for installing an AFCI-protective device at the first outlet in the branch circuit. Because of the inherent restrictions of the existing exception, this alternative was not practical and resulted in reluctance to manufacture devices with limited application. This revision broadens that exception and provides for increased flexibility and more practical application. The length restriction was removed; however, the branch-circuit wiring to the first outlet must be in rigid metal conduit, intermediate metal conduit, electrical metallic tubing, or a steel armor cable, Type AC, which qualifies as an equipment grounding conductor in accordance with 250.118. The AFCI outlet-type protective device must be installed at the first outlet in the branch circuit and the wiring from the branch-circuit overcurrent device to the first outlet must be one of the listed types. This change provides additional alternatives for providing arc-fault circuit-interrupter protection as required in dwelling units. It also responds to efforts to include device-type AFCI protection as an option to address challenges in retrofitting existing electrical systems to include the arc-fault protection, such as those encountered when fuses are being used as the branch-circuit overcurrent protection for the dwelling unit. Although additional options are provided by these revisions, the limitations of the wiring methods necessary for application continue to limit where they can be practically applied in the field.

Code Language
210.12(B)

Dwelling Units
Exception No. 1
Where RMC, IMC, EMT or steel armored cable, Type AC, meeting the requirements of 250.118 using metal outlet and junction boxes is installed for the portion of the branch circuit between the branch-circuit overcurrent device and the first outlet, it shall be permitted to install a combination AFCI at the first outlet to provide protection for the remaining portion of the branch circuit.

Summary of Change

The 1.8 m (6 ft) length restriction is no longer included. Type AC cable has been included in the list of recognized wiring methods. This revision provides alternatives for use of listed combination AFCI protection (outlet device-type) installed at the first outlet in the branch circuit. There is no longer a length restriction of the metallic wiring method from the point of origin of the branch circuit to the first outlet, where ACFI protection is provided.

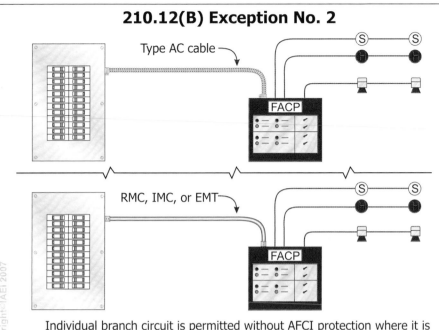

210.12(B) Exception No. 2

Type AC cable

FACP

RMC, IMC, or EMT

FACP

Individual branch circuit is permitted without AFCI protection where it is installed using RMC, IMC, EMT, or a Type AC cable assembly.

210.12(B) Exception No. 2

Dwelling Units
NEC, p. 51

Proposal 2-142
Log 3488
ROP, p. 89

Comment 2-137
Log 840
ROC, p. 73

Analysis and Effect

Reorganization in Article 760 required the renumbering of some sections; 760.21 was changed to 760.41(B) and 760.41 was changed to 760.121(B) and both have been revised to require individual branch circuits. This new exception to 210.12(B) correlates between 760.41(B) and 760.121(B) that prohibit AFCI and GFCI protection in branch circuits supplying either power-limited fire alarm circuits or non-power-limited fire alarm circuits. It also requires specific metallic wiring methods. Branch circuits supplying fire alarm systems covered by Article 760 must be in rigid metal conduit, intermediate metal conduit, electrical metallic tubing, or Type AC cable that qualifies as an equipment grounding conductor in accordance with 250.118. A fire alarm system in a dwelling unit must meet the requirements in 760 that prohibit AFCI and GFCI protection, and the required dedicated individual branch circuit must be installed in a metallic wiring method when installed in areas that now require AFCI protection. This exception is consistent with Exception No. 1 regarding concerns about physical protection of the branch circuit and its performance as an effective ground-fault current path. Single and multi-station smoke alarms include an initiating device and an audible appliance in the same unit, while smoke detectors installed as part of a fire alarm system are typically only initiating devices. Smoke alarms installed and connected to branch circuits in dwellings do not qualify for application of this exception.

Code Language
210.12(B)

Dwelling Units
Exception No. 2

Where a branch circuit to a fire alarm system installed in accordance with 760.41(B) and 760.121(B) is installed in RMC, IMC, EMT, or steel armored cable, Type AC, meeting the requirements of 250.118, with metal outlet and junction boxes, AFCI protection shall be permitted to be omitted.

Summary of Change

A new Exception No. 2 has been added and the existing exception to this section has been renumbered as Exception No. 1.

Change at a Glance

AFCIs are not permitted for the individual branch circuits supplying fire alarm systems in dwellings, and such branch circuits must be installed in a metallic wiring method when installed in those areas requiring AFCI protection.

210.19
(A)(1)
Exception
No. 2

Branch Circuits Not More
Than 600 Volts
NEC, p. 51

Proposal 2-166
Log 1319
ROP, p. 95

Comment 2-188
Log 1900
ROC, p. 84

Analysis and Effect

This revision clarifies the sizing requirements for grounded conductors of associated branch circuits. The exception specifically addresses the grounded (often a neutral) conductor of branch circuits. It is generally understood that grounded conductors are not permitted to be connected to an overcurrent device, other than the allowances in the exceptions to Section 230.90(B) and 240.22. This exception provides straightforward sizing allowances for the grounded conductor of a branch circuit allowing it to be sized at 100% of the continuous and non-continuous load. Where a grounded conductor is terminated to an overcurrent device, the requirements for 125% of the overcurrent device rating must be applied. This exception also predicated a need to revise the language provided in Annex D, Example D3(a) [see the analysis of this revision following chapter 9 of this text]. The revised text in Example D3(a) in Annex D correlates with the revisions to this section.

Change at a Glance

The additional 25% load requirement applies only to branch-circuit conductors that are terminated in an overcurrent protective device, unless the overcurrent device is listed for operation at 100% of its rating.

Code Language
210.19(A)(1)

Grounded Conductors
Exception No. 2
Grounded conductors that are not connected to an overcurrent device shall be permitted to be sized at 100 percent of the continuous and non-continuous load.

Summary of Change

A new exception addressing grounded conductor sizing for feeders has been added to Section 210.19(A)(1).

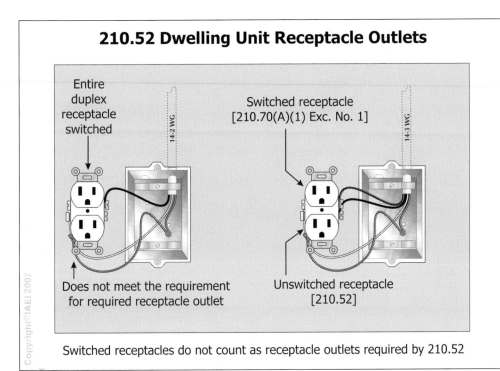

210.52 Dwelling Unit Receptacle Outlets

Entire duplex receptacle switched

Switched receptacle [210.70(A)(1) Exc. No. 1]

14-2 WG

14-3 WG

Does not meet the requirement for required receptacle outlet

Unswitched receptacle [210.52]

Switched receptacles do not count as receptacle outlets required by 210.52

Copyright©IAEI 2007

Dwelling Unit
Receptacle Outlets
NEC, p. 54

Proposal 2-190
Log 3324
ROP, p. 99

Comment
None

Analysis and Effect

This change provides a clarification for receptacles that are controlled by switches to meet the requirements for switched lighting outlets in 210.70(A)(1) Exception No. 1. Note that this allowance for switched receptacles applies to receptacles in other than the bathrooms or kitchens of dwelling units. The net result of this revision clarifies that only one receptacle of a duplex receptacle is permitted to be controlled by a switch. This revision makes it clear that the receptacles required by 210.52 placement rules must meet the objective of providing convenience receptacles in those prescribed locations for users. Switching both receptacles of a duplex-type receptacle leaves an area of the wall space without a receptacle that provides continuous service to meet the minimum requirements of 210.52 for receptacles that should be provided. The effect for installers is that duplex receptacles that are provided in accordance with 210.52 and located to meet the spacing rules of 210.52(A) must provide continuity of service to that location. It is clear that one receptacle on the mounting strap or yoke of the device is permitted to be switched; but where both are switched, an additional receptacle would be necessary to meet the objectives and requirements of 210.52.

Code Language
210.52

Dwelling Unit Receptacle Outlets

This section provides requirements for 125-volt, 15- and 20-ampere receptacle outlets. The receptacles required by this section shall be in addition to any receptacle that is:
(1) Part of a luminaire or appliance, or
(2) Controlled by a wall switch in accordance with 210.70(A)(1), Exception No. 1, or
(3) Located within cabinets or cupboards, or
(4) Located more than 1.7 m (5 ½ ft) above the floor.

Summary of Change

The words "or is controlled by a wall switch in accordance with 210.70(A)(1) Exception No. 1" have been added to this section.

Change at a Glance

Switched receptacles do not count as the receptacle outlets required by 210.52.

2

210.52(E)

Outdoor Outlets
NEC, p. 56

Proposal 2-229
Log 637
ROP, p. 108

Comment 2-227
Log 1411
ROC, p. 92

Change at a Glance

An accessible receptacle outlet is required on balconies, decks, or porches of dwelling units above grade level.

Analysis and Effect

The revisions in this section involve restructuring the various requirements for outdoor receptacle outlets into a list format. These structural changes improve clarity and usability and are in concert with the *NEC Style Manual* requirements for subdividing sections and establishing list formats where possible. A new subdivision (3) has been added to require at least one receptacle outlet to be installed at each balcony, deck, or porch that is accessible from inside the dwelling unit. This new requirement applies to all porches, decks, or balconies and does not have to be accessible from grade level. The revised text takes into consideration those units that are above the first floor level that may have balconies, decks or porches. It is common for holiday lighting and other electrical appliances to be used on the balconies of these units. The requirement for a receptacle outlet in these locations should help reduce instances of extension cords run from inside the unit that could create hazards by being pinched between sliding doors or windows. Action by CMP-2 responds to those concerns for reducing the need for an extension cord use to provide power for these spaces.

Summary of Change

This section has been reorganized and restructured into a list format to meet the requirements of the *NEC Style Manual*. A new subdivision (3) has been added to require a receptacle outlet accessible from balconies, decks, or porches.

Code Language

(E)
Outdoor Outlets.
(1) One-Family and Two-Family Dwellings. For a one-family dwelling and each unit of a two-family dwelling that is at grade level, at least one receptacle outlet accessible while standing at grade level and located not more than 2.0 m (6 1/2 ft) above grade shall be installed at the front and back of the dwelling.

(2) Multifamily Dwellings. For each dwelling unit of a multifamily dwelling where the dwelling unit is located at grade level and provided with individual exterior entrance/egress, at least one receptacle outlet accessible from grade level and not more than 2.0 m (6 1/2 ft) above grade shall be installed.

(3) Balconies, Decks, and Porches. Balconies, decks, and porches that are accessible from inside the dwelling unit shall have at least one receptacle outlet installed within the perimeter of the balcony, deck, or porch. The receptacle shall not be located more than 2.0 m (6 1/2 ft) above the balcony, deck, or porch surface.

Analysis of Changes *NEC*-2008

210.52 (E)(3)

Outdoor Outlets
NEC, p. 56

Proposal 2-229
Log 637
ROP, p. 108

Comment 2-230
Log 2032
ROC, p. 93

Analysis and Effect

This new exception relaxes the receptacle outlet requirement when the dwelling unit deck, porch, or balcony provides a floor or platform area less than 1.86 m² (20 ft²). CMP-2 responded favorably to the substantiation in Comment 2-230, which clearly indicated that some balconies, decks, or porches are very small areas and serve only decorative or architectural purposes. The exception applies only to those balconies, decks, or porches that provide less than 1.86 m² (20 ft²) of floor or platform area. This action provides relief from the receptacle outlet requirement, but it is recognized that there could be situations where power would be desired in those areas for holiday lighting or other uses. The *NEC* continues to include other rules in 400.8 that restrict cords from use where installed through doors and windows, and so forth, but most occupants are unaware of such rules.

Code Language
210.52(E)(3)

Balconies, Decks, and Porches
Exception to (3): Balconies, decks, or porches with a usable area of less than 1.86 m² (20 ft²) are not required to have a receptacle installed.

Summary of Change

A new exception to list item (3) is included in Section 210.52(E).

Change at a Glance

Small balconies or deck spaces are exempt from the new receptacle outlet requirement.

2

210.52(G)

Basement and Garages
NEC, p. 56

Proposal 2-240
Log 1265
ROP, p. 110

Comment 2-237
Log 1083
ROC, p. 94

Change at a Glance

Required receptacle outlets are in addition to any receptacle outlets installed for specific equipment such as fire alarm systems, sump pumps, and so forth.

210.52(G) Basements and Garages

Water treatment equipment

Float switch

Float

Sump pump

Copyright©IAEI 2007

At least one receptacle outlet shall be installed in addition to those for specific equipment.

Analysis and Effect

The changes to this section provide needed clarification about receptacle outlet requirements for basements and attached or detached garages of dwelling units. The requirements before the revision could have been interpreted to allow a single receptacle, in addition to the receptacle supplied for laundry purposes or other specific equipment uses to meet the requirements of this section. For example, a single receptacle installed for a sump pump in addition to the one for laundry equipment would be all that is needed for compliance. The revisions in item (1) clarify what is anticipated to meet the objective of this receptacles requirement. A general-use receptacle is necessary to provide convenience of power in those locations without having to resort to extension cords that would possibly be connected to receptacles that are not GFCI-protected. The receptacles required by Section 210.52(G) are required to be protected by ground-fault circuit interrupters in accordance with 210.8(A).

Code Language
210.52(G)

Basements and Garages

For a one-family dwelling, the following provisions shall apply:
(1) At least one receptacle outlet, in addition to those for specific equipment, shall be installed in each basement, in each attached garage, and in each detached garage with electric power.
(2) Where a portion of the basement is finished into one or more habitable rooms, each separate unfinished portion shall have a receptacle outlet installed in accordance with this section.

Summary of Change

This rule has been restructured into a list format for improved clarity and usability. The words "in addition to those for specific equipment" have been added in item (1).

University Hall

210.60
(A)

Guest Rooms, Guest Suites, Dormitories, and Similar Occupancies
NEC, p. 56

Proposal 2-242
Log 1184
ROP, p. 110

Comment 1-238a
Log CC200
ROC, p. 95

Analysis and Effect

This revision clarifies that sleeping rooms in dormitories are included in the requirements of 210.60(A). The wording "and similar occupancies" in the first sentence of this rule is intended to apply to dormitory occupancies. As a result, rooms in hotels, motels, and sleeping rooms in dormitories, in addition to similar types of occupancies must have the receptacle outlets installed in accordance with placement requirements of 210.52(A).

In addition, bathrooms in dorms must meet the requirements of 210.52(D) for receptacle placement. This is a logical clarification because the use of bathrooms does not vary, typically in these types of occupancies.

This revision results in requirements for adequate numbers of receptacles to meet the electrical needs of dorm rooms and to limit the excessive use of extension cords and receptacle power strips. Students today often require computers and a variety of other electrical utilization equipment. It is also very common that more than one student share a single dorm. This revision to require a minimum number of receptacles in those rooms improves this situation, which the *NEC* did not clearly address in previous editions. Installers and inspectors will now have clear language in the *Code* to remove the question as to how many receptacles are required in sleeping rooms of dormitories. Typically, inspectors required these occupancies to meet the receptacle placement rules in 210.52, but had no clear text in the *Code* to support this interpretation.

Code Language
210.60(A)
General

Guest rooms or guest suites in hotels, motels, sleeping rooms in dormitories, and similar occupancies shall have receptacle outlets installed in accordance with 210.52(A) and 210.52(D). Guest rooms or guest suites provided with permanent provisions for cooking shall have receptacle outlets installed in accordance with all of the applicable rules in 210.52.

Summary of Change

This section and the title of the section have been revised to include to sleeping rooms in dormitories and similar occupancies.

Change at a Glance

Sleeping rooms of dormitories and similar occupancies must meet the same receptacle-outlet location requirements for dwelling units as provided in 210.52(A) and (D).

210.62

Show Windows
NEC, p. 57

Proposal 2-244
Log 1895
ROP, p. 111

Comment
None

Change at a Glance

Receptacle outlets are required to be located within 450 mm (18 in.) of the top of a show window.

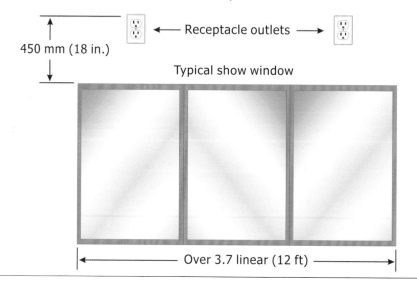

210.62 Show Windows

At least one receptacle outlet is required to be installed within 450 mm (18 in.) of the top of a show window for each 3.7 linear m (12 ft) or major fraction thereof measured horizontally at its maximum width.

450 mm (18 in.)

← Receptacle outlets →

Typical show window

Over 3.7 linear (12 ft)

Copyright©IAEI 2007

Analysis and Effect

The requirement for a receptacle at a show window has been in the *NEC* for considerable time. The requirements of this section must be applied to all types and configurations of what is defined as a show window. In some cases, this presented some unique challenges for installers and inspectors to satisfy the intent of the requirement. The revisions to this section result in more specific location criteria that must be applied to show window receptacle installations. The new rule requires the receptacle to be located within 450 mm (18 in.) of the top of any show window. This change provides installers with clear direction on how to meet the placement criteria for show window receptacles while at the same time providing enforcement with a means to apply the rule more consistently to all show windows. The effect for users is receptacles located for the convenient and practical use for which they were intended without having to resort to extension cord use, or other remedial means of supplying power for show window applications, which can lead to less than safe conditions.

Code Language
210.62
Show Windows

At least one receptacle outlet shall be installed within 450 mm (18 in.) of the top of a show window for each 3.7 linear m (12 linear ft) or major fraction thereof of show window area measured horizontally at its maximum width.

Summary of Change

This section has been revised by replacing the word "above" with the words "within 450 mm (18 in.) of" after the word "installed."

215.2 (A)(1) Exception No. 2

Feeders Not More Than 600 Volts
NEC, p. 58

Proposal 2-275
Log 1322
ROP, p. 116

Comment
None

Analysis and Effect

This revision clarifies the sizing requirements for grounded conductors of associated feeders. The exception specifically addresses the grounded (often a neutral) conductor of feeders. It is generally understood that grounded conductors are not permitted to be connected to an overcurrent device, other than the allowances in the exceptions to Section 230.90(B) and 240.22. This exception provides straightforward sizing allowances for the grounded conductor of a feeder allowing it to be sized at 100% of the continuous and non-continuous load. Where a grounded conductor is terminated to an overcurrent device, the requirements for 125% of the overcurrent device rating must be applied.

Change at a Glance

The additional 25% load requirement applies only to conductors that are terminated in an overcurrent protective device, unless the overcurrent device is listed for operation at 100% of its rating.

Code Language
215.2
Grounded Conductors
Exception No. 2:
Grounded conductors that are not connected to an overcurrent device shall be permitted to be sized at 100 percent of the continuous and non-continuous load.

Summary of Change

A new exception addressing grounded conductor sizing for feeders has been added to Section 215.2(A)(1).

215.6

Feeder Equipment Grounding Conductor
NEC, p. 59

Proposal 2-283
Log 524
ROP, p. 118

Comment 2-250
Log 24
ROC, p. 98

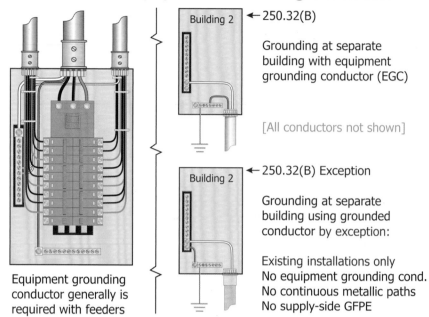

215.6 Feeder Equipment Grounding Conductor

Building 2 ← 250.32(B)

Grounding at separate building with equipment grounding conductor (EGC)

[All conductors not shown]

Building 2 ← 250.32(B) Exception

Grounding at separate building using grounded conductor by exception:

Existing installations only
No equipment grounding cond.
No continuous metallic paths
No supply-side GFPE

Copyright©IAEI 2007

Equipment grounding conductor generally is required with feeders

Analysis and Effect

The title to Section 215.6 has been revised to clarify that the grounding means previously addressed here is the feeder equipment grounding conductor for the feeder. This change is consistent with the efforts of the NEC TCC Task Group on Grounding and Bonding to address how words and terms related to grounding and bonding are used throughout the *NEC*. The revision correlates effectively with the provisions of 250.32(B) Exception that specifically relate to the equipment grounding conductor of feeders that supply buildings or structures. This revision also correlates between the two sections that address feeder equipment grounding conductors and rules that apply to how they are connected at separate buildings or structures.

Change at a Glance

The revision provides a correlation with 250.32(B) Exception that includes provisions for using the grounded conductor of a feeder as a grounding means at existing separate buildings or structures only.

Code Language

215.6

Feeder Equipment Grounding Conductor
Where a feeder supplies branch circuits in which equipment grounding conductors are required, the feeder shall include or provide an equipment grounding conductor in accordance with the provisions of 250.134, to which the equipment grounding conductors of the branch circuits shall be connected. Where the feeder supplies a separate building or structure, the requirements of 250.32(B) shall apply.

Summary of Change

This section was revised for technical clarity in the use of grounding and bonding terms. A new last sentence was added and provides a direct correlation with Section 250.32(B).

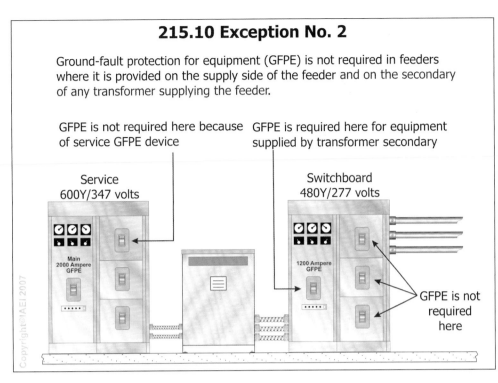

215.10 Exception No. 2

Ground-fault protection for equipment (GFPE) is not required in feeders where it is provided on the supply side of the feeder and on the secondary of any transformer supplying the feeder.

GFPE is not required here because of service GFPE device

GFPE is required here for equipment supplied by transformer secondary

Service 600Y/347 volts

Main 2000 Ampere GFPE

Switchboard 480Y/277 volts

1200 Ampere GFPE

GFPE is not required here

Ground-Fault Protection of Equipment
NEC, p. 59

Proposal 2-286, 2-287
Log 3499, 3498
ROP, p. 119

Comment
None

Analysis and Effect

The revisions to Exception No. 2 clarify where GFPE is required. The intent of the exception is not to require GFPE on a feeder disconnect if that feeder has GFPE protection provided upstream. However, some users are misinterpreting that GFPE could be provided on the primary of a transformer to meet this exception. Of course, GFPE on the primary side of a transformer provides no protection to equipment connected to the secondary since the ground-fault on the secondary only returns current to the secondary of the transformer. The objective of this exception is to relax the GFPE requirement for distribution equipment connected to feeders where a GFPE device is supplied upstream of the feeder, at the service equipment, for example. When a transformer is inserted in a feeder, essentially this is a new derived system or source. The requirement for ground-fault protection for equipment is related to the size of the equipment supplied by the feeder, as indicated in 215.10. Current, including ground-fault current, will always try to return to the source. In this case, the source is the transformer. The GFPE on the supply side of such transformers would not protect the equipment in accordance with the requirements of this rule because the ground-fault current would not be attempting to return to the service and utility transformer, but to the transformer on the supply side of the feeder. The effect of this change clarifies for users that this exception does not apply to field installations where the feeder is derived from a transformer that is supplied from the service equipment on its supply side.

Code Language
215.10

Ground-Fault Protection of Equipment
Exception No. 2:

The provisions of this section shall not apply if ground-fault protection of equipment is provided on the supply side of the feeder and on the load side of any transformer supplying the feeder.

Summary of Change

Section 215.10 Exception No. 3 (*NEC*-2005) has been revised by adding the words "and on the load side of any transformer supplying the feeder" and has been renumbered as Exception No. 2 because 215.10 Exception No. 2 (*NEC*-2005) was deleted as a result of CMP-2 action on Proposal 2-286.

Change at a Glance

GFPE on the primary side of transformers does not provide feeder ground-fault protection for equipment on the secondary side.

215.12(C)

Ungrounded Conductors
NEC, p. 59

Proposal 2-290, 2-291, 2-292
Log 671, 2682, 2736
ROP, p. 119, 120

Comment 2-254
Log 1898
ROC, p. 98

Change at a Glance

Identification means must distinguish both phase and system conductors and is required where feeder conductors terminate or are spliced.

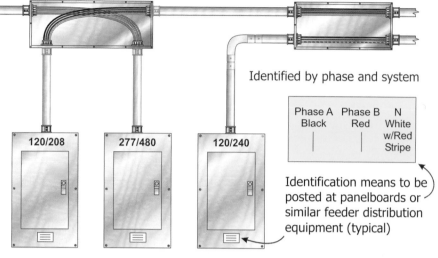

215.12(C) Ungrounded Conductors

Feeder identification is required where more than one nominal voltage exists

Identified by phase and system

Phase A	Phase B	N
Black	Red	White w/Red Stripe

Identification means to be posted at panelboards or similar feeder distribution equipment (typical)

120/208   277/480   120/240

Copyright©IAEI 2007

Means of identification are permitted to be by separate color coding, marking tape, tagging, or other approved means (applies to each system)

Analysis and Effect

Section 215.12(C) was new in *NEC*-2005 and essentially paralleled the new identification requirements for branch circuits covered by 210.5(C). The changes to this section correlate with similar revisions to Section 210.5(C) for consistency. The first revision expands the identification requirements for feeders by clarifying that conductors of feeders are to be identified by both phase and system. These requirements should result in more readily identifiable feeder system origins as well as indicating to which phase of that system the conductors are connected. The term *where accessible* previously imposed the identification requirements to conditions that were not necessarily practical in all cases. The adjustment in wording to specifically require the identification means to be applied "at all termination, connection and splice points" clarifies that the identification means does not have to be applied in conduit bodies or other access points where the feeder conductors are accessible but pass through such fittings. The change results in ease of feeder and system verification by inspectors and enhanced safety levels for installers and workers by improving the means of identifying feeders and the systems from which they are supplied. These revisions also have been expanded to allow readily available documentation to serve as a feeder identification means in addition to the means posted at the equipment where the feeder originates.

Code Language
215.12(C)

Ungrounded Conductors

Where the premises wiring system has feeders supplied from more than one nominal voltage system, each ungrounded conductor of a feeder shall be identified by phase or line and system at all termination, connection, and splice points....The method utilized for conductors originating within each feeder panelboard or similar feeder distribution equipment shall be documented in a manner that is readily available or shall be permanently posted at each feeder panelboard or similar feeder distribution equipment.

Summary of Change

This section has been revised by adding the words "phase or line and" before the word "system" and replacing the words "where accessible" with the words "at all termination, connection and splice points."

Analysis of Changes *NEC*-2008

General Loads
NEC, p. 66

Proposal 2-338, 2-340
Log 1165, 3249
ROP, p. 128, 129

Comment
None

Analysis and Effect

The revisions to Section 220.82(B)(2), (3) and (4) clarify the requirements for general calculations applying to dwelling units covered by this section. The requirement to provide small appliance and laundry branch circuits actually is located in 210.11(C), not 220.52, which is clarified by changing the reference. This helps clarify that multiwire branch circuits are permitted to be used for the small appliance branch circuits in addition to the two-wire circuits mentioned in 210.11(C)(1) and (2). The reference to "clothes dryers" in (3) was expanded to make it clear that a gas dryer connected to the laundry branch circuit requires no additional calculation. The changes to (4) in this section clarify that motors already covered by (3) are not included in the calculation.

Change at a Glance

Multiwire branch circuits are permitted to be used for the small appliance branch circuits in addition to the two-wire circuits mentioned in 210.11(C)(1) and (2). Gas dryers can be connected to a laundry branch circuit without additional calculation.

Code Language
220.82(B) and (C)

General Loads and Heating and Air-Conditioning Load

(2) 1500 volt-amperes for each 2-wire, 20-ampere small-appliance branch circuit and each laundry branch circuit covered in 210.11(C)(1) and (2).

(3) The nameplate rating of the following:
a. All appliances that are fastened in place, permanently connected, or located to be on a specific circuit
b. Ranges, wall-mounted ovens, counter-mounted cooking units
c. Clothes dryers that are not connected to the laundry branch circuit specified in item (2)
d. Water heaters

(4) The nameplate ampere or kVA rating of all permanently connected motors not included in item (3).

Summary of Change

Subdivision (2) to Section 220.82(B) has been revised to replace the reference to 220.52 with 210.11(C)(1) and (2). Subdivision (4) has also been revised to remove the words "low power factor loads" and add a reference to (3). Subdivision (3) has been restructured into a list format and has expanded the information about clothes dryers that are gas types.

220.82 (C)(2)

Heating & Air-Conditioning Load
NEC, p. 66

Proposal 2-343
Log 1897
ROP, p. 129

Comment 2-267, 2-268
Log 595, 1204
ROC, p. 100

Change at a Glance

Heat pumps loads are to be calculated at 100% of the nameplate rating when used without any supplemental electric heating.

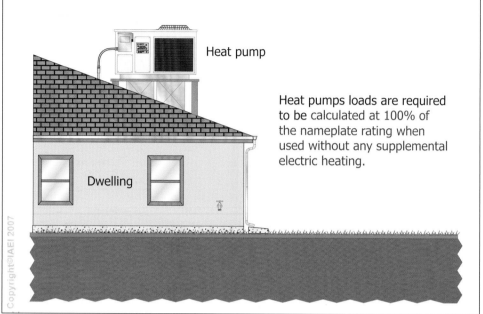

220.82(C)(2) Heating and Air-Conditioning Load

Heat pump

Heat pumps loads are required to be calculated at 100% of the nameplate rating when used without any supplemental electric heating.

Dwelling

Copyright©IAEI 2007

Analysis and Effect

This section has been rearranged to provide a more logical order and revised to clarify the load calculation requirements for heat pumps where supplemental heat is not used. Since the heat pump compressor and related accessories are being used to generate the heat without the use of supplemental electric heating strips, the nameplate rating of the heat pump would be used for the general load. The text as used in *NEC*-2005 indicates the use of the heating load on the nameplate when, in fact, there would be no specific heating load for this air conditioner. This revision provides needed clarification and the proper location of the data necessary to be used in the optional calculation method.

Summary of Change

Section 220.82(C)(2) has been revised by deleting the word "heating" and replacing it with the words "heat pump." The word "a" has been changed to the word "the."

Code Language
220.82

(C) Heating and Air-Conditioning Load. The largest of the following six selections (load in kVA) shall be included:
(1) 100 percent of the nameplate rating(s) of the air conditioning and cooling.
(2) 100 percent of the nameplate rating(s) of the heat pump when the heat pump is used without any supplemental electric heating.
(3) 100 percent of the nameplate rating(s) of the heat pump compressor and 65 percent of the supplemental electric heating for central electric space-heating systems. If the heat pump compressor is prevented from operating at the same time as the supplementary heat, it does not need to be added to the supplementary heat for the total central space heating load.
(4) 65 percent of the nameplate rating(s) of electric space heating if less than four separately controlled units.
(5) 40 percent of the nameplate rating(s) of electric space heating if four or more separately controlled units.
(6) 100 percent of the nameplate ratings of electric thermal storage and other heating systems where the usual load is expected to be continuous at the full nameplate value. Systems qualifying under this selection shall not be calculated under any other selection in 220.82(C).

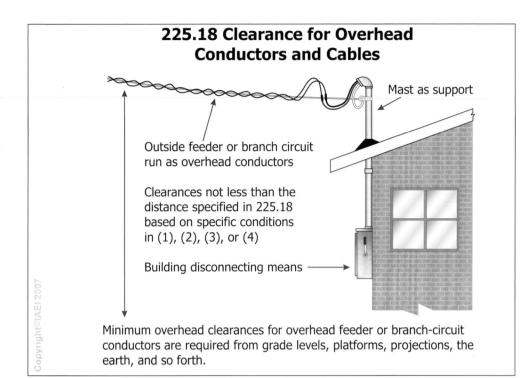

225.18 Clearance for Overhead Conductors and Cables

Mast as support

Outside feeder or branch circuit run as overhead conductors

Clearances not less than the distance specified in 225.18 based on specific conditions in (1), (2), (3), or (4)

Building disconnecting means

Minimum overhead clearances for overhead feeder or branch-circuit conductors are required from grade levels, platforms, projections, the earth, and so forth.

Copyright©IAEI 2007

Clearance for Overhead Conductors and Cables
NEC, p. 71

Proposal 4-12
Log 620
ROP, p. 137

Comment 4-7
Log 1216
ROC, p. 102

Analysis and Effect

The title of this section has been revised to promote consistent use of defined terms related to grounding and bonding. This revision is consistent with the efforts of the *NEC* TCC Task Group on Grounding and Bonding. *Ground* is a defined term in Article 100 and primarily relates to the concepts of grounding and bonding. The words used in this section are *finished grade, sidewalks* and *platform or projection.* This section has been revised to correlate with the code-wide effort to identify that *ground* is associated with requirements of Article 250. Terms related to grounding and bonding concepts and requirements should mean what they imply as defined in the *Code* where used in any other requirements throughout the *NEC*. Removing *ground* from the title of this section will help reduce the confusion with the use of the term outside of Article 250. Similar editorial revisions have also been incorporated in 230.24 and 230.50 for correlation and consistency.

Code Language
225.18
Clearance for Overhead Conductors and Cables

Summary of Change

Change the title to "Clearance for Overhead Conductors and Cables." The word "ground" was removed and the words "for overhead conductors and cables" were added to the title of Section 225.18.

Change at a Glance

Clearances for overhead conductors and cables, regardless from what grade or level they are taken, are addressed in more general fashion.

2

225.22,
Exception

Raceways on Exterior Surfaces
of Buildings or Other
Structures
NEC, p. 72

Proposal 4-14
Log 2608
ROP, p. 138

Comment 4-11
Log 2152
ROC, p. 103

Change at a Glance

Flexible metal conduit is
no longer to be used in wet
locations.

Analysis and Effect

Action by CMP-4 reverses the original rejection of Proposal 4-14. Affirmative action by CMP-8 on Proposals 8-26, 8-27, and 8-28 provided the basis for deleting this exception. Substantiation in those proposals indicated that the *Code* already restricts liquids from entering an enclosure to which flexible metal conduit is connected. Flexible metal conduit does not have a continuous outer surface and does not provide a protective covering over its interlocking metal tape armor construction. Installations of flexible metal conduit with listed fittings do not provide sufficient protection from wetness entering the conduit and enclosures to which it is connected. The deletion of this exception correlates with the actions of CMP-8 to clarify that flexible metal conduit is no longer permitted to be used in wet locations as provided in 348.12(1). This revision removes questions about applications of flexible metal conduit, regardless of the type of conductors it contains.

Code Language

Deleted

*Exception: Flexible metal conduit,
where permitted in 348.12 (1), shall
not be required to be raintight.*

Summary of Change

The exception to 225.22
has been deleted.

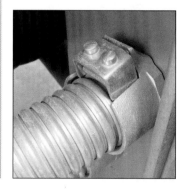

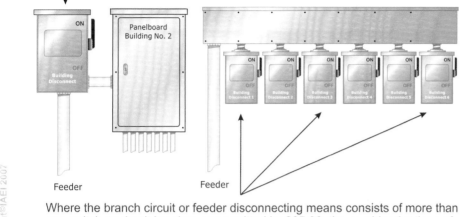

225.39 Rating of Disconnect

The feeder disconnect is required to be rated at not less than the calculated load to be carried, determined in accordance with Parts I and II of Article 220 for branch circuits, Parts III or IV for feeders, or Part V for farm loads.

Where the branch circuit or feeder disconnecting means consists of more than one switch or circuit breaker, as permitted by 225.33, the combined ratings of all the switches or circuit breakers used shall be permitted.

225.39

Rating of Disconnect
NEC, p. 74

Proposal 4-25
Log 2156
ROP, p. 140

Comment
None

Analysis and Effect

Sections 225.31 and 225.33 address requirements for disconnecting means in feeders supplying separate buildings or structures. The disconnecting means requirements are similar to those for service disconnecting means covered in 230.70 and 230.71. Section 230.80 includes methods of establishing a combined rating for installations where multiple disconnects in separate enclosures are used as the service disconnecting means. It is important to note that the term *disconnecting means* is defined in Article 100 and can be a single disconnect or a group of disconnects. This section in Article 225 has been revised by adding a new second sentence to clarify that when more than one switch or circuit breaker is used as the disconnecting means for a feeder supplying a separate building or structure, the combined ratings of the switches or circuit breakers used as the disconnecting means can be added together to achieve the minimum rating required for the disconnecting means. This revision incorporates methods of establishing combined ratings of several disconnects in 225.39 that are similar the requirements already provided in 230.80 for services.

Change at a Glance

The combined ratings of the separate switches or circuit breakers used as the service disconnecting means can be added together to achieve the minimum rating required for the disconnecting means.

Code Language
225.39
Rating of Disconnect

The feeder or branch-circuit disconnecting means shall have a rating of not less than the calculated load to be supplied, determined in accordance with Parts I and II of Article 220 for branch circuits, Parts III or IV of Article 220 for feeders, or Part V of Article 220 for farm loads. Where the branch circuit or feeder disconnecting means consists of more than one switch or circuit breaker, as permitted by 225.33, combining the ratings of all the switches or circuit breakers for determining the rating of the disconnecting means shall be permitted.

Summary of Change

This section has been revised by adding a new second sentence pertaining to combined ratings of disconnecting means.

2

230.24(B)

Vertical Clearance for Service-Drop Conductors
NEC, p. 77

Proposal 4-40
Log 619
ROP, p. 142

Comment 4-7
Log 1216
ROC, p. 102

Change at a Glance

This section addresses clearances for overhead conductors and cables, regardless from what grade or level the clearance is taken, in a more general fashion.

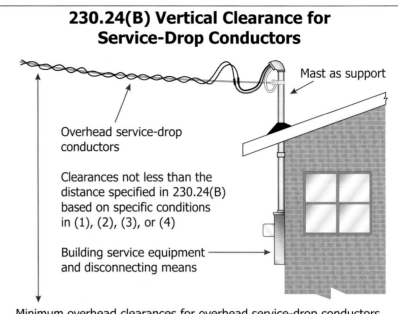

230.24(B) Vertical Clearance for Service-Drop Conductors

Mast as support

Overhead service-drop conductors

Clearances not less than the distance specified in 230.24(B) based on specific conditions in (1), (2), (3), or (4)

Building service equipment and disconnecting means

Copyright©IAEI 2007

Minimum overhead clearances for overhead service-drop conductors are required from different grade levels, platforms, projections, earth, and so forth.

Analysis and Effect

The title of this section has been revised to promote consistent use of defined terms related to grounding and bonding. This revision is consistent with the efforts of the *NEC* TCC Task Group on Grounding and Bonding. *Ground* is a defined term in Article 100 and primarily relates to the concepts of grounding and bonding. The words used in this section are *finished grade*, *sidewalks*, and *platform or projection*. This section has been revised to correlate with the code-wide effort to identify that *ground* is associated with requirements of Article 250. Terms related to grounding and bonding concepts and requirements should mean what they imply as defined in the *Code* where used in any other requirements throughout the *NEC*. Removing *ground* from the title of this section will help reduce the confusion with the use of *ground* outside of Article 250. Similar editorial revisions have also been incorporated in 225.18 and 230.50 for correlation and consistency.

Code Language
230.24(B)
Vertical Clearance for Service-Drop Conductors

Summary of Change

The word "ground" was removed and the words "for service-drop conductors" were added to the title of Section 230.24(B).

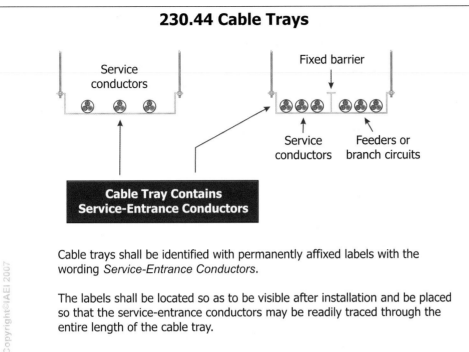

230.44 Cable Trays

Service conductors

Fixed barrier

Service conductors

Feeders or branch circuits

Cable Tray Contains Service-Entrance Conductors

Cable trays shall be identified with permanently affixed labels with the wording *Service-Entrance Conductors*.

The labels shall be located so as to be visible after installation and be placed so that the service-entrance conductors may be readily traced through the entire length of the cable tray.

Copyright©IAEI 2007

230.44 Exception

Cable Trays
NEC, p. 79

Proposal 4-52
Log 1898
ROP, p. 146

Comment 4-23, 4-24
Log 597, 1213
ROC, p. 105

REVISION

Analysis and Effect

This section has been revised to include specific labeling requirements that clearly indicate where the cable tray is being used for service-entrance conductors. The last two sentences were added to ensure that the cable tray containing a barrier separating the service-entrance conductors is clearly identified from feeders and branch circuits installed in the other side of the cable tray. The labels should be visible after the installation of the cable tray since an installer may not be able to differentiate between section/partition of the tray containing the service-entrance conductors and may inadvertently install protected conductors with unprotected conductors. The effect of this revision is that cable trays containing service-entrance conductors must be identified with permanently affixed labels with the wording *Service-Entrance Conductors*.

Change at a Glance

Cable trays containing service-entrance conductors must be labeled to indicate this use, and the labels must be readily traced.

Code Language
230.44
Cable Trays
Exception
...Cable trays shall be identified with permanently affixed labels with the wording "Service-Entrance Conductors." The labels shall be located so as to be visible after installation and placed so that the service-entrance conductors may be readily traced through the entire length of the cable tray.

Summary of Change

The exception to Section 230.44 has been revised to include two additional sentences addressing labeling requirements.

230.49 and 230.50

Protection Against Physical Damage
NEC, p. 79

Proposal 4-52a
Log CP 400
ROP, p. 146

Comment
None

REORGANIZE

Change at a Glance

Sections 230.49 and 230.50 have been combined and structured into a list format for clarity and usability.

Analysis and Effect

Sections 230.49 and 50 both cover protection against physical damage. The changes include combining the two sections and restructuring all previous requirements to provide a more logical layout for clarity and usability. The sections were combined since both addressed protection from physical damage, 230.49 for underground service-entrance conductors and 230.50 for all others. The new section, as revised, provides specific information and requirements without using the phrase "above ground" and clarifies the physical protection requirements for service-entrance conductors. The words "rigid nonmetallic conduit" have been changed to "PVC conduit" to correlate with changes in Article 352 and throughout the *NEC*.

Summary of Change

Sections 230.49 and 230.50 have been combined into one section and restructured to incorporate the provisions of both sections covering protection into one more usable section.

Code Language
230.50

Protection Against Physical Damage

(A)

Underground Service-Entrance Conductors
Underground service-entrance conductors shall be protected against physical damage in accordance with 300.5.

(B)

All Other Service-Entrance Conductors
All other service-entrance conductors, other than underground service-entrance conductors, shall be protected against physical damage as specified in 230.50(B)(1) or (B)(2).

(1) Service Cables. Service cables, where subject to physical damage, shall be protected by any of the following:
(1) Rigid metal conduit
(2) Intermediate metal conduit
(3) Schedule 80 PVC conduit
(4) Electrical metallic tubing
(5) Other approved means

(2) Other Than Service Cable. Individual open conductors and cables, other than service cables, shall not be installed within 3.0 m (10 ft) of grade level or where exposed to physical damage.

Exception: Type MI and Type MC cable shall be permitted within 3.0 m (10 ft) of grade level where not exposed to physical damage or where protected in accordance with 300.5(D).

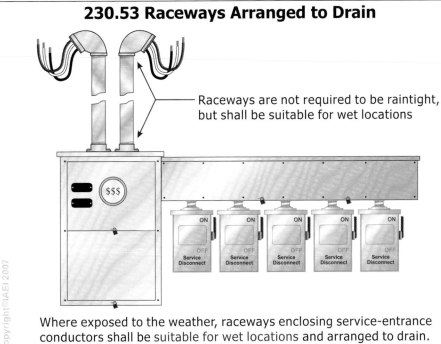

230.53 Raceways Arranged to Drain

Raceways are not required to be raintight, but shall be suitable for wet locations

Where exposed to the weather, raceways enclosing service-entrance conductors shall be suitable for wet locations and arranged to drain.

Copyright©IAEI 2007

Raceways to Drain
NEC, p. 80

Proposal 4-57
Log 1975
ROP, p. 147

Comment 4-27
Log 489
ROC, p. 106

Analysis and Effect

This revision clarifies the objectives intended by the use of the word "raintight" as previously provided in this section. It recognizes that raceways are generally not raintight, but many certainly are suitable for use in wet locations as specifically recognized in other *Code* rules. The word "raintight" as used in this section previously presented inconsistencies with how this word is defined in Article 100. This revision clarifies and improves the usability of this requirement that raceways are to be suitable for use in wet locations and, that where necessary, they must be arranged to drain any wetness that may enter from normal operating and environmental conditions. The revision also promotes more uniform and consistent use of defined *Code* words and terms.

Code Language
230.53

Raceways to Drain

Where exposed to the weather, raceways enclosing service-entrance conductors shall be suitable for wet locations and arranged to drain. Where embedded in masonry, raceways shall be arranged to drain.

Summary of Change

The words "suitable for wet locations" have replaced the word "raintight."

Change at a Glance

Raceways for service conductors do not have to be raintight, but are required to be suitable for wet location use.

2

230.54(A) and (B)

Overhead Service Locations
NEC, p. 80

Proposal 4-59, 4-60
Log 1970, 1971
ROP, p. 147

Comment 4-29, 4-30
Log 487, 488
ROC, p. 106

Analysis and Effect

Action by CMP-4 reverses the initial panel action on Proposals 4-59 and 4-60. This revision results in the removal of *raintight* from the title and text of 230.54(A) and (B). *Raintight*, as previously used in this section, presented inconsistencies with how the word is defined in Article 100. Weather heads, fittings and other equipment used at the overhead service drop connections are now required to meet the requirements in 314.15, which requires fittings and equipment to be placed or equipped in a manner that will prevent the entrance of moisture and to be listed for use in wet locations. This revision promotes consistent use of defined *Code* terms, while improving clarity and practical applicability in the requirements to field conditions. The existing exception to 230.54(B) for service-entrance cable goosenecks was not affected by this revision.

Change at a Glance

Service heads (weather heads) for service raceways and service cables are required for overhead service raceway or cable installations. The service heads must be placed or equipped to prevent the entrance of moisture, and they must be listed for use in wet locations.

Code Language
230.54
Overhead Service Locations

(A)
Service Head
Service raceways shall be equipped with a service head at the point of connection to service-drop conductors. The service head shall comply with the requirements for fittings in 314.15.

(B)
Service Cable Equipped with Service Head or Gooseneck
Service cables shall be equipped with a service head. The service head shall comply with the requirements for fittings in 314.15.

Summary of Change
The term *raintight* has been removed from 230.54(A) and (B). A new sentence referencing 314.15 has been added to each of these subdivisions.

230.71

Maximum Number of Disconnects
NEC, p. 81

Proposal 4-66
Log 2602
ROP, p. 149

Comment 4-32
Log 813
ROC, p. 106

Analysis and Effect

The editorial revisions to this section improve clarity and usability. In addition to the editorial improvements, it is now clear that the disconnecting means referred to in this portion of the rule must be part of or installed in the equipment. It cannot be a field-installed switch or a circuit breaker installed remote from the switchboard or panelboard. Many equipment manufacturers provide the option of surge protective devices and other apparatus identified in (1) through (4) as integral components in their assemblies. The disconnects provided in the equipment for these devices are not required to be included in the six disconnect maximum provisions of 230.71.

Change at a Glance

The disconnecting means for a surge protective device(s), power monitoring equipment, control circuit for a ground-fault protection system, and power-operable service disconnecting means is required to be part of the listed equipment.

Code Language
230.71(A)
General

The service disconnecting means.... in any one location.

For the purpose of this section, disconnecting means installed as part of listed equipment and used solely for the following shall not be considered a service disconnecting means:

(1) Power monitoring equipment
(2) Surge-protective device(s)
(3) Control circuit of the ground-fault protection system
(4) Power-operable service disconnecting means

Summary of Change

The last sentence of this section has been structured into a list format and the words "installed as part of and" have been added for clarity and editorial improvements. The term *transient voltage surge suppressors* has been changed to *surge protective devices* consistent with the revisions in Article 285.

2

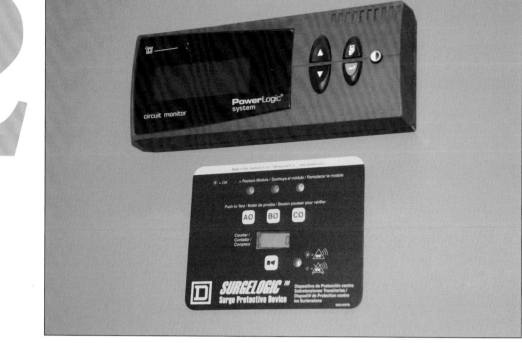

230.71, 230.82, 230.94

Surge Protective Devices
NEC, p. 81, 82, 83

Proposal 4-66, 4-77
Log 2602, 3476
ROP, p. 149, 152

Comment 4-32
Log 813
ROC, p. 106

Change at a Glance

Transient voltage surge suppressors are re-identified as *surge protective devices* in these three sections and throughout the *NEC*.

Analysis and Effect

These revisions change the term *transient voltage surge suppressors* to *surge protective devices* not only in these three sections but also throughout the *NEC*. These revisions are common to several other related changes affecting Articles 100, 230, 250, 280, 285, 501, and 502, which result from changes and restructuring of UL Standard 1449. This standard is being renamed as *Surge Protective Devices (SPDs)*. The reorganization and revisions to this product standard combine the categories of Surge Arresters (Article 280) and Transient Voltage Surge Suppressors (Article 285) into one category and one common standard. It is anticipated that UL Standard 1449 will include SPD designations Type 1 and Type 2 for permanently connected devices for use on circuits not exceeding 600 V. The technology of low-voltage surge arresters and TVSSs are now basically the same, thereby justifying coverage under one standard, UL 1449, and one test program with consideration given to the installation location on the line side (Type 1) or load side (Type 2) of the service-disconnect overcurrent protection. The *surge arrester* designation will be retained for devices used in circuits of 1 kV and over addressed by Article 280 and evaluated to IEEE C62.11-1999. Two new definitions of these terms have been added to Article 100.

Code Language

Surge Protective Devices
See the full text of Sections 230.71, 230.82 and 230.94 in the 2008 *Code* for the exact language.

Summary of Change

The changes replace the term *transient voltage surge suppressors* with *surge protective devices* in Section 230.71. The revision to Section 230.82(4) references Type 1 surge protective devices; the revision to subdivision (8) removes the term *transient voltage surge suppressors* and references Type 2 surge protective devices. Section 230.90 has been revised to reference Type 1 surge protective devices.

230.79 Rating of Service Disconnect

The service disconnect is required to be rated at not less than the calculated load to be carried, determined in accordance with Parts III, IV, or V of Article 220.

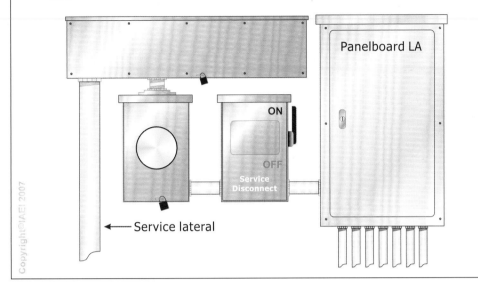

Panelboard LA

ON

OFF

Service Disconnect

← Service lateral

Copyright©IAEI 2007

230.79

Rating of Service Disconnecting Means
NEC, p. 82

Proposal 4-69
Log 925
ROP, p. 149

Comment
None

Analysis and Effect

The revisions to this section clarify that the rating of the service disconnect is to be not less than the *calculated* load to be carried and not the *actual* load carried. This revision logically implies that the load to be carried can vary from time to time, but a calculated load is the maximum anticipated that the disconnect would need to be capable of handling. The word "calculated" was used to be consistent with the changes in the text in Article 220 and other parts of *NEC*-2005 where the word "computed" was formerly used. The words "Parts III, IV, or V" were added to be consistent with the *NEC Style Manual* and to identify the applicable parts of Article 220, to which this section refers.

Change at a Glance

Parts III, IV, or V of 220 are required for determining the minimum rating for a service disconnecting means.

Code Language
230.79

Rating of Service Disconnecting Means

The service disconnecting means shall have a rating not less than the calculated load to be carried, determined in accordance with Parts III, IV, or V of Article 220, as applicable.

Summary of Change

The words "calculated" and "Parts III, IV, or V" were added to the first sentence of Section 230.79. References to Parts III, IV, and V of Article 220 provide specific direction for the calculations necessary to determine the minimum rating for a service disconnecting means.

230.82(3)

Equipment Connected to the Supply Side of Service Disconnect
NEC, p. 82

Proposal 4-4, 4-73
Log 1533, 3334
ROP, p. 135, 150

Comment 4-39a, 4-35
Log CC403, 1086
ROC, p. 108, 107

230.82(3) Meter Disconnect Switches

Meter socket disconnects permitted on supply side of service under conditions
- Rated 600 volts or less
- Rated for at least the available short-circuit current
- Housings and service enclosures are grounded per 250 Part VII and bonded per 250 Part V and are capable of interrupting the load served.

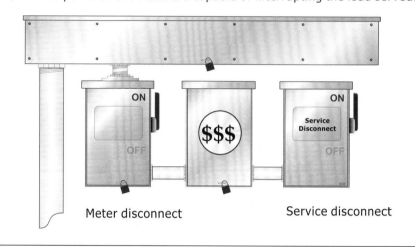

Meter disconnect   Service disconnect

Analysis and Effect

This section has been revised by requiring meter socket disconnects to be grounded and bonded electrically as required in Part V of Article 250. Both grounding and bonding functions are necessary in meter socket enclosures, and this change clarifies those essential requirements for this equipment. The second change provides information about the capabilities of meter socket disconnects. The substantiation in Comment 4-35 indicated that these switches provide not only safety for utility workers and other workers removing and inserting meters into their bases, but also can be operated by users with loads connected. Therefore, it is logical that these disconnecting means be capable of carrying and interrupting the load as well.

Change at a Glance

Meter socket disconnects must be capable of interrupting the load, and they shall be grounded and bonded to meet the applicable requirements in Parts V and VII of Article 250.

Code Language
230.82(3)

Meter Disconnect Switches
Meter disconnect switches nominally rated not in excess of 600 volts that have a short-circuit current rating equal to or greater than the available short-circuit current, provided all metal housings and service enclosures are grounded in accordance with Part VII and bonded in accordance with Part V of Article 250. A meter disconnect switch shall be capable of interrupting the load served.

Summary of Change

Specific references to the appropriate Parts V and VII of Article 250 and a new last sentence have been added.

Location
NEC, p. 84

Proposal 4-87
Log 2952
ROP, p. 154

Comment
None

Analysis and Effect

The definition of *service point* in Article 100 clarifies the point where the utility rules govern installations, and where the rules in the *NEC* start having application to the premises' wiring systems. There are many installations where the service point is at the edge of the property, and a medium or high voltage switching means or mechanism is the actual service disconnecting means, by definition, for the distribution system of the premises. The wiring on the load side of this point is actually a feeder, by definition, for multiple buildings on the property. As a result, the disconnect requirements in Articles 230 and 225 for feeders would apply to the buildings in this situation. In many cases, the switching mechanisms for pole cutouts in these systems are not readily accessible to persons or occupants as generally would be required by 230.70(A)(1), nor should they be, in most cases, for safety reasons. It should be emphasized that the *NEC* includes rules that could be applied to these types of installations; but in some cases, it falls short of addressing many installations and conditions that currently exist on the load side of what the *Code* presently defines as the *service point*. This change enforces needed language that can be applied to existing and new installations that fall under the scope of the *NEC* for these situations and allows for requirements that are more practical for users. The *NEC* continues to see growth regarding the rules that apply to medium and high-voltage systems and installations that fall under its scope.

Code Language
230.205(A)

Location

The service disconnecting means shall be located in accordance with 230.70.

For either overhead or underground primary distribution systems on private property, the service disconnect shall be permitted to be located in a location that is not readily accessible.

Summary of Change

An additional sentence has been incorporated into this section.

Change at a Glance

Service disconnects in underground or overhead primary power distribution systems are not required to be readily accessible.

2

240.4(D)

Small Conductors
NEC, p. 86

Proposal 10-10
Log 2931
ROP, p. 156

Comment
None

Change at a Glance

The requirements for small conductors have been expanded to include overcurrent protection for copper conductors in 16 AWG and 18 AWG sizes.

Analysis and Effect

These revisions expand the requirements for small conductors to include overcurrent protection rules for copper conductors in 16 AWG and 18 AWG sizes. This section has been restructured and organized into a list format to conform with the *NEC Style Manual* and to place the contained provisions in logical order. This change also correlates with NFPA 79-2002, *Electrical Standard for Industrial Machinery*. In order to remain competitive in the global marketplace, U. S. industrial machinery manufacturers on the committee for NFPA 79 expressed the need to be able to utilize power circuit conductors that are smaller than 14 AWG, which is the existing minimum allowed for branch circuits in the *NEC*. The use of 16 and 18 AWG conductors for other than control loads should be allowed provided conditions of use are established, and proper overcurrent protection is provided. The ampacity levels provided for 16 and 18 AWG conductors correlate with those in UL 508A, UL 508, and *NEC* Table 400.5(A) and the associated restrictions. These revisions do not allow for the expanded use of 16 AWG and 18 AWG conductors for general branch-circuit applications; they simply provide protection requirements for these conductors if their limited usage is allowed and specifically covered by other sections of the *NEC*. A UL special service investigation was conducted for the protection of 16 and 18 AWG copper conductors using Class CC, J, or T fuses, and the report of this testing and its results substantiated this change.

Code Language

240.4(D)

Small Conductors

Unless specifically permitted in 240.4(E) or (G), the overcurrent protection shall not exceed that required by (D)(1) through (D)(7) after any correction factors for ambient temperature and number of conductors have been applied.

(1) 18 AWG Copper. 7 amperes, provided all the following conditions are met:

   (1) Continuous loads do not exceed 5.6 amperes

   (2) Overcurrent protection is provided by one of the following:

     a. Branch-circuit-rated circuit breakers listed and marked for use with 18 AWG copper wire

     b. Branch-circuit-rated fuses listed and marked for use with 18 AWG copper wire

     c. Class CC, Class J, or Class T fuses

(2) 16 AWG Copper. 10 amperes, provided all the following conditions are met:

   (1) Continuous loads do not exceed 8 amperes

   (2) Overcurrent protection is provided by one of the following:

     a. Branch-circuit-rated circuit breakers listed and marked for use with 16 AWG copper wire

     b. Branch-circuit-rated fuses listed and marked for use with 16 AWG copper wire

     c. Class CC, Class J, or Class T fuses

(3) 14 AWG Copper. 15 amperes

(4) 12 AWG Aluminum and Copper-Clad Aluminum. 15 amperes

(5) 12 AWG Copper. 20 amperes

(6) 10 AWG Aluminum and Copper-Clad Aluminum. 25 amperes

(7) 10 AWG Copper. 30 amperes

Summary of Change

This section has been revised for clarity, and has been expanded to include overcurrent protection requirements for sizes 16 AWG and 18 AWG copper conductors.

2

240.15

Ungrounded Conductors
NEC, p. 88, 89

Proposal 10-16
Log 2938
ROP, p. 159

Comment
None

Change at a Glance

Change in arrangement and location of operational characteristics of overcurrent protection devices

Analysis and Effect

This change involves relocation of the requirements presently provided in Section 240.20 in Part II of Article 240 to a new Section 240.15 located in Part I. The revision provides a more logical presentation of the requirements within the article. The information contained in 240.20 applies to more than just locations of overcurrent protection devices. Information in the substantiation indicated that the requirements in this section address operational characteristics rather than locations. There are no changes in any of the existing technical requirements contained in this section; the relocation is intended to improve usability by arranging requirements in a more logical sequence within the general requirements in Article 240.

Code Language
240.15
Ungrounded Conductors

[A]
Overcurrent Device Required (text unchanged)

[B]
Circuit Breaker as Overcurrent Device (text unchanged)
　　(1) Multiwire Branch Circuit (text unchanged)
　　(2) Grounded Single-Phase and 3-Wire dc Circuits (text unchanged)
　　(3) 3-Phase and 2-Phase Systems (text unchanged)

[C]
Closed-Loop Power Distribution Systems (text unchanged)

Summary of Change
Section 240.20 is relocated to Part I of Article 240 in a new Section 240.15.

240.21(C) Transformer Secondary Conductors

Each set of conductors feeding a single load, or each set of conductors feeding separate loads are required to meet the requirements specified in 240.21(C)(1) through (6).

The provisions of 240.4(B) shall not be permitted for transformer secondary conductors.

240.21
(B)(1) FPN
& 240.21
(C)(2) FPN

Location in Circuit
NEC, p. 89, 91

Proposal 9-7a, 9-7b
Log CP901, CP902
ROP, p. 160, 163

Comment 10-9, 10-10
Log 53, 54
ROC, p. 112

Analysis and Effect

CMP-9 has removed the categories of "lighting and appliance branch circuit panelboard" and "power panelboard" from Article 408 by virtue of its action on Proposal 9-117 which included the following changes in Article 408:

1. Permit more than 42 circuits in all panelboards
2. Eliminate the category of "Lighting and Appliance Branch Circuit Panelboard" and "Power Panelboards"
3. Require that all panelboards (for new installations) be protected on the line side by a single integral or a remote main overcurrent protective device (except as presently permitted for service equipment).

The revisions to Sections 408.34, 408.35, and 408.36 clearly resulted in the need for correlating the references in these two fine print notes in 240.21(B)(1) and (C)(2) to Article 408 for consistency with that action. Revisions to these sections will be covered in detail in chapter 4 of this *Analysis of Changes* textbook.

Code Language

240.21(B)(1)
Feeder Taps

FPN: For overcurrent protection requirements for panelboards, see 408.36.

240.21(C)(2)
Transformer Secondary Conductors

FPN: For overcurrent protection requirements for panelboards, see 408.36.

Summary of Change

The fine print notes (FPNs) to Sections 240.21(B)(1) and 240.21(C)(2) have been revised and simplified for correlation with Article 408.

Change at a Glance

The overcurrent protection requirements for panelboards are provided in Section 408.36. Section 240.21 provides overcurrent protection requirements for conductors.

2

240.21(C)
(2)(4)

Transformer Secondary Conductors
NEC, p. 91

Proposal 10-27
Log 3387
ROP, p. 163

Comment 10-11
Log 65
ROC, p. 112

Change at a Glance

This rule now clearly applies to transformer secondary conductors that leave an enclosure or vault.

Analysis and Effect

This revision to the secondary conductor sizing requirements correlates with the conventional ten-foot tap rule that originally inspired it. The existing language was problematic for instrumentation supplied with the gear that often includes smaller conductors that do not meet the restriction in size specified in this section. In addition, if the transformer installation is located within a vault, there is little likelihood of a problem in such short conductors affecting the building as a whole. These were the principle reasons that the allowances were inserted in the rules for conventional ten-foot feeder taps in *NEC*-1993, and they apply equally now that these rules are being applied to transformer secondary conductors. This change clarifies that the sizing provisions of 240.21(C)(2)(4) are applicable to conductors that are field-installed outside of transformer enclosures or vaults. This sizing provision would not have to be applied where the secondary conductors do not leave the vault or enclosure.

Code Language
240.21(C)(2)(4)
Transformer Secondary Conductors
For field installations where the secondary conductors leave the enclosure or vault in which the supply connection is made, the rating of the overcurrent device protecting the primary of the transformer, multiplied by the primary to secondary transformer voltage ratio, shall not exceed 10 times the ampacity of the secondary conductor.

Summary of Change

The words "For field installations where the secondary conductors leave the enclosure or vault in which the supply connection is made," have been added to new item (4), which was previously 240.21(C)(2)(1)c. The section has been renumbered to meet the *NEC Style Manual* requirements.

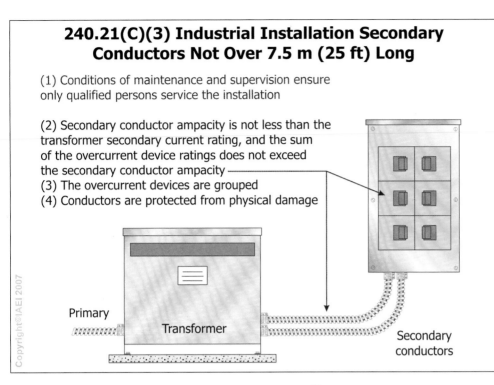

240.21(C)(3) Industrial Installation Secondary Conductors Not Over 7.5 m (25 ft) Long

(1) Conditions of maintenance and supervision ensure only qualified persons service the installation

(2) Secondary conductor ampacity is not less than the transformer secondary current rating, and the sum of the overcurrent device ratings does not exceed the secondary conductor ampacity
(3) The overcurrent devices are grouped
(4) Conductors are protected from physical damage

Primary

Transformer

Secondary conductors

Copyright©IAEI 2007

Transformer Secondary Conductors
NEC, p. 91

Proposal 10-4, 10-3a
Log 669, CP1000
ROP, p. 154, 163

Comment
None

Analysis and Effect

This revision clarifies what qualifies an industrial installation to install transformer secondary conductors under the provisions of this section. A new item (1) is included as one of the conditions that must be met in order for this section to be applied to field installations. Many industrial exceptions and provisions throughout the *NEC* call for conditions of maintenance and supervision to ensure that only qualified persons service the systems as a condition of using the requirement in designs and field installations. This revision clarifies when industrial allowances are permitted, and helps develop consistent field applications of these requirements for industrial installations. Proposal 10-4 was to insert a definition of *industrial installation* in Section 240.2, which would have been limited for use and application to those instances where it is used in Article 240. The term *industrial installation* is used in other articles of the *NEC*, and probably warrants consideration for a definition that can be applied across the entire *NEC* where the term is used.

Change at a Glance

To qualify as an industrial installation, four conditions are required: servicing only by qualified personnel; correlation of ampacity and secondary current ratings; OCPDs grouped; and protection from physical damage.

Code Language
240.21(C)(3)

Industrial Installation Secondary Conductors Not Over 7.5 m (25 ft) Long

For industrial installations only, where the length of the secondary conductors does not exceed 7.5 m (25 ft) and complies with all of the following:

(1) Conditions of maintenance and supervision ensure that only qualified persons service the systems.

(2) The ampacity of the secondary conductors is not less than the secondary current rating of the transformer, and the sum of the ratings of the overcurrent devices does not exceed the ampacity of the secondary conductors.

(3) All overcurrent devices are grouped.

(4) The secondary conductors are protected from physical damage by being enclosed in an approved raceway or by other approved means.

Summary of Change

A new item (1) has been added to create four conditions in this section. With the new item (1) inserted, the other three conditions have been renumbered accordingly.

2

240.21(H)

Battery Conductors
NEC, p. 91

Proposal 10-33
Log 1672
ROP, p. 165

Comment 10-13
Log 1846
ROC, p. 112

Change at a Glance

Overcurrent protection is to be installed as close to the battery terminals as practicable, but generally not in a hazardous location.

Analysis and Effect

Section 240.21 has addressed overcurrent protection of conductors and tap conductor length for several cycles without specifically addressing OCP location requirements for conductors connected to batteries. Substantiation with the proposal identified the increased applications of large battery power systems installed as standby power supply systems for numerous facilities. Action by CMP-10 on Comment 10.13 reverses the initial action on Proposal 10-33 and directs the relative location of the disconnecting means to be at the load end of the conductors connected to batteries. Conductors connected to a battery system carry current when the batteries are under load and during charging operations when the conductors are protected by the charging equipment. OCPDs protect the conductors when load is connected to the battery bank. One of the concerns is the level of hydrogen gases produced during charging processes. In many cases, significant ventilation systems are required, and the area can even be classified as a hazardous location because of excessive hydrogen gas accumulations. The objective is to locate the disconnecting means and overcurrent protection outside the hazardous (classified) location. The new provision permits the OCP to be located as close as practicable to the battery terminals, but in an unclassified location. The new text recognizes that the OCP could be installed within the hazardous location, but the equipment would be required to be suitable for such use. This provision does not contain any maximum length for the connected conductors as compared to similar requirements for feeders and transformer secondary conductors addressed in 240.21(B) and (C). The length of the conductors is typically based on the size and capacity of the system, building construction features, and so forth.

Code Language
240.21(H)
Battery Conductors
Overcurrent protection shall be permitted to be installed as close as practicable to the storage battery terminals in a non-hazardous location. Installation of the overcurrent protection within a hazardous location shall also be permitted.

Summary of Change
A new subdivision (H) covering battery conductors has been added to 240.21.

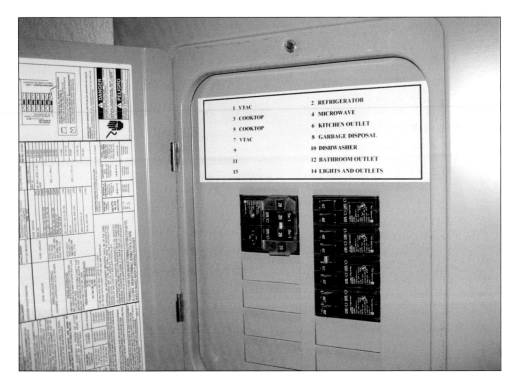

Occupancy
NEC, p. 92

Proposal 10-37
Log 2035
ROP, p. 166

Comment
None

Analysis and Effect

These revisions clarify the requirements for occupants to have access to their overcurrent protective devices. The exceptions have been rewritten into affirmative text and references to transient occupants have been removed. Section 210.18 was added in *NEC*-2005 to clarify what specific criteria constitutes treating occupancies as dwelling units for the purposes of applying all dwelling unit *Code* requirements, the main one of which calls for occupants to have ready access to all overcurrent devices supplying that particular occupancy. Where guest rooms or suites do not include perma-nent provisions for cooking, the branch-circuit overcurrent devices are permitted to be accessible only to authorized man-agement personnel. Where the dwelling unit includes per-manent provisions for cooking, 210.18 applies for branch circuits and outlets and access to the overcurrent protective devices. Hotels and motels not intended for extended occupancy and not including permanent provisions for cooking do not have to provide access to overcurrent devices to transient occupants.

Change at a Glance

When electric service is provided by and continu-ously supervised by build-ing management, only authorized personnel have access to service and feeder OCPDs of multiple-oc-cupancy buildings and to branch-circuit OCPDs of guest rooms or suites with-out cooking facilities.

Code Language 240.24(B)

Occupancy

Each occupant shall have ready access to all overcurrent devices protecting the conductors supplying that occupancy, un-less otherwise permitted in 240.24(B)(1) and (B)(2).

(1) Service and Feeder Overcurrent Devices. Where electrical service and electrical maintenance are provided by the building management and where these are under continuous building management supervision, the service overcurrent devices and feeder overcur-rent devices supplying more than one occupancy shall be permitted to be ac-cessible only to authorized management personnel in the following:

    (1) Multiple-occupancy buildings

    (2) Guest rooms or guest suites

(2) Branch-Circuit Overcurrent De-vices. Where electrical service and elec-trical maintenance are provided by the building management and where these are under continuous building manage-ment supervision, the branch-circuit overcurrent devices supplying any guest rooms or guest suites without permanent provisions for cooking shall be permitted to be accessible to only authorized man-agement personnel.

Summary of Change

The exceptions have been rewritten into positive text and the section has been arranged to provide a more logical layout for improved clarity and application of the overcurrent device accessibility requirements.

240.24(F)

Not Located Over Steps
NEC, p. 92

Proposal 10-40
Log 1633
ROP, p. 167

Comment 10-15, 10-16
Log 267, 1099
ROC, p. 113

Change at a Glance

Overcurrent devices are not permitted to be located over the steps of stairs, but could be located in stair landings where the minimum requirements of 110.26 are met.

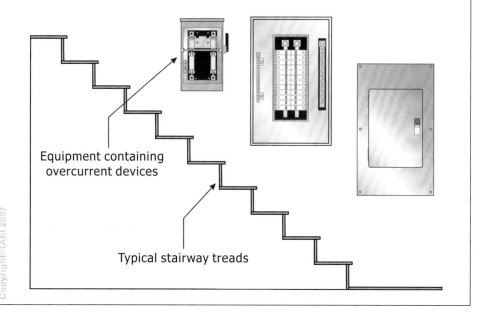

240.24(F) Not Located Over Steps

Overcurrent protective devices shall not be located over steps of a stairway.

Equipment containing overcurrent devices

Typical stairway treads

Copyright©IAEI 2007

Analysis and Effect

Section 240.24 provides requirements specific to overcurrent device locations. New subdivision (F) restricts overcurrent protective devices from being installed over stair steps. CMP-10 responded favorably and progressively to Comments 10-15 and 10-16 resulting in the reversal of an initial action to reject the original Proposal 10-40. Substantiation for the proposal indicated two significant problems which have been effectively addressed by the acceptance of this new requirement. Inspection authorities have commonly rejected panelboards and other equipment containing OCPDs from being installed over steps in stairways, but had no clear *Code* language that would prohibit this location. The uneven surface of stairs in front of electrical equipment creates additional safety concerns for workers having to service or operate such equipment. The restriction from installation of OCPDs in these locations reduces those inherent safety concerns and eliminates the problems inspectors had determining that maximum height requirements of 240.24(A) have been met. The negative statements to Proposal 10-40 and Comments 10-15 and 10-16 clearly indicate that the concerns of the panel are that installing OCPDs in stairways is not practical, and the *NEC* should not permit it. This new requirement cleanly addresses the concerns of the floor or working platform being one that can safely accommodate workers without inherent obstructions that increase injury possibili-

ties. This rule removes the unwritten allowance of a practice that most of the enforcement communities would not allow anyway. This restriction does not prohibit the installation of OCPDs in stairways at landings where the applicable provisions of 110.26 have been met. Most building codes normally prohibit any electrical raceways, devices, or other from being in an egress corridor or an egress stairway, but this would not be applicable in residential occupancies.

Code Language
240.24(F)
Not Located Over Steps
Overcurrent devices shall not be located over steps of a stairway.

Summary of Change
A new subdivision (F) addressing additional restricted overcurrent device locations has been added to Section 240.24.

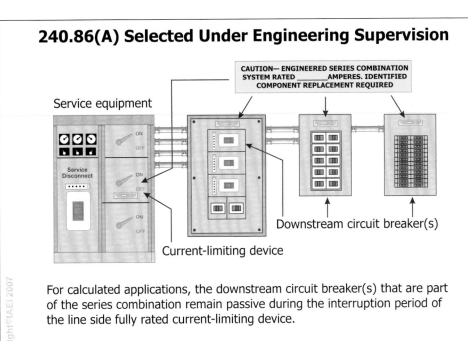

240.86(A) Selected Under Engineering Supervision

CAUTION— ENGINEERED SERIES COMBINATION SYSTEM RATED _____ AMPERES. IDENTIFIED COMPONENT REPLACEMENT REQUIRED

Service equipment

Current-limiting device

Downstream circuit breaker(s)

For calculated applications, the downstream circuit breaker(s) that are part of the series combination remain passive during the interruption period of the line side fully rated current-limiting device.

Note that Section 240.86(A) applies to existing installations only.

240.86(A)

Selected Under Engineering
Supervision in Existing
Installations
NEC, p. 94

Proposal 10-52, 10-50a
Log 567, CP1001
ROP, p. 171

Comment 10-22
Log 348
ROC, p. 114

Analysis and Effect

This revision improves usability and helps minimize misapplication while promoting consistency within the electrical inspection and installation communities. A new last sentence has been added to provide engineers with specific criteria that must be applied when selecting an engineered series rated combination of overcurrent protective devices in accordance with this section. It is important that the operating characteristics of the downstream device remain passive during the interruption period of the fully rated, current-limiting device on the line side of the engineered combination. Because each of these engineered combinations is unique and not standardized as listed series rated combination devices are, more cautionary markings for the equipment in these applications are warranted and are now required in 110.22. This revision parallels tested series rated combination systems field marking requirements.

Change at a Glance

The downstream overcurrent protective devices in an engineered series rated combination system must remain passive during operation of the higher rated current-limiting device located on its supply (line) side.

Code Language
240.86(A)

Selected Under Engineering Supervision in Existing Installations

The series rated combination devices shall be selected by a licensed professional engineer engaged primarily in the design or maintenance of electrical installations. The selection shall be documented and stamped by the professional engineer. This documentation shall be available to those authorized to design, install, inspect, maintain, and operate the system. This series combination rating, including identification of the upstream device, shall be field marked on the end use equipment. For calculated applications, the engineer shall ensure that the downstream circuit breaker(s) that are part of the series combination remain passive during the interruption period of the line side fully rated, current-limiting device.

(B) Tested Combinations. The combination of line-side overcurrent device and load-side circuit breaker(s) is tested and marked on the end use equipment, such as switchboards and panelboards.

FPN to (A) and (B): See 110.22 for marking of series combination systems.

Summary of Change

An additional sentence clarifies the operating characteristics of devices applied in specifically engineered combinations under the provisions of this section. Fine print notes add direction for rules pertaining to engineered series rated combinations and those that apply to tested series combination systems.

240.92(B) and Table 240.92(B)

Feeder Taps
NEC, p. 95

Proposal 10-21
Log 2877
ROP, p. 160

Comment 10-32
Log 1419
ROC, p. 119

Change at a Glance

In supervised industrial installations only, conductors are permitted to be protected using a combination of overcurrent protective devices and the conductors' short-circuit withstand capabilities.

240.92(B) Feeder Taps

For feeder taps specified in 240.21(B)(2), (B)(3), and (B)(4), the tap conductors shall be permitted to be sized in accordance with Table 240.92(B).

Table 240.92(B) Tap Conductors Short-Circuit Current Ratings (in part)

Tap conductors shall be considered to be protected under short-circuit conditions when their short-circuit temperature limit is not exceeded. Conductor heating under short-circuit conditions is determined by (1) or (2):

(1) Short-Circuit Formula for Copper Conductors

$$(I^2/A^2)t = 0.0297 \log_{10}[(T^2 + 234)(T^1 + 234)]$$

(2) Short-Circuit Formula for Aluminum Conductors

$$(I^2/A^2)t = 0.0125 \log_{10}[(T^2 + 228)/(T^1 + 228)]$$

See Table 240.92(B) for complete Table and legend

Analysis and Effect

This revision results in recognized conductor protection concepts that relate to the conductors' ability to withstand short-circuit current conditions for various durations of time. It is generally understood that fast overcurrent device operation increases conductor withstand ratings. The overcurrent device selected in designs of electrical systems has a direct impact on the withstand capability of conductors. A new table provides information about calculating maximum conductor withstand capabilities for both copper and aluminum conductors to determine maximum conductor heating under short-circuit conditions. Two calculation formulas have been included in this table, and this allowance is limited to applications of supervised industrial installations only. This action will increase the enforceability needed by the inspection community, but still limits the application to supervised industrial installations only. This action recognizes the performance of overcurrent protective device characteristics as a significant factor in determining the tap conductor size since time (in cycles) is the key to the maximum amount of short-circuit current wire-type conductors can withstand. It also provides another engineering alternative in Part VIII of Article 240 that can be applied to tap conductors and in some cases resulting in smaller sizes of tap conductors that are provided with suitable overcurrent protection within their short-time capacities.

Code Language
240.92(B)
Feeder Taps

For feeder taps specified in 240.21(B)(2), (B)(3), and (B)(4), the tap conductors shall be permitted to be sized in accordance with Table 240.92(B).

See actual NEC text for table.

Summary of Change

Insert a new provision and table in Section 240.92 and renumber existing 240.92(B), (C), and (D) as 240.92(C), (D), and (E).

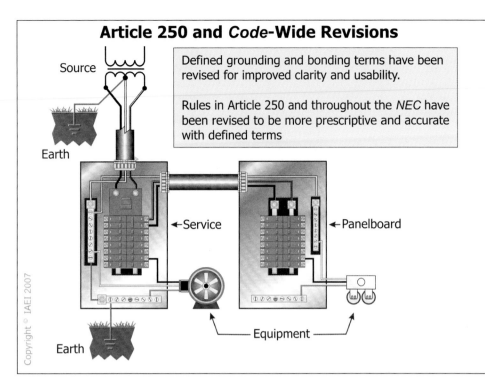

Article 250 and *Code*-Wide Revisions

Source

Defined grounding and bonding terms have been revised for improved clarity and usability.

Rules in Article 250 and throughout the *NEC* have been revised to be more prescriptive and accurate with defined terms

Earth

←Service

←Panelboard

Equipment

Earth

Copyright © IAEI 2007

Grounding & Bonding Requirements
NEC, Various pages

Proposal 5-76, 5-77
Log 1520, 1521
ROP, p. 180

Comment 5-24, 5-25
Log 1229, 1232
ROC, p. 120

Analysis and Effect

The revisions to the requirements using terms related to grounding and bonding are the result of the objectives of *NEC* Technical Correlating Committee Task Group on Grounding and Bonding to clarify *Code* requirements that use grounding and bonding terms. Many of the existing *Code* definitions of terms related to grounding and bonding have been revised, and a few new definitions have been added as a result of this work (see Article 100). The primary objectives of the Task Group on Grounding and Bonding were to clarify the existing defined terms for clarity and simplicity, and to revise rules throughout Article 250 and the entire *NEC* that use these defined terms. It is very important that terms mean what they imply as defined in the *Code*. Using inappropriate terms related to grounding and bonding within *Code* rules can result in inconsistent application of the necessary minimum requirements, which ultimately can result in installations that might meet the literal language in the *Code* rule itself, but not meet the desired objectives and requirements for a safe installation. For example, the phrase "shall be grounded" could literally mean that a conductive object required to be grounded could to be connected to the earth with a ground rod and a conductor to the ground rod, without a connection to the equipment grounding conductor. This installation would literally meet the requirements of the previous language used throughout the *NEC*. By revising such phrases to read "shall be connected to an equipment grounding conductor" where appropriate, the *Code* rules should be very clear about what is intended to be accomplished from a performance standpoint. In this case, not only is the equipment connected to the earth through the equipment grounding conductor connection, but an effective ground-fault current path is also in place, which is an essential requirement for electrical safety. Both performance concepts (grounding and bonding) satisfy the safety objectives anticipated in *Code* rules that use this language.

Change at a Glance

Grounding and bonding terms are used more consistently with their defined meaning. Many general grounding rules throughout Article 250 and the entire *NEC* have been revised to be more specific and prescriptive for users.

2

Code Language

Article 250
Grounding and Bonding

Common examples of revisions to text in Article 250 and other *Code* rules related to grounding and bonding requirements:

1. Change the term "shall be grounded" to "shall be connected to an equipment grounding conductor." [250.86, 250.112, 250.114, and so forth]

2. Change the phrase "shall be grounded to the equipment grounding terminal bar of the panelboard" to the phrase "shall be connected to an equipment grounding terminal bar of the panelboard." [680.24(F)]

3. Change the phrase "to provide a permanent, reliable electrical bond" to *"to provide a reliable bonding connection"* [250.97 Exception]

Summary of Change

These revisions are throughout Article 250 and are code-wide where rules related to grounding and bonding requirements were inconsistent with what is intended to be accomplished from a performance perspective and what is required by the actual text used in the *Code*.

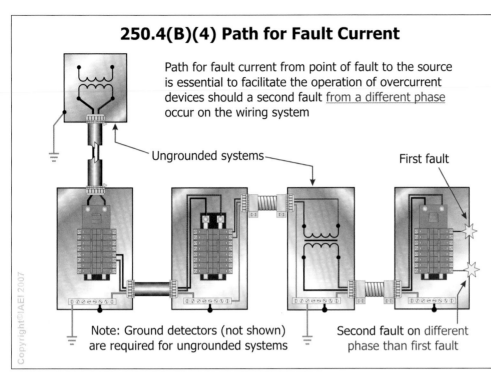

250.4(B)(4) Path for Fault Current

Path for fault current from point of fault to the source is essential to facilitate the operation of overcurrent devices should a second fault <u>from a different phase</u> occur on the wiring system

Ungrounded systems

First fault

Note: Ground detectors (not shown) are required for ungrounded systems

Second fault on different phase than first fault

Copyright©IAEI 2007

250.4 (B)(4)

Ungrounded Systems
NEC, p. 99

Proposal 5-69, 5-71
Log 339, 1900
ROP, p. 178

Comment 5-40
Log 1020
ROC, p. 124

Analysis and Effect

This revision clarifies that a first phase-to-ground fault condition creates an accidental connection to ground from one ungrounded phase conductor of an ungrounded system. If a second ground fault should occur on the same phase as the first ground fault, the ground-fault condition would still exist without facilitating overcurrent device operation. However, if a second phase-to-ground fault event on a different ungrounded phase conductor were to occur, it should facilitate overcurrent device operation by the ground-fault current path in an ungrounded system. No technical changes have been made to this section, only clarification. It was always the objective that the second ground fault on the wiring system was intended to occur on another phase conductor, other than the initial faulted phase conductor that created the first phase-to-ground fault condition. Ground detectors are now required for ungrounded systems in accordance with 250.21(B); and they provide necessary indication of a first phase-to-ground fault event, so that qualified persons can respond to and repair the condition to avoid potential effects of a second phase-to-ground fault event. Action by CMP-5 on Comment 5-40 removed the word "permanent" from this section, which continues to have the same meaning without the subjectivity, ambiguity, and inconsistency of application of the performance requirements. This revision is consistent with similar revisions that removed the word "permanent" throughout Article 250 and the entire *NEC*.

Change at a Glance

A second phase-to-ground fault event on a different ungrounded phase conductor, other than the phase with initial ground fault, is the condition that should facilitate overcurrent device operation by the ground-fault current path in an ungrounded system.

Code Language
250.4(B)(4)
Path for Fault Current
Electrical equipment, wiring, and other electrically conductive material likely to become energized shall be installed in a manner that creates a low-impedance circuit from any point on the wiring system to the electrical supply source to facilitate the operation of overcurrent devices should a second ground fault from a different phase occur on the wiring system. The earth shall not be considered as an effective fault-current path.

Summary of Change

This section has been revised by adding the words "ground fault from a different phase" at the end of the first sentence. The word "permanent" has been removed from this section.

250.8

Connection of Grounding and Bonding Equipment
NEC, p. 100

Proposal 5-84
Log 3365
ROP, p. 186

Comment 5-44
Log 2249
ROC, p. 125

Change at a Glance

Acceptable methods of connecting grounding and bonding conductors are listed in 250.8, and the reference to sheet metal screws has been removed.

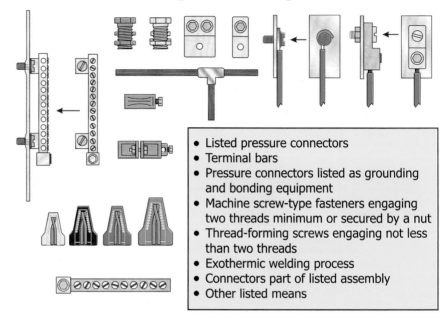

250.8 Grounding and Bonding Connections

- Listed pressure connectors
- Terminal bars
- Pressure connectors listed as grounding and bonding equipment
- Machine screw-type fasteners engaging two threads minimum or secured by a nut
- Thread-forming screws engaging not less than two threads
- Exothermic welding process
- Connectors part of listed assembly
- Other listed means

Copyright©IAEI 2007

Analysis and Effect

The panel action on this proposal incorporates acceptable concepts included in other proposals to revise this section and clarify acceptable methods of grounding conductor and bonding jumper connections. Proposal 5-57 in the 2004 *NEC Report on Proposals* and Comment 5-40 (Log No. 2173) in the 2004 *NEC Report on Comments* were held for further study owing to the introduction of new material that did not have an opportunity for public review and comment. The revisions to this section result in a list of acceptable methods for connections of grounding conductors and bonding jumpers. The change also removes the term *sheet metal screws* from this section, providing further emphasis that sheet metal screws are not an acceptable means of attaching grounding conductors, bonding jumpers or connection devices to enclosures. Connections of grounding conductors and bonding jumpers are an important element of the electrical wiring system. The path for ground-fault current must remain effective to ensure the performance under all anticipated conditions. This revision clarifies for installers and enforcement the issue about sheet metal screws being used as fastening means for these conductors or devices. By providing an inclusive list of acceptable methods, the rule improves the meeting the its objective.

Code Language

250.8

Connection of Grounding and Bonding Equipment

(A) Permitted Methods. Grounding conductors and bonding jumpers shall be connected by one of the following means:

(1) Listed pressure connectors

(2) Terminal bars

(3) Pressure connectors listed as grounding and bonding equipment

(4) Exothermic welding process

(5) Machine screw-type fasteners that engage not less than two threads or are secured with a nut

(6) Thread-forming machine screws that engage not less than two threads in the enclosure

(7) Connections that are part of a listed assembly

(8) Other listed means

(B) Methods Not Permitted. Connection devices or fittings that depend solely on solder shall not be used.

Summary of Change

This section has been rewritten into a list format meeting the requirements of Section 2.1.5.1 of the *NEC Style Manual*, and also expanded to include acceptable means of connection methods for grounding conductors and bonding jumpers.

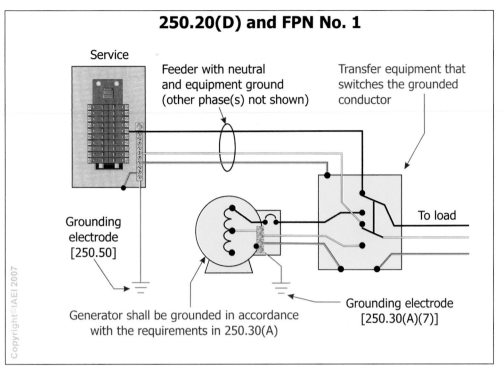

250.20(D) and FPN No. 1

Service

Feeder with neutral and equipment ground (other phase(s) not shown)

Transfer equipment that switches the grounded conductor

To load

Grounding electrode [250.50]

Generator shall be grounded in accordance with the requirements in 250.30(A)

Grounding electrode [250.30(A)(7)]

Copyright©IAEI 2007

Separately Derived Systems
NEC, p. 100–102

Proposal 5-95
Log 341
ROP, p. 188

Comment
None

Analysis and Effect

The changes in this section and the new information added to FPN No. 1 improve clarity and usability. The information in the fine print note has been incorporated into affirmative text to provide clear direction in the form of a rule where systems that meet these criteria are installed. Generator grounding and bonding connections always seem to be questionable items in the field where generators and transfer switches are installed and used. The method of grounding and bonding connections for separately derived systems is directly related to the type of transfer equipment installed in the system. Having more concise and clearer language in the rule and the additional text in FPN No. 1 provides better direction for installers and *Code* enforcement, and should result in more consistent application of the appropriate requirements that apply to method of grounding for separately derived systems based on the type of transfer equipment utilized in the design. Transfer equipment that includes a switching action in the grounded conductor common to both systems predicates the grounding requirements for the generator or other source.

Change at a Glance

More specific direction indicates when generators are separately derived systems and must be grounded according to 250.30(A). Relationship to transfer switch operation is included in both the rule and the fine print note.

Code Language
250.20(D)

Separately Derived Systems
Separately derived systems, as covered in 250.20(A) or (B), shall be grounded as specified in 250.30(A). Where an alternate source such as an on-site generator is provided with transfer equipment that includes a grounded conductor that is not solidly interconnected to the service-supplied grounded conductor, the alternate source (derived system) shall be grounded in accordance with 250.30(A).

FPN No. 1: An alternate ac power source such as an on-site generator is not a separately derived system if the grounded conductor is solidly interconnected to a service-supplied system grounded conductor. An example of such situations is where alternate source transfer equipment does not include a switching action in the grounded conductor and allows it to remain solidly connected to the service-supplied grounded conductor when the alternate source is operational and supplying the load served.

FPN No. 2: For systems that are not separately derived and are not required to be grounded as specified in 250.30, see 445.13 for minimum size of conductors that must carry fault current.

Summary of Change
The revisions to this section include adding an additional sentence in the requirement and to FPN No. 1. The reference to Section 250.30 has been revised to include the specific subdivision (A).

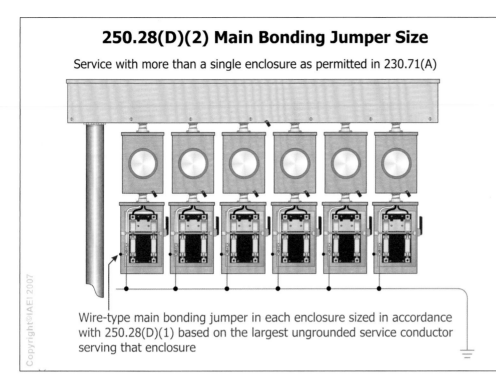

250.28(D)(2) Main Bonding Jumper Size

Service with more than a single enclosure as permitted in 230.71(A)

Copyright©IAEI 2007

Wire-type main bonding jumper in each enclosure sized in accordance with 250.28(D)(1) based on the largest ungrounded service conductor serving that enclosure

250.28(D)

Size
NEC, p. 102

Proposal 5-107
Log 2012
ROP, p. 190

Comment 5-53
Log 1758
ROC, p. 126

REVISION

Analysis and Effect

The changes in this section improve usability and provide clarity in the *NEC* regarding the sizing of main bonding jumpers and system bonding jumpers of the wire types in various installation configurations. The previous rule addressed these sizing requirements only from a general perspective, and for single enclosures. This revision includes restructuring the rule into a list format in accordance with Section 2.1.5 of the *NEC Style Manual*. The new language included in items (2) and (3) of the list address specific main bonding jumper sizing requirements for configurations in the field that include separate service disconnecting means enclosures as permitted in 230.71(A) and system bonding jumper sizing requirements where a separately derived system supplies more than a single enclosure. This revision also clarifies the sizing of main and system bonding jumpers (wire-types) where multiple enclosures are installed. The method of sizing has not been altered by this revision. Table 250.66 is required to be used, and the 12.5% rule where applicable, is based on the cm area of the largest ungrounded service-entrance conductor for services or the derived phase conductor for separately derived systems.

Change at a Glance

Main bonding jumpers and system bonding jumper sizing requirements are listed for installations that include multiple service disconnects of first system overcurrent device enclosures.

250.28(D)(3) System Bonding Jumper Size

System bonding jumpers in each enclosure shall be sized in accordance with 250.28(D)(1) based on the largest ungrounded feeder conductor serving that enclosure.

Single system bonding jumper installed at the source and sized in accordance with 250.28(D)(1) based on the sum of the circular mil areas of all ungrounded derived conductor sets

Multiple enclosures

Transformer

Secondary conductor sets

Copyright©IAEI 2007

Code Language
250.28(D)

Size

Main bonding jumpers and system bonding jumpers shall be sized in accordance with 250.28(D)(1) through (D)(3).

(1) General. Main bonding jumpers and system bonding jumpers shall not be smaller than the sizes shown in Table 250.66. Where the supply conductors are larger than 1100 kcmil copper or 1750 kcmil aluminum, the bonding jumper shall have an area that is not less than 12 1/2 percent of the area so the largest phase conductor except that, where the phase conductors and the bonding jumper are of different materials (copper or aluminum), the minimum size of the bonding jumper shall be based on the assumed use of phase conductors of the same material as the bonding jumper and with an ampacity equivalent to that of the installed phase conductors.

(2) Main Bonding Jumper for Service with More Than One Enclosure. Where a service consists of more than a single enclosure as permitted in 230.71(A), the main bonding jumper for each enclosure shall be sized in accordance with 250.28(D)(1) based on the largest ungrounded service conductor serving that enclosure.

(3) Separately Derived Systems with More Than One Enclosure. Where a separately derived system supplies more than a single enclosure, the system bonding jumper for

each enclosure shall be sized in accordance with 250.28(D)(1) based on the largest ungrounded feeder conductor serving that enclosure or a single system bonding jumper shall be installed at the source and sized in accordance with 250.28(D)(1) based on the equivalent size of the largest supply conductor determined by the largest sum of the areas of the corresponding conductors of each set.

Summary of Change

This section has been restructured to include three list items under (D) and to include expanded requirements for sizing main bonding jumpers and system bonding jumpers of the wire types where multiple enclosures are used.

Analysis of Changes *NEC*-2008

250.30(A)(4) Multiple Separately Derived Systems

- Common grounding electrode conductor is required to be sized at minimum 3/0 copper or 250 aluminum.

- The grounding electrode conductor tap connection to the system is required to be located where the system bonding jumper is installed.

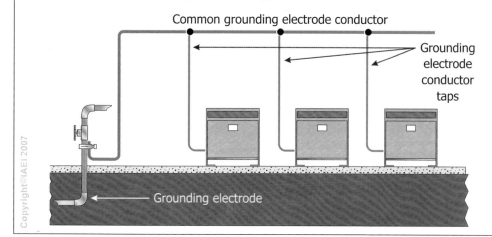

Common grounding electrode conductor

Grounding electrode conductor taps

Grounding electrode

Grounded Systems
NEC, p. 104

Proposal 5-110
Log 1649
ROP, p. 191

Comment
None

Analysis and Effect

The revision to this section provides users with clear direction as to the appropriate location of the grounding electrode conductor connection where the common grounding electrode conductor tap concept is utilized in accordance with Section 250.30(A)(4). Previous editions of the *NEC* required the grounding electrode conductor connection for separately derived systems in general to be located at the same point where the system bonding jumper is installed. This change provides consistency between similar requirements presently contained in Section 250.30(A)(3) for a single separately derived system, while at the same time providing needed clarification for installers and enforcement as to the required location for the grounding electrode conductor connections where multiple separately derived systems are installed and grounded using the concepts provided in 250.30(A)(4).

Change at a Glance

Where multiple separately derived systems are grounded using the common grounding electrode conductor tap concepts provided in 250.30(A)(4), the system bonding jumper must be installed where the grounding electrode conductor tap is connected to the separately derived system.

Code Language
250.30(A)(4)

Grounding Electrode Conductor, Multiple Separately Derived Systems
Where more than one separately derived system is installed, it shall be permissible to connect a tap from each separately derived system to a common grounding electrode conductor. Each tap conductor shall connect the grounded conductor of the separately derived system to the common grounding electrode conductor. The grounding electrode conductors and taps shall comply with 250.30(A)(4)(a) through (A)(4)(c). This connection shall be made at the same point on the separately derived system where the system bonding jumper is installed.

Summary of Change

A new sentence has been added to the end of this section and reads as follows: "This connection shall be made at the same point on the separately derived system where the system bonding jumper is installed."

250.32(B) and Exception

Grounded Systems
NEC, p. 105

___

Proposal 5-119
Log 2395
ROP, p. 193

___

Comment 5-58
Log 1518
ROC, p. 127

Change at a Glance

Equipment grounding conductors are required to be installed with all branch circuits and feeders supplying separate buildings or structures.

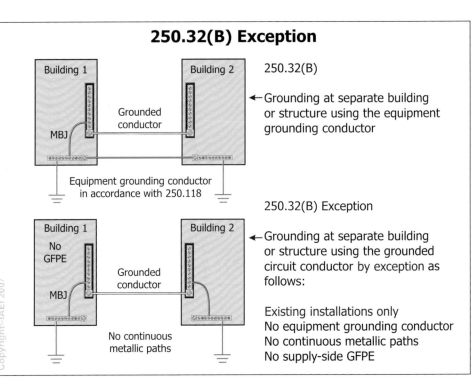

250.32(B) Exception

Building 1 | Building 2
Grounded conductor
MBJ

Equipment grounding conductor in accordance with 250.118

250.32(B)
← Grounding at separate building or structure using the equipment grounding conductor

Building 1 | Building 2
No GFPE
Grounded conductor
MBJ
No continuous metallic paths

Copyright©IAEI 2007

250.32(B) Exception
← Grounding at separate building or structure using the grounded circuit conductor by exception as follows:

Existing installations only
No equipment grounding conductor
No continuous metallic paths
No supply-side GFPE

Analysis and Effect

The revisions to this section are consistent with the efforts of Code-Making Panel 5 to continue to migrate away from the use of the grounded conductor for grounding on the load side of the service disconnecting means. The original proposal was to delete Section 250.32(B)(2) completely, which would have not left any language that could be applied to existing installations. The changes in this section also include a restriction for application to existing installations only. The conditions specified in former Section 250.32(B)(2) for use of the grounded conductor for grounding equipment were already restrictive in nature for new designs and installations contemplating its use. This revision results in users having to develop designs and installations of feeders or branch circuits that include an equipment grounding conductor in accordance with the requirements of 215.6 and 250.32(B) for all feeders or branch circuits installed to supply separate buildings or structures. This change should help reduce the number of designs that purposely invite the possibilities of inappropriate neutral-to-ground connections that can and often do happen at a later date, which is uncontrollable by any *NEC* rule. Existing installations meeting the requirements of Section 250.32(B)(2) in previous editions of the *NEC* would be allowed to remain operational. It should be noted that the restrictive conditions of the new exception [former 250.32(B)(2)] still have to be met and are subject to approval of the applicable authority having jurisdiction.

For a grounded system at the separate building or structure, an equipment grounding conductor as described in 250.118 shall be run with the supply conductors and be connected to the building or structure disconnecting means and to the grounding electrode(s). The equipment grounding conductor shall be used for grounding or bonding of equipment, structures, or frames required to be grounded or bonded. The equipment grounding conductor shall be sized in accordance with 250.122. Any installed grounded conductor shall not be connected to the equipment grounding conductor or to the grounding electrode(s).

Exception: For existing premises wiring systems only, the grounded conductor run with the supply to the building or structure shall be permitted to be connected to the building or structure disconnecting means and to the grounding electrode(s) and shall be used for grounding or bonding of equipment, structures, or frames required to be grounded or bonded where all the requirements of (1), (2), and (3) are met:

(1) An equipment grounding conductor is not run with the supply to the building or structure.
(2) There are no continuous metallic paths bonded to the grounding system in each building or structure involved.
(3) Ground-fault protection of equipment has not been installed on the supply side of the feeder(s).

Where the grounded conductor is used for grounding in accordance with the provision of this exception, the size of the grounded conductor shall not be smaller than the larger of either of the following:

(1) That required by 220.61
(2) That required by 250.122

Summary of Change

Former Section 250.32(B)(2) has been rewritten into an exception to the general requirements in Section 250.32(B).

250.35

Permanently Installed Generators
NEC, p. 106

Proposal 5-128
Log 3503
ROP, p. 195

Comment 5-67
Log 1797
ROC, p. 129

Change at a Glance

Detailed direction about grounding and bonding connections and sizing for equipment bonding jumpers installed between a generator and the equipment enclosure to which the feeder is connected for generators that are separately derived systems and those that are not.

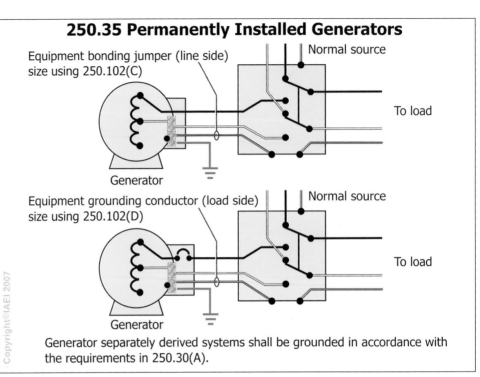

250.35 Permanently Installed Generators

Equipment bonding jumper (line side) size using 250.102(C)

Normal source

To load

Generator

Equipment grounding conductor (load side) size using 250.102(D)

Normal source

To load

Generator

Generator separately derived systems shall be grounded in accordance with the requirements in 250.30(A).

Copyright©IAEI 2007

Analysis and Effect

Action by CMP-5 results in a new section that provides sizing rules for generator feeder equipment grounding conductor and equipment bonding jumper in Article 250. If generators are installed with transfer equipment that includes a switching means in the grounded (neutral) conductor, then the generator is required to be grounded in accordance with the rules in 250.30(A). This new section addresses sizing requirements where the generator is not a separately derived system. Prior to this edition of the *NEC*, there were no applicable rules that addressed the sizing of these conductors. Essentially, where the generator includes an overcurrent device, the equipment grounding conductor is required to be sized using 250.102(D) and Table 250.122 based on the rating of the overcurrent protective device. Where the conductors from the generator to the first system overcurrent device are not provided with overcurrent protection at the source (generator), the equipment bonding jumper(s) shall be sized in accordance with 250.102(C) using Table 250.66 or the 12.5% rule if applicable. This revision provides users with clear requirements for sizing equipment grounding conductors (load side) or equipment bonding jumpers (line side) installed with feeder conductors supplied by generators that are not grounded as separately derived systems in accordance with 250.30.

250.35 Permanently Installed Generators

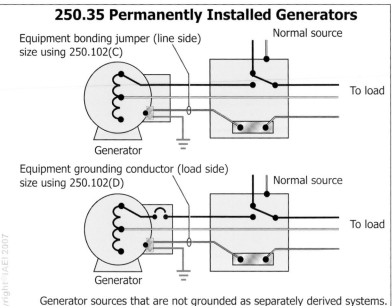

Equipment bonding jumper (line side) size using 250.102(C)

Normal source

To load

Generator

Equipment grounding conductor (load side) size using 250.102(D)

Normal source

To load

Generator

Generator sources that are not grounded as separately derived systems.

Copyright IAEI 2007

Code Language

250.35

Permanently Installed Generators

A conductor that provides an effective ground-fault current path shall be installed with the supply conductors from a permanently installed generator(s) to the first disconnecting mean(s) in accordance with (A) or (B).

(A)

Separately Derived System

Where the generator is installed as a separately derived system, the requirements in 250.30 shall apply.

(B)

Nonseparately Derived System

Where the generator is not installed as a separately derived system, an equipment bonding jumper shall be installed between the generator equipment grounding terminal and the equipment grounding terminal or bus of the enclosure of supplied disconnecting mean(s) in accordance with (B)(1) or (B)(2).

(1) Supply Side of Generator Overcurrent Device. The equipment bonding jumper on the supply side of each generator overcurrent device shall be sized in accordance with 250.102(C) based on the size of the conductors supplied by the generator.

(2) Load Side of Generator Overcurrent Device. The equipment grounding conductor on the load side of each generator overcurrent device shall be sized in accordance with 250.102(D) based on the rating of the overcurrent device supplied.

Summary of Change

New Section 250.35 provides requirements for sizing equipment grounding conductors and equipment bonding jumpers installed with generators that are not grounded as separately derived systems in accordance with 250.30.

250.52
(A)(3)

Concrete-Encased Electrode
NEC, p. 108

Proposal 5-137, 5-152
Log 2642, 202
ROP, p. 197, 202

Comment 5-86
Log 381
ROC, p. 134

Change at a Glance

Concrete-encased grounding electrodes can be horizontally installed or vertically installed as long as they meet the criteria of this section, and only one is required to be used in the grounding electrode system for a building or structure.

250.52(A)(3) Concrete-Encased Electrode

Encased by at least 50 mm (2 in.) of concrete, located horizontally near the bottom or vertically and within the portion of a concrete footing or foundation in direct contact with the earth.

Where multiple concrete-encased electrodes are present at a building or structure, it is permissible to bond one into the grounding electrode system.

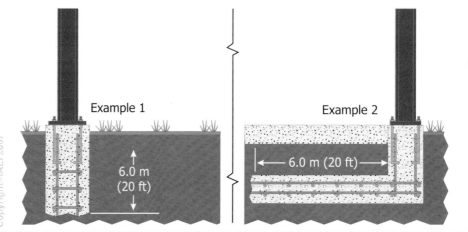

Example 1

6.0 m (20 ft)

Example 2

6.0 m (20 ft)

Copyright©IAEI 2007

Analysis and Effect

There are different configurations for constructing footings and foundations for buildings and other structures. In some, the reinforcing steel within the concrete foundation or footing is installed in multiple separate sections that are not connected physically. In these, several electrodes meeting the criteria in 250.52(A)(3) can be present within the same footing or foundation. This revision clarifies that where these conditions are encountered, one of the multiple qualifying concrete-encased grounding electrodes is required to be connected and used in the grounding electrode system. Incidental conductivity is provided between the separate sections of steel reinforcing bars by common concrete encasement. Although bonding these isolated sections of rebar in the footing or foundation together would be permitted, it would only be required to connect and use one in the grounding electrode system to meet these requirements. The other significant change recognizes concrete-encased grounding electrodes that are horizontally installed and in contact with the earth, such as at the bottom of a footing or foundation, and those that are installed vertically, such as concrete pier-style footings. The key is that the concrete footing or foundation, whether installed horizontally or vertically, is in direct contact with the earth and meets all other specific requirements of this section such as length of reinforcing bars or 4 AWG conductor and sizes, thus qualifying as a concrete-encased grounding electrode.

Code Language
250.52(A)(3)

Concrete-Encased Electrode
An electrode encased by at least 50 mm (2 in.) of concrete, located horizontally near the bottom or vertically, and within that portion of a concrete foundation or footing that is in direct contact with the earth, consisting of at least 6.0 m (20 ft) of one or more bare or zinc galvanized or other electrically conductive coated steel reinforcing bars or rods of not less than 13 mm (1/ 2 in.) in diameter, or consisting of at least 6.0 m (20 ft) of bare copper conductor not smaller than 4 AWG. Reinforcing bars shall be permitted to be bonded together by the usual steel tie wires or other effective means. Where multiple concrete-encased electrodes are present at a building or structure, it shall be permissible to bond only one into the grounding electrode system.

Summary of Change

This revision addresses horizontal and vertical concrete footings or foundations that meet the criteria of a concrete-encased electrode. A new last sentence has been added (see above).

250.52(A)(6) Other Listed Electrodes

Other listed grounding electrodes shall be permitted to be used

Required to be listed as grounding and bonding equipment [UL 467]

Courtesy of
ERICO International

Electrodes Permitted
for Grounding
NEC, p. 108

Proposal 5-164
Log 3309
ROP, p. 205

Comment 5-97
Log 2082
ROC, p. 137

Analysis and Effect

Section 250.52(A) provides an inclusive list of the grounding electrodes that are required or permitted to be used for grounding. CMP-5 responded favorably to the substantiation provided in Comment 5-97 resulting in a new item (6) within this section that covers other listed grounding electrodes. This new provision incorporates text that recognizes listed products manufactured specifically for use as grounding electrodes. Various manufacturers of listed grounding and bonding equipment produce listed grounding electrode products that are often installed in special applications such as information technology system facilities and electronics manufacturing plants, but are not limited to those types of facilities. An important feature of this new provision is that these other electrodes are required to be listed. This means they are manufactured and evaluated to applicable product safety standards. In this case, UL Standard 467 is the standard to which this special grounding equipment would be required to evaluated, tested, and listed. Another aspect of listing is the requirement to install and use the equipment in accordance with any installation instructions included with the listing or labeling as required in 110.3(B). The effect of this change is that the *NEC* will now recognize listed grounding electrode products for use in 250.52(A) and to provide a ready means for installers and enforcement to attain approvals of installations that include these more specialized grounding electrode products that were not previously addressed by *NEC* rules.

Code Language
250.52(A)

Electrodes Permitted for Grounding
(6) Other Listed Electrodes. Other listed electrodes shall be permitted.

Renumber previous items (6) and (7) as (7) and (8) as follows:

(7) Plate Electrodes.

(8) Other Local Metal Underground Systems or Structures.

Summary of Change

A new item (6) addressing other listed electrodes is included in Section 250.52(A). Existing items (6) and (7) have been renumbered as (7) and (8) accordingly.

Change at a Glance

Listed grounding electrodes other than ground rods are now recognized in 250.52(A)(6).

2

250.64(D)

**Service with Multiple
Disconnecting Means
Enclosures**
NEC, p. 110

Proposal 5-192
Log 2396
ROP, p. 210

Comment
None

Change at a Glance

Three methods for grounding electrode conductor connections at services disconnecting means enclosures are clarified under this revision.

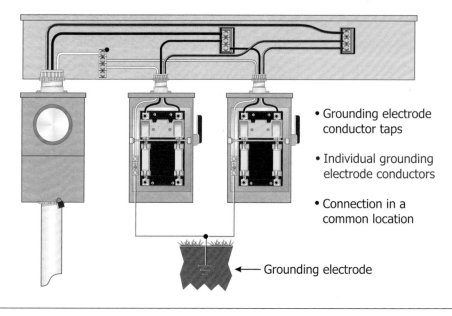

250.64(D) Service With Multiple Disconnecting Means Enclosures

- Grounding electrode conductor taps
- Individual grounding electrode conductors
- Connection in a common location

← Grounding electrode

Analysis and Effect

This section has been revised and expanded to provide a logical layout and to address the installation of multiple individual grounding electrode conductors for separate disconnecting means enclosures. The previous language addressed only grounding electrode conductor taps to the common grounding electrode conductor, but did not address individual grounding electrode conductors from separate disconnecting means enclosures. This change inserts text that recognizes the methods permitted for utilizing the grounding electrode conductor tap concept in accordance with this section, and also recognizes that individual grounding electrode conductors could be installed from each separate disconnecting means enclosure where they are installed as separate enclosures under the provisions of 230.71(A). Specific sizing requirements are included that clearly require the individual grounding electrode conductors to be sized in accordance with 250.66 based on the size of the largest service-entrance conductor(s) supplying the individual service disconnecting means. A new item (3) recognizes that a single grounding electrode conductor connection for the service could also be made in an accessible location and would need to be sized in accordance with 250.66 based on the service-entrance conductor(s) at the common location where the connection is made. This connection is required to be made by using the exothermic welding process or by using a connector that is listed as grounding and bonding equipment in accordance with UL 467.

Code Language
250.64

See actual *Code* text in 250.64(D)(1)(2) and (3)

(D) Service with Multiple Disconnecting Means Enclosures.
(1) Grounding Electrode Conductor Taps.
(2) Individual Grounding Electrode Conductors.
(3) Common Location.

Note: See Section 250.64(D) for complete text as restructured by this revision.

Summary of Change
Section 250.64(D) has been rearranged, revised, and structured into a list format meeting the requirements in Section 2.1.5.1 of the *NEC Style Manual*.

Accessibility
NEC, p. 111

Proposal 5-213
Log 3393
ROP, p. 215

Comment
None

Analysis and Effect

The revisions to subdivision (A) in this section have clarified that all grounding electrode conductor connections of the mechanical types are generally required to be accessible unless otherwise meeting the provisions of either exception. Exception No. 2 has been clarified by inserting a reference to the mechanical means, such as a mechanical bolt and nut combination, that is typically used to fasten the irreversible compression connector to the metal framing member and then is coated or encapsulated in fireproofing material. The provisions of this exception in the previous edition of the *Code* could have been interpreted to mean that the irreversible compression connector had to be connected directly to the metal framing member without the use of fastening hardware. The effect of this revision is that it provides needed clarity for users, while remaining consistent with the objectives of the technical committee regarding accessibility requirements for grounding electrode conductor connections and the fastening means permitted under the allowance of this exception.

Change at a Glance

Mechanical means such as bolts and nuts can be used to connect irreversible compression connectors to structural metal framing that is encapsulated or coated with fireproofing materials.

Code Language
250.68

Grounding Electrode Conductor and Bonding Jumper Connection to Grounding Electrodes

(A)
Accessibility

All mechanical elements used to terminate a grounding electrode conductor or bonding jumper to a grounding electrode shall be accessible.

Exception No. 1: An encased or buried connection to a concrete-encased, driven, or buried grounding electrode shall not be required to be accessible.

Exception No. 2: Exothermic or irreversible compression connections used at terminations, together with the mechanical means used to attach such terminations to fireproofed structural metal whether or not the mechanical means is reversible, shall not be required to be accessible.

Summary of Change

Section 250.68(A) now references mechanical elements used to terminate a grounding electrode conductor or bonding jumper to a grounding electrode. Exception No. 2 has been revised to reference the mechanical means of attachment of grounding electrode conductors.

250.94

Bonding for Other Systems
NEC, p. 113

Proposal 5-220
Log 1886
ROP, p. 217

Comment 5-122
Log 1151
ROC, p. 143

Change at a Glance

An intersystem bonding termination means that includes provisions for connecting at least three grounding or bonding conductors required for communications systems by chapter 8 is required to be installed at one of three specific locations.

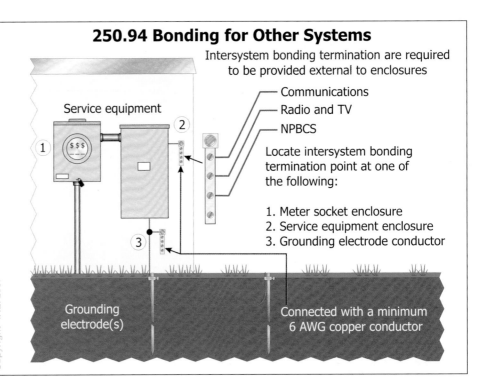

250.94 Bonding for Other Systems

Intersystem bonding termination are required to be provided external to enclosures

Service equipment

— Communications
— Radio and TV
— NPBCS

Locate intersystem bonding termination point at one of the following:

1. Meter socket enclosure
2. Service equipment enclosure
3. Grounding electrode conductor

Grounding electrode(s)

Connected with a minimum 6 AWG copper conductor

Copyright©AEI 2007

Analysis and Effect

This section has been completely revised and expanded to include more specific requirements to provide an intersystem bonding termination means for all limited energy systems grounding and bonding conductors required in accordance with chapters 7 and 8 of the *NEC*. Intersystem bonding accomplished by connection of a communication grounding conductor to the power system grounding electrode system is an important safety measure to prevent occurrences of voltages between communication system and power system. With the expansion of limited energy systems, experience is frequently indicating that the existing requirements are inadequate. The grounding and bonding for these systems is essential for safety, and is becoming more difficult to implement due to changes in building construction practices such as increased prevalence of flush construction and use of nonmetallic conduits for services, and so forth. Frequently, in new construction, the grounding electrode(s), the metallic service raceway, and the grounding electrode conductor are hidden behind walls and are not accessible for establishing the required intersystem grounding and bonding connections. This change inserts a requirement for a dedicated and well-defined location for terminating the bonding and grounding conductors on a specific set of terminals listed as grounding and bonding equipment. The termination must provide sufficient capacity to handle multiple communication systems (telecom, satellite, CATV) on premises, but not less than three terminals are required. Specified locations for these termination points for the intersystem bonding and grounding conductor termination are a key part of the revision. This termination means is required to be secured to (electrically and mechanically) the meter enclosure, located at the service equipment enclosure, or located at the grounding electrode conductor. Where it is attached to a service or metering equipment enclosure, it must not interfere with opening the enclosure. Where it is not connected to the meter socket enclosure as in accordance with 250.94(1), each intersystem termination means is required to be electrically connected to the equipment grounding terminal bar in the service equipment in accordance with 250.94(2), or connected to the grounding electrode conductor in accordance with 250.94(3). The size of the conductor used to establish this connection must not be smaller than 6 AWG copper. These grounding conductors also provide the necessary connection between communication and power systems (intersystem bonding). As a result, limited energy system installers and technicians should encounter fewer challenges regarding completing the required intersystem bonding and grounding connections because of these new requirements for a dedicated termination means having to be located in one of three prominent locations.

Code Language

250.94

Bonding for Other Systems
See revised Section 250.94 and Exception for actual *Code* text.

Summary of Change

This section has been completely revised by adding more specific requirements for intersystem bonding and grounding terminations. The existing text has been retained and rewritten into an exception to the new requirements. This revision is one of several correlated changes (100 Definitions, 250.94, Chapter 8 articles) to improve the requirements related to intersystem bonding and grounding of communication systems.

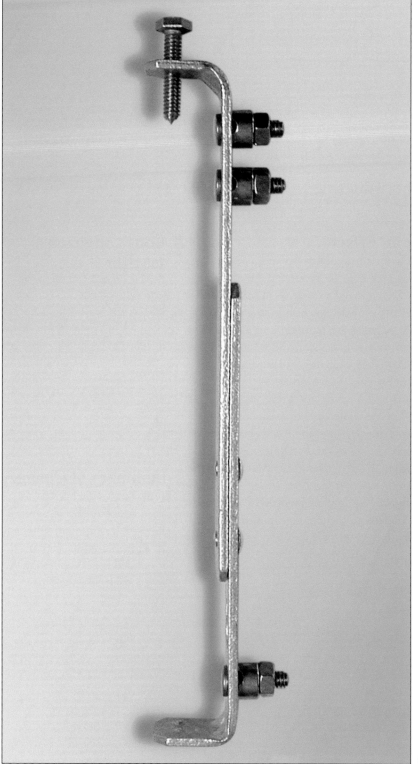

Courtesy of Thomas and Betts

250.112(I)

Remote Control, Signaling, and Fire Alarm Circuits
NEC, p. 116

Proposal 5-252
Log 3339
ROP, p. 224

Comment
None

Change at a Glance

Equipment or enclosures supplied by Class 1 circuits or systems are required to be grounded unless the circuit operates at less than 50 volts.

250.112(I) Remote-Control, Signaling, and Fire Alarm Circuits

Class 1 circuit

Equipment

Equipment supplied by Class 1 circuits is required to be grounded unless the system operates at less than 50 volts.

Section 250.20(A) provides the conditions and requirements for grounding systems less than 50 volts.

Analysis and Effect

This revision clarifies that equipment supplied by Class 1 circuits are required to be grounded generally, unless the Class 1 circuit operates at less than 50 volts. Section 250.20(A) provides the conditions where systems less than 50 volts are required to be grounded systems. The revisions to this section address the equipment supplied by Class 1 circuits, not the circuit itself. Another important *Code* provision to keep in mind is Section 250.21(A)(3), which recognizes omission of system grounding on some control circuits that operate at higher voltages. This revision resolves these questionable situations and requires equipment grounding in such cases. The effect is that the void in this section has been closed that could have allowed equipment supplied by a 480-volt Class 1 circuit to remain ungrounded if applied literally to these installations and systems.

Code Language
250.112(I)

Remote-Control, Signaling, and Fire Alarm Circuits

Equipment supplied by Class 1 circuits shall be grounded unless operating at less than 50 volts. Equipment supplied by Class 1 power-limited circuits, Class 2, and Class 3 remote-control and signaling circuits, and by fire alarm circuits shall be grounded where system grounding is required by Part II or Part VIII of this article.

Summary of Change

A new first sentence has been added to this section as follows: "Equipment supplied by Class 1 circuits shall be grounded unless operating at less than 50 volts."

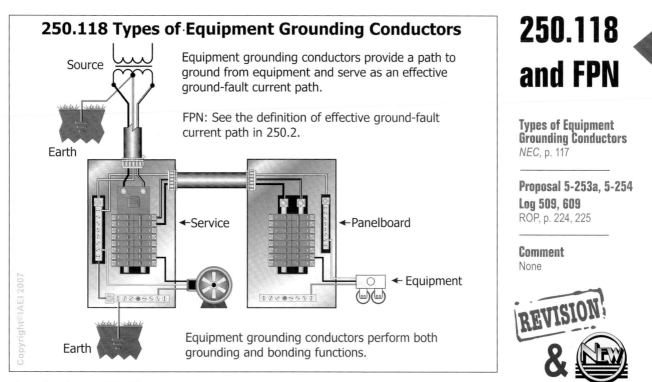

250.118 Types of Equipment Grounding Conductors

Equipment grounding conductors provide a path to ground from equipment and serve as an effective ground-fault current path.

FPN: See the definition of effective ground-fault current path in 250.2.

Source

Earth

←Service

←Panelboard

←Equipment

Earth

Equipment grounding conductors perform both grounding and bonding functions.

Copyright©IAEI 2007

250.118 and FPN

Types of Equipment Grounding Conductors
NEC, p. 117

Proposal 5-253a, 5-254
Log 509, 609
ROP, p. 224, 225

Comment
None

REVISION & NEW

Analysis and Effect

This revision is a continuation of larger efforts being extended to use the correct terms related to grounding and bonding in *Code* rules. The changes to this section primarily address two items. First, the new fine print note (FPN) provides users with clear information about the functionality of the equipment grounding conductor by referencing the definition of the term *effective ground-fault current path* in Section 250.2. The equipment grounding conductors provided in 250.118 serve as a means of grounding equipment and, equally important, serve as an effective ground-fault current path. The new FPN No. 1 to the revised definition of *grounding conductor, equipment* (EGC) in Article 100 indicates that the EGC also performs bonding. The second item clarified in the revisions to this section has to do with the fittings used with any of the wiring methods identified. This section previously required fittings that are "listed for grounding" to be used with these wiring methods that qualify as equipment grounding conductors. The problem is that the fittings (connectors and couplings, etc) perform bonding functions. The connectors connect (bond) the raceways to enclosures and the couplings connect (bond) conduit raceways and tubing together. The more appropriate term to use in this section

where the term *listed for grounding* is used is *listed for bonding* because bonding is really what is being accomplished by the fittings. This is also how they are evaluated by testing laboratories. *Bonding (Bonded)* is defined in Article 100 as "connected to establish electrical continuity and conductivity." The revision changes the term *listed for grounding* by removing the words "for grounding" because listed fittings provide the characteristics required within the rule. The listed fittings used with these wiring methods provide bonding functions inherent to their use. It is recognized that product standards and the guide card directory information also currently indicate that such fittings are listed for grounding. Words and terms related to grounding and bonding should mean what they imply by definition. The revisions to this section provide the needed clarification and accuracy in their use.

Change at a Glance

Equipment grounding conductors included in 250.118 serve as a grounding means and effective ground-fault current path by performing both grounding and bonding functions.

Code Language
250.118

Types of Equipment Grounding Conductors
See revised Section 250.118 and new FPN for actual *Code* text.

Summary of Change

A new fine print note (FPN) has been added to reference the definition of *effective ground-fault current path* in Section 250.2. The words "for grounding" after the word "listed" have been deleted throughout this section.

2

250.119 Exception

Identification of Equipment Grounding Conductors
NEC, p. 118

Proposal 5-264
Log 878
ROP, p. 227

Comment 5-140, 5-141
Log 1966, 633
ROC, p. 146, 147

Change at a Glance

Green insulated conductors of limited energy cables, such as thermostat cables, are permitted to be used as other than equipment grounding conductors.

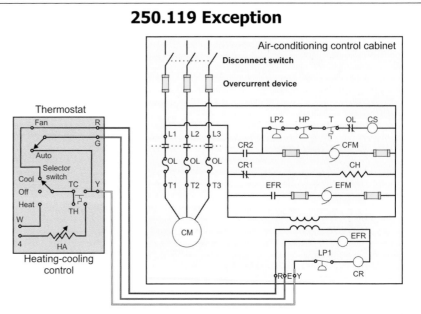

Green insulated conductors of limited energy cables, such as thermostat cables, are permitted to be used as other than equipment grounding conductors.

Analysis and Effect

Section 250.119 provides general requirements that reserve the use of the color green or green with one or more yellow stripes for identifying equipment grounding conductors. This rule applies to circuits and wiring that provide an equipment grounding conductor, such as feeders and branch circuits. A new exception has been added that addresses multi-conductor power-limited cables and Class 2 or Class 3 cables used for circuits operating at 50 volts or less. The new exception recognizes low-voltage installations where low-voltage and limited energy cable assemblies include an insulated conductor that is identified using the color green. The green conductors of such cable assemblies are typically not used as equipment grounding conductors, but are used for conductors of control circuits, signaling circuits, communication circuits, audio circuits, and so forth. As an example, the insulated green conductor of a Class 2 control circuit to a thermostat for a heating/cooling system is usually terminated on the "G" terminal in the thermostat and at the equipment. This circuit conductor is typically used as the fan control circuit for this type of equipment. Prior to this exception, the *NEC* included no recognition of using the color green for other than the purposes of identifying equipment grounding conductors. The new exception provides recognition of such uses and removes the apparent conflict regarding the use of the color green as an identification means for conductors that are part of cable assemblies operating at less than 50 volts.

Code Language
250.119

Green Insulated Conductors
Exception: Power-limited, Class 2, or Class 3 circuit cables containing only circuits operating at less than 50 volts shall be permitted to use a conductor with green insulation for other than equipment grounding purposes.

Summary of Change

A new exception has been added to 250.119 addressing green insulated conductors of limited energy cables.

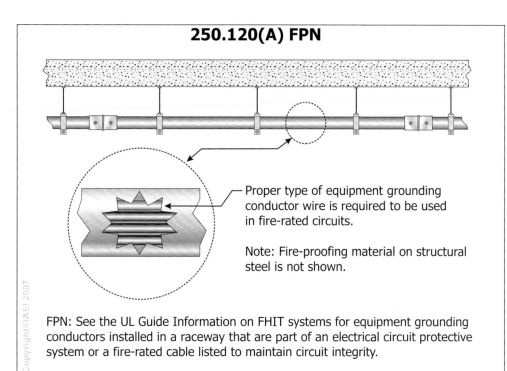

250.120(A) FPN

Proper type of equipment grounding conductor wire is required to be used in fire-rated circuits.

Note: Fire-proofing material on structural steel is not shown.

FPN: See the UL Guide Information on FHIT systems for equipment grounding conductors installed in a raceway that are part of an electrical circuit protective system or a fire-rated cable listed to maintain circuit integrity.

Copyright©IAEI 2007

Raceway, Cable Trays, Cable Armor, Cablebus, or Cable Sheaths
NEC, p. 118

Proposal 5-256
Log 3021
ROP, p. 226

Comment 5-136
Log 1987
ROC, p. 145

Analysis and Effect

Fire-rated cables are required for life safety circuits in Articles 695 and 700 in various applications where fire rating is required. Circuit integrity and reliability are the primary concerns for these circuits and systems. These circuits typically include an equipment grounding conductor, to which these specific fire rating requirements must also be applied. This new fine print note raises awareness for selecting the proper equipment grounding conductors for fire-rated circuits as outlined in the UL Guide Information FHIT that provides requirements for fire-rated assemblies. The UL Guide Information for FHIT systems specifically states, "If not specified, the ground shall be the same as the fire-rated wire described in the system." Use of any other ground wire violates the system fire rating. As an example, a THHN type equipment grounding conductor should not be used with a fire-rated system, unless specified in the system. The new FPN clarifies the importance of using the proper type of equipment grounding conductor wire used with these systems. Similar fine print notes have been added to 300.19(B), 695.6(A)(3)(d)(3) Exception, and 700.9 (D)(1)(2).

Change at a Glance

Equipment grounding conductors in circuits that require fire rating, circuit integrity, and survivability must meet minimum fire rating provisions or be a listed fire-rated cable.

Code Language 250.120(A)

FHIT Systems

FPN: See the UL Guide Information on FHIT systems for equipment grounding conductors installed in a raceway that are part of an electrical circuit protective system or a fire-rated cable listed to maintain circuit integrity.

Summary of Change

A new fine print note references the UL Guide Information on FHIT systems that have application to equipment grounding conductors.

250.122(C)

Multiple Circuits
NEC, p. 119

Proposal 5-282a
Log CP513
ROP, p. 231

Comment
None

Change at a Glance

A single equipment grounding conductor is permitted for multiple circuits installed in the same cable tray in accordance with the requirements in 392.3(B)(1)(c).

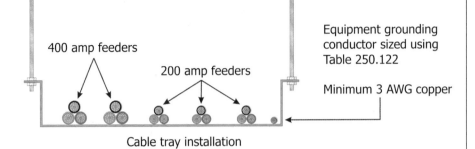

250.122(C) Multiple Circuits

400 amp feeders

200 amp feeders

Equipment grounding conductor sized using Table 250.122

Minimum 3 AWG copper

Cable tray installation

Copyright©IAEI 2007

A single equipment grounding conductor is permitted for multiple circuits installed in the same cable tray.

The equipment grounding conductor shall be sized based on the rating of the largest overcurrent device protecting the conductors in the tray.

Equipment grounding conductors installed in cable trays shall also meet the requirements in 392.3(B)(1)(c).

Analysis and Effect

The revisions to this section reference cable trays and provide direction for users on installation requirements for equipment grounding conductors installed in cable trays. This change, working in conjunction with present language of 300.3(B), clarifies that a common (single) equipment grounding conductor is permitted to be used within a cable tray where multiple circuits are installed. This long established trade practice in the field warrants the revision in the *Code* to recognize and assign appropriate requirements that should be complied with for such designs and installations. This revision brings the *Code* current with long-standing industry practices associated with cable tray installations. The reference to Section 392.3(B)(1)(c) is an appropriate correlation with the article covering cable tray installations, because there is a minimum size of 4 AWG established for single equipment grounding conductors used in such installations. Other than the specific minimum requirements for size in 392.3(B)(1)(c), the common single equipment grounding conductors in cable tray installations are required to meet the minimum sizes specified in 250.122.

Code Language
250.122(C)
Multiple Circuits
Where a single equipment grounding conductor is run with multiple circuits in the same raceway, cable, or cable tray, it shall be sized for the largest overcurrent device protecting conductors in the raceway, cable or cable tray. Equipment grounding conductors installed in cable trays shall meet the minimum requirements of 392.3(B)(1)(c).

Summary of Change

References to cable trays have been incorporated into the first sentence, and a new second sentence has been added as follows: "Equipment grounding conductors installed in cable trays shall meet the minimum requirements of 392.3(B)(1)(c)."

Conductors in Parallel
NEC, p. 119

Proposal 5-287
Log 3491
ROP, p. 232

Comment
None

Analysis and Effect

This section of the *NEC* was introduced into the 1999 edition as a concept that placed a listing requirement on the ground-fault protection equipment with the expectations that a product would be listed for this to protect undersized equipment grounding conductors under restrictive conditions. Substantiation with the proposal indicated there is no listing requirement, and there is no product standard with listing requirements for this application and there has been no equipment introduced to support this application. Action by CMP-5 removes this provision from the section to clarify that equipment grounding conductors in parallel installations are required to meet the rules in 250.122(F), whether part of a cable assembly or not. This revision eliminates the unnecessary potential for misapplication of this type of equipment with the expectations that it would provide protection for undersized equipment grounding conductors of feeders within cable systems, such as MC cables that are installed parallel. Equipment grounding conductors for feeders installed in parallel configurations shall be sized at a minimum based on Table 250.122 using the rating of the overcurrent device protecting the feeder.

Change at a Glance

Ground-fault protection devices previously addressed in this section are listed and designed to protect electrical equipment, not equipment grounding conductors in raceways or cable assemblies.

Code Language
250.122(F)

Conductors in Parallel

Where conductors are run in parallel in multiple raceways or cables as permitted in 310.4, the equipment grounding conductors, where used, shall be run in parallel in each raceway or cable.

Each parallel equipment grounding conductor shall be sized on the basis of the ampere rating of the overcurrent device protecting the circuit conductors in the raceway or cable in accordance with Table 250.122.

Summary of Change

List item (2) has been deleted from Section 250.122(F). Numbering for item (1) is no longer necessary and the section has been revised editorially.

250.142(B) (2) Exc. No. 2 (2)

Load-Side Equipment
NEC, p. 122

Proposal 5-294
Log 3351
ROP, p. 233

Comment
None

250.142(B) Exception No. 2 (2)

Exception No. 2(2) applies to all metering equipment enclosures including CT enclosures and meter socket enclosures.

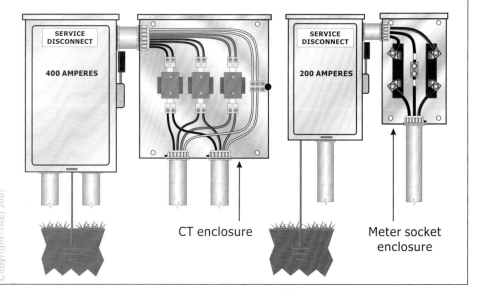

CT enclosure

Meter socket enclosure

Analysis and Effect

This section has been revised to broaden the requirements to cover other enclosures related to metering functions, such as metering current transformer (CT) or metering potential transformer (PT) enclosures. By not limiting the provisions of this exception to just meter socket enclosures, the exception can be more readily applied to installations that include not only meter socket enclosures, but also might include enclosures for metering equipment such as potential transformers (PTs) and current transformers (CTs).

Change at a Glance

This exception is applicable to meter socket enclosures and other meter instrument enclosures, such as a CT enclosure associated with a meter.

Code Language
250.142(B)(2)

Load-Side Equipment
Exception No. 2: It shall be permissible to ground meter enclosures by connection to the grounded circuit conductor on the load side of the service disconnect where all of the following conditions apply:

(1) No service ground-fault protection is installed.
(2) All meter enclosures are located immediately adjacent to the service disconnecting means.
(3) The size of the grounded circuit conductor is not smaller than the size specified in Table 250.122 for equipment grounding conductors.

Summary of Change

The word "socket" has been deleted from item (2) in Exception No. 2 to 250.142(B).

250.146 Connecting Grounding Terminal to Box

Connecting Receptacle Grounding Terminal to Box
NEC, p. 122

Proposal 5-297
Log 628
ROP, p. 234

Comment
None

← Equipment bonding jumper

Equipment bonding jumper is sized based on the branch-circuit overcurrent device rating using Table 250.122.

Copyright©IAEI 2007

Analysis and Effect

This revision provides *Code* users with specific sizing information for the equipment bonding jumpers addressed in this section used at outlet and junction boxes. While it is understood that equipment bonding jumper sizing rules in 250.102(D) are to be used and applied to this installation, there continues to be many installations in the field where the equipment bonding jumper is smaller than the branch-circuit conductors (14 AWG for 20-ampere branch circuits, for example). Exhibit 314.3 in the 2005 *NEC* Handbook provides an example of an installation that would be in violation of minimum equipment bonding jumper sizing rules if the conductor from the wire connector (red wire nut) to the outlet box is a 14 AWG conductor. The *Code* presently includes the minimum sizing requirements for wire-type equipment grounding conductors in 250.122 and load-side equipment bonding jumpers in 250.102(B). The minimum sizing for equipment bonding jumpers on the load side of an overcurrent device is provided in Table 250.122. Including the sizing requirement within the rule that requires the bonding jumper adds usability and clarity to a requirement that often is misapplied in field installations. The revision to this section enhances clarity and usability by including sizing requirements within this rule to correlate with other existing sizing rules for equipment bonding jumpers in Article 250.

Code Language
250.146

Connecting Receptacle Grounding Terminal to Box
An equipment bonding jumper shall be used to connect the grounding terminal of a grounding-type receptacle to a grounded box unless grounded as in 250.146(A) through (D). The equipment bonding jumper shall be sized in accordance with Table 250.122 based on the rating of the overcurrent device protecting the circuit conductors.

Summary of Change

A new second sentence has been added to this section as follows: "The equipment bonding jumper shall be sized in accordance with Table 250.122 based on the rating of the overcurrent device protecting the circuit conductors."

Change at a Glance

Equipment bonding jumpers that connect a grounding terminal of a receptacle to a grounded metal box must be sized according to Table 250.122 using the rating of the overcurrent device (fuse or circuit breaker) for the circuit.

2

250.146(A)

Surface-Mounted Box
NEC, p. 122

Proposal 5-300
Log 2484
ROP, p. 234

Comment
None

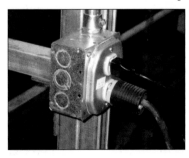

Change at a Glance

Clarification has been provided about the types of boxes and cover combinations that provide adequate grounding and bonding continuity between a box and cover.

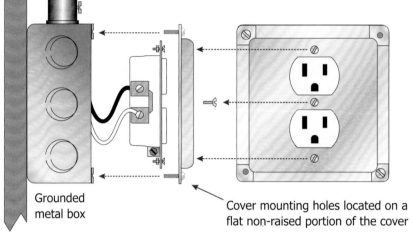

250.146(A) Surface-Mounted Box

Two permanent fasteners for attaching the device to the cover (rivets or thread locking screw locking means)

Grounded metal box

Cover mounting holes located on a flat non-raised portion of the cover

Listed exposed work cover is permitted as the grounding and bonding means

Copyright©IAEI 2007

Analysis and Effect

This section has been revised to clarify what type of box and cover combinations are acceptable to provide the required bonding connections from the receptacle to the box without using an equipment bonding jumper as required in the general provisions of 250.146. The new sentence clarifies for installers and inspectors that a listed exposed work cover is acceptable for establishing the grounding and bonding means to grounding-type receptacle as follows:

    1. the device is attached to the cover with at least two fasteners that are permanent (such as a rivet) or have a thread locking or screw locking means, and

    2. when the cover mounting holes are located on a flat non-raised portion of the cover.

    This revision results in improved clarity as to what type of listed cover provides the required grounding and bonding connection anticipated and the specific physical characteristics of the type of cover that is referred to in this section.

Summary of Change

A new last sentence has been added to 250.146(A).

Code Language
250.146(A)
Surface-Mounted Box

Where the box is mounted on the surface, direct metal-to-metal contact between the device yoke and the box or a contact yoke or device that complies with 250.146(B) shall be permitted to ground the receptacle to the box. At least one of the insulating washers shall be removed from receptacles that do not have a contact yoke or device that complies with 250.146(B) to ensure direct metal-to-metal contact. This provision shall not apply to cover-mounted receptacles unless the box and cover combination are listed as providing satisfactory ground continuity between the box and the receptacle. A listed exposed work cover shall be permitted to be the grounding and bonding means when (1) the device is attached to the cover with at least two fasteners that are permanent (such as a rivet) or have a thread locking or screw locking means and (2) when the cover mounting holes are located on a flat non-raised portion of the cover.

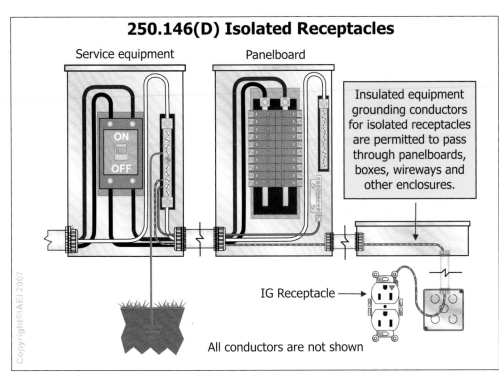

250.146(D) Isolated Receptacles

Service equipment

Panelboard

ON
OFF

Insulated equipment grounding conductors for isolated receptacles are permitted to pass through panelboards, boxes, wireways and other enclosures.

IG Receptacle →

All conductors are not shown

Copyright©IAEI 2007

250.146 (D)

Isolated Receptacles
NEC, p. 122

Proposal 5-302
Log 438
ROP, p. 235

Comment 5-155
Log 337
ROC, p. 150

REVISION

Analysis and Effect

The changes to the requirements in this section provide clarity and enhance usability of the provisions. It is logical to presume that isolated, insulated equipment grounding conductors installed in accordance with 250.146(D) and 408.40 Exception, not only have to pass through one or more panelboards so they may be connected at a point of grounding for the applicable service or separately derived system, but they generally must also pass through outlet boxes, junction and pull boxes, wireways, and so forth without connection to the grounding means in those items so the conductor remains an isolated insulated equipment grounding conductor. This revision brings the *NEC* current and consistent with actual ongoing installations and practices that include isolated equipment grounding conductors in designs and in the field. The change results in a requirement that accurately and practically can be applied to enclosures, boxes, and so forth, other than just panelboards that include insulated, isolated equipment grounding conductors in accordance with this section.

Change at a Glance

Isolated, insulated equipment grounding conductors used with isolated receptacles are permitted to pass through panelboards, boxes, wireways, or other enclosures without connection to such enclosures.

Code Language
250.146(D)

Isolated Receptacles

Where installed for the reduction of electrical noise (electromagnetic interference) on the grounding circuit, a receptacle in which the grounding terminal is purposely insulated from the receptacle mounting means shall be permitted. The receptacle grounding terminal shall be grounded to an insulated equipment grounding conductor run with the circuit conductors. This equipment grounding conductor shall be permitted to pass through one or more panelboards without a connection to the panelboard grounding terminal bar as permitted in 408.40, Exception, so as to terminate within the same building or structure directly at an equipment grounding conductor terminal of the applicable derived system or service. Where installed in accordance with the provisions of this section, this equipment grounding conductor shall also be permitted to pass through boxes, wireways, or other enclosures without being connected to such enclosures.

Summary of Change

This section has been revised to replace the word "required" in the first sentence with "installed." A new last sentence addresses the insulated equipment grounding conductor routing permitted under the provision of this section.

2

Article 280

Surge Arresters, Over 1 kV
NEC, 126–127

Proposal 5-335
Log 2599
ROP, p. 246

Comment 5-162
Log 975
ROC, p. 151

Change at a Glance

Article 280 was revised and restructured to provide uniformity with revisions to UL 1449 *Standard for Surge Protective Devices*.

Analysis and Effect

Article 280 has been restructured and revised to correlate with pending revisions to UL Standard 1449. Article 280 will now cover only surge arresters installed in premises wiring systems over 1000 volts. This significant change results from UL combining the categories of surge arresters and transient voltage surge suppressors into a single category and product standard, which is being renamed UL 1449 *Standard for Surge Protective Devices*. The technology of both low-voltage surge arresters and transient voltage surge suppressors (TVSS) is now essentially the same, thereby justifying one product standard and one evaluation and test program, with consideration to the installation location on the line side (Type 1) or load side (Type 2) of the service disconnect overcurrent protection. Another change is that surge arresters are to be listed devices in a new Section 280.5. Smaller voltage surge arrester grounding conductor requirements in former 280.22 have been deleted. As a result, all conductors between surge arresters and the grounding connection shall not be smaller than 6 AWG copper or aluminum. This revision clarifies when Article 280 applies to surge arrester installations and whether those surge arresters are required to be listed, providing enforcement with a basis for approvals of installations that incorporate surge arresters. A new definition of *surge arrester* has also been included in Article 100 to point out what these devices are and what they are intended to accomplish.

Revisions to Article 285 cover surge arresters for use on premises wiring systems of 1000 volts or less.

Code Language
Article 280

Surge Arresters, Over 1 kV
   I. General
   II. Installation
   III. Connecting Surge Arresters
See revised Article 280 for actual *Code* text.

Summary of Change

The title and scope of Article 280 have been revised and various specific requirements have been either changed or added. The article has been restructured to include three parts as part of this overall revision. The technical changes are in addition to other revisions throughout the *Code* where surge arresters are covered by other *NEC* rules such as those in Articles 100, 230, 250, 280, 285, 501, and 502.

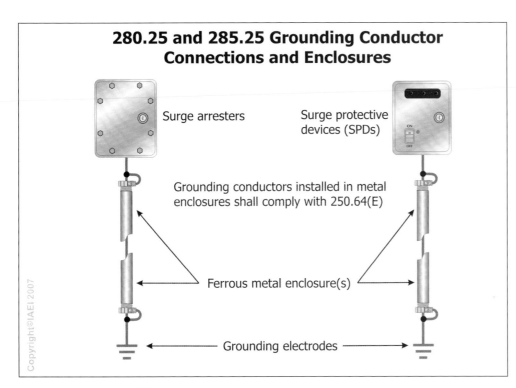

280.25 and 285.25 Grounding Conductor Connections and Enclosures

Surge arresters

Surge protective devices (SPDs)

Grounding conductors installed in metal enclosures shall comply with 250.64(E)

Ferrous metal enclosure(s)

Grounding electrodes

Copyright©IAEI 2007

Grounding Conductor Connections and Enclosures
NEC, p. 127, 129

Proposal 5-347,5-351
Log 802, 803
ROP, p. 251, 253

Comment 5-162, 5-168
Log 975, 2351
ROC, p. 151, 154

Analysis and Effect

Grounding conductors for surge arresters and surge protective devices (SPDs) have similar requirements in Articles 280 and 285. The requirements for grounding electrode conductors installed in metallic enclosures already exist in Section 250.64(E), so an additional sentence has been included in each of these sections to refer to Section 250.64(E) for the specific metal enclosure installation and bonding rules. This revision provides consistency between two rules in two separate articles that cover the same requirements. The revision to the title of each of these sections is appropriate to reflect what is covered by the rule itself. By referencing Section 250.64(E), these installations will be required to comply with the rules that apply to grounding electrode conductors that are installed in ferrous metal enclosures rather than all metal enclosures previously required by each of these rules in Articles 280 and 285.

Change at a Glance

Ferrous metal enclosures for grounding conductors installed for surge arresters or surge protective devices (SPDs) must meet the protection from magnetic field requirements in 250.64(E).

Code Language
280.25

Grounding Conductor Connections and Enclosures

Except as indicated in this article, surge-arrester grounding conductor connections shall be made as specified in Article 250, Parts III and X. Grounding conductors installed in metal enclosures shall comply with 250.64(E).

285.28

Grounding Conductor Connections and Enclosures

Except as indicated in this article, SPD grounding connections shall be made as specified in Article 250, Part III. Grounding conductors installed in metal enclosures shall comply with 250.64(E).

Summary of Change

Both Sections 280.25 and 285.28 have been revised by expanding the title of each section and including a new additional sentence as follows: "Grounding conductors installed in metal enclosures shall comply with 250.64(E)."

Article 285

**Surge Protective Devices,
1kV or Less**
NEC, 128, 129

Proposal 5-349
Log 2604
ROP, p. 252

Comment 5-168
Log 2351
ROC, p. 154

Change at a Glance

Transient voltage surge suppressors are now identified by the *NEC* as *surge protective devices* (SPDs).

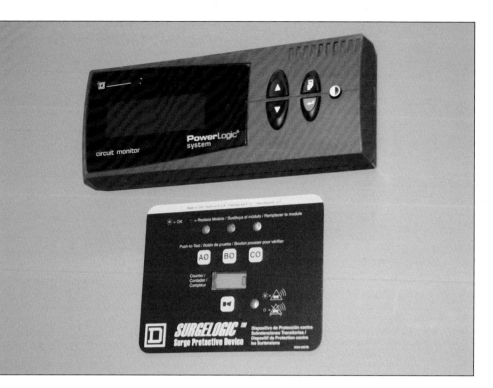

Analysis and Effect

Article 285 has been restructured and revised to correlate with pending revisions to UL Standard 1449. The title has been changed from "Transient Voltage Surge Suppressors" to "Surge Protective Devices, 1 kV or Less." Use of *transient voltage surge suppressor* has been replaced by *surge protective devices* (SPDs) throughout Article 285 and the *NEC*. For the 2008 *NEC*, the acronym "SPD" will be followed by (*surge arrester or TVSS*) as a practical transition. Article 285 will now cover only surge protective devices (both surge arresters and transient voltage surge suppressors) installed in premises wiring systems of 1000 volts or less. This change results from UL combining surge arresters and transient voltage surge suppressors into a single category and product standard, which is being renamed as UL 1449 *Standard for Surge Protective Devices*. The technology of both low-voltage surge arresters and transient voltage surge suppressors (TVSS) is essentially the same, thereby justifying one product standard, and one evaluation and test program, with consideration to the installation location on the line side (Type 1) or load side (Type 2) of the service disconnect overcurrent protection. Part III includes specific rules related to installation and connection of surge protective devices. Sections 285.21 through 285.25 specifically address the three types of surge protective devices (Types 1, 2 and 3). Requirements addressing installation criteria, locations and minimum length of conductors for Type 3 devices are included. TVSSs are now identified as surge protective devices (SPDs), but still provide transient voltage surge protection. A new definition of *surge protective devices* (SPDs), including the three types of devices, has been included in Article 100 to point out what these devices are and what they are intended to accomplish.

Code Language
Article 285

See revised Article 285 for actual *Code* text.

Summary of Change

The title and scope of Article 285 have been revised and various specific requirements have been either changed or added. These revisions are in addition to others throughout the *NEC* where surge protective devices are covered by rules such as those in Articles 100, 230, 250, 280, 285, 501, and 502 and so forth.

Chapter 3

Selected Changes

300.4(A)(1)

Bored Holes
NEC, p. 131

Proposal 3-21
Log 3045
ROP, p. 258

Comment
None

REVISION

Change at a Glance

Multiple protective plates or bushings can be installed to provide protection for cables and raceways installed through wood members.

300.4(A)(1) Bored Holes

Multiple plates (stacked) or bushings are permitted to provide protection

Copyright©IAEI 2007

← Protective plates →

Protective steel plates to cover the area of the wiring with appropriate length and width protection.

Analysis and Effect

This revision clarifies that more than one protective plate or bushing can be installed to provide the physical protection required by this section. Where necessary, multiple plates or bushings can be used in a continuous row to afford protection for the entire length and width of the area of the framing where the wiring method is located less than 32 mm (1 1/4 in.) from the nearest edge of the wood member. Although this revision is simple in nature, literally the text in previous editions required only a single plate for protection. Where wiring is installed through multiple framing members that are sandwiched together, multiple protective plates are necessary to meet the protection requirements. This revision provides a clarification that actually reflects current accepted practices being used to meet the requirements for physical protection where wiring is installed, such as at corners, and supports the framing requirement of multiple members used together.

Code Language

300.4(A)

Cables and Raceways Through Wood Members

(1) Bored Holes. In both exposed and concealed locations, where a cable- or raceway-type wiring method is installed through bored holes in joists, rafters, or wood members, holes shall be bored so that the edge of the hole is not less than 32 mm (1 1/4 in.) from the nearest edge of the wood member. Where this distance cannot be maintained, the cable or raceway shall be protected from penetration by screws or nails by a steel plate(s) or bushing(s), at least 1.6 mm (1/16 in.) thick, and of appropriate length and width installed to cover the area of the wiring.

Summary of Change

The last sentence of Section 300.4(A)(1) has been revised by adding an "(s)" to "plate" and adding "bushing(s)" in the last sentence.

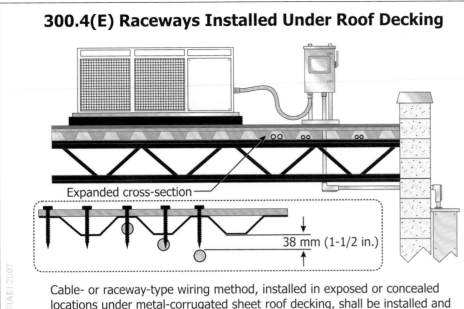

300.4(E) Raceways Installed Under Roof Decking

Expanded cross-section

38 mm (1-1/2 in.)

Cable- or raceway-type wiring method, installed in exposed or concealed locations under metal-corrugated sheet roof decking, shall be installed and supported so the nearest outside surface of the cable or raceway is not less than 38 mm (1-1/2") from the nearest surface of the roof decking.

Copyright IAEI 2007

300.4(E), FPN, and Exception

Cables and Raceways Installed Under Roof Decking
NEC, p. 132

Proposal 3-31
Log 3310
ROP, p. 260

Comment 3-10
Log 2040
ROC, p. 157

Analysis and Effect

This new requirement for protection of cables and raceways is in response to substantiation that construction roofing processes can cause damage to wiring methods installed in close proximity to metal roof decking. The fastening devices used to hold down roofing materials are typically driven through the metal decking as a normal part of their installation. Where cables and raceways are installed on the underside of the decking and spacing is not maintained between the decking and the wiring, they are vulnerable to damage by roof material fasteners that can penetrate the wiring when they are installed. Action by CMP-3 results in a new requirement that will restrict raceways and cables from being installed closer than 38.1 m (1 1/2 in.) from the underside of the decking. The original proposal included an alternative protection that could have been provided by nail plates, but this could prove rather impractical in most situations. It was determined that a greater degree of protection could be achieved by maintaining minimum spacing, which is practical for users and enforceable for inspectors. The new exception recognizes that rigid metal conduit and intermediate metal conduit provide a greater degree of protection from damage that can occur from these nails and fasteners. The information provided in the substantiation demonstrated the need to address wiring protection in this specific type of installation and to coincide with the general concepts of property protection provided in 90.1(A).

Code Language
300.4(E)

Cables and Raceways Installed Under Roof Decking. A cable- or raceway-type wiring method, installed in exposed or concealed locations under metal-corrugated sheet roof decking, shall be installed and supported so the nearest outside surface of the cable or raceway is not less than 38 mm (1 1/2 in.) from the nearest surface of the roof decking.

FPN: Roof decking material is often repaired or replaced after the initial raceway or cabling and roofing installation and may be penetrated by the screws or other mechanical devices designed to provide "hold down" strength of the waterproof membrane or roof insulating material.

Exception: Rigid metal conduit and intermediate metal conduit shall not be required to comply with 300.4(E).

Summary of Change

A new subdivision (E) has been included in Section 300.4 and addresses protection for cables and raceways installed under metal roof decking. A new exception relaxes this requirement for rigid metal conduit and intermediate metal conduit. The existing 2005 *NEC* subdivisions (E) and (F) have been re-identified as (F) and (G).

Change at a Glance

Cables and raceways other than RMC and IMC require protection where installed within 38 mm (1 1/2 in.) of metal roof decking.

3

300.4(G)

Insulated Fittings
NEC, p. 132

Proposal 3-33
Log 1338
ROP, p. 261

Comment 3-12
Log 2255
ROC, p. 158

Change at a Glance

Insulation fittings or bushings are required for protection of insulated circuit conductors.

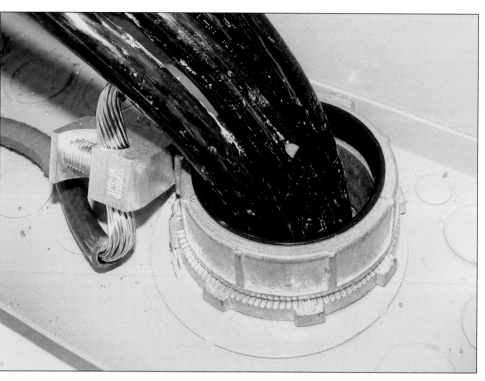

Analysis and Effect

This requirement addresses protection for conductors from abrasion at the location where the conductors enter a cabinet, box, enclosure, or raceway. These protection requirements apply to conductors in sizes 4 AWG or larger. Although the requirements of this section have been typically applied to both ungrounded and grounded circuit conductors, the requirement taken literally applied only to ungrounded conductors. This revision clarifies that this rule applies not only to ungrounded conductors but to all insulated circuit conductors. Protection to insulated conductors of circuits is the objective of the requirement and should not be limited to just ungrounded conductors. The change expands the requirement for protection against abrasion to all insulated circuit conductors whether ungrounded or grounded and provides consistency with current industry practices. As revised, this section provides clear requirements for protection of all insulated circuit conductors when the raceway wiring method system enters an enclosure.

Code Language
300.4(G)
Insulated Fittings

Where raceways contain 4 AWG or larger insulated circuit conductors and these conductors enter a cabinet, box enclosure, or raceway, the conductors shall be protected by a substantial fitting providing a smoothly rounded insulating surface, unless the conductors are separated from the fitting or raceway by substantial insulating material that is securely fastened in place.

Summary of Change

Section 300.4(G) has been revised by removing the word "ungrounded" and replacing it with the words "insulated circuit" conductors.

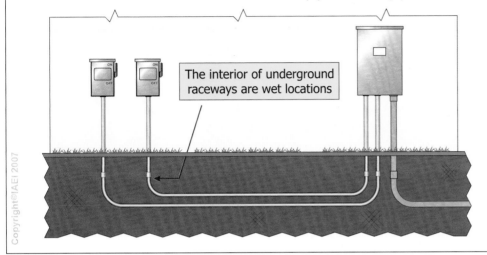

300.5(B) Wet Locations

The interior of enclosures or raceways installed underground shall be considered to be a wet location.

Insulated conductors installed in wet locations are required to be listed for use in wet locations and shall comply with 310.8(C).

The interior of underground raceways are wet locations

Copyright©IAEI 2007

300.5(B)

Underground Installations
NEC, p. 132

Proposal 3-42
Log 2874
ROP, p. 263

Comment 3-20a, 3-21
Log CC300, 274
ROC, p. 160, 161

Analysis and Effect

This revision clarifies the requirements for conductors and splices in wet locations. Substantiation in the proposal indicated that some confusion exists about whether the interior of a raceway or enclosure installed underground is a wet location or other than a wet location. Since all underground installations were already covered by 300.5 and rather than requiring only insulated conductors and cables to be listed for wet locations, the text was modified to clarify that the interior of raceways and enclosures installed in underground installations are considered wet locations. Substantiation in Comments 3-21 and 3-52 provided enough justification for panel action that clarifies and differentiates the interior of underground raceways as wet locations in contrast to dry locations. These revisions provide users with clear direction on this issue and remove the questions about what type of conductors and splicing methods must be used in installations that are wet locations as specified. Conductors and cables installed in such locations are required to be listed for such locations. Splices in these locations are required to be approved for a wet location.

Change at a Glance

The interior of enclosures and raceways installed underground are considered wet locations.

Code Language

300.5

Underground Installations
(A) Minimum Cover Requirements (unchanged)

(B) Wet Locations. The interior of enclosures or raceways installed underground shall be considered to be a wet location. Insulated conductors and cables installed in these enclosures or raceways in underground installations shall be listed for use in wet locations and shall comply with 310.8(C). Any connections or splices in an underground installation shall be approved for wet locations.

Summary of Change

The title of subdivision (B) was changed from *Listed* to *Wet Locations*. The first sentence was revised to address the interior of raceways. Any insulated conductors or cables installed in these raceways or enclosures shall meet the requirements of 310.8(C). A new last sentence was added to include approval requirements for connectors and splicing means.

300.5(C)

Underground Cables Under Buildings
NEC, p. 132

Proposal 3-45
Log 3333
ROP, p. 263

Comment 3-22
Log 409
ROC, p. 161

Change at a Glance

Cables installed under buildings must be in a raceway.

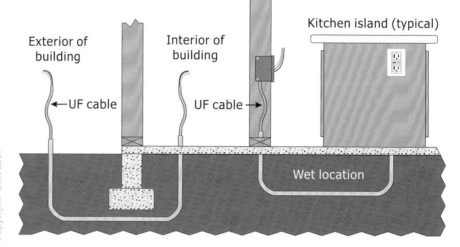

300.5(C) Underground Cable Under Buildings

Underground cables installed under buildings shall be in a raceway.

This requirement applies to cables routed from under the building to outside the building perimeter and to raceways that remain within the outside perimeter of the building.

Exterior of building

Interior of building

Kitchen island (typical)

←UF cable

UF cable →

Wet location

Copyright©IAEI 2007

Analysis and Effect

The revisions to this section clarify the objectives of the rule. This rule is applicable to underground cables installed under buildings and allows for practical access to such cables that would otherwise be rendered inaccessible owing to the burial under building floors. The change allows cables to be installed specifically under a building with or without a concrete slab, if they are installed in a raceway that allows for access to the wiring method for removal where necessary. The existing requirement for the raceway to extend beyond the outside walls of the building was deleted to permit the cables to emerge and terminate within the building. This is seen in kitchens where a length of UF cable is installed in a short section of raceway under the slab or floor from an island to an interior wall. The previous text did not account for such conditions. Action by CMP-3 also results in the removal of the reference to structures within this section because, by definition, a structure is that which is built or constructed; and structures can be an entity other than a building, such as, installations of 4 x 4 wood posts or poles with plywood backing for a panelboard or temporary service equipment in an undeveloped field or a construction site. It would not be necessary to require a direct burial cable to be in a raceway under these types of structures.

Code Language
300.5(C)
Underground Cables Under Buildings

Underground cable installed under a building shall be in a raceway.

Summary of Change

This section has been revised and the intent of the requirement has been clarified by removing the references to structures.

Analysis of Changes *NEC*-2008

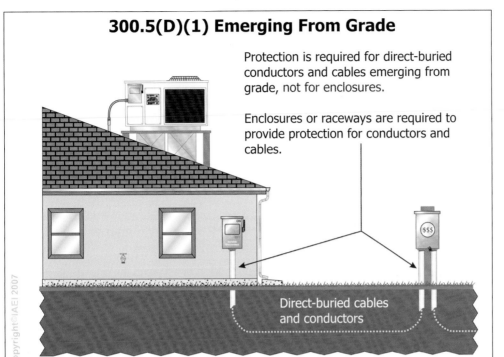

300.5(D)(1) Emerging From Grade

Protection is required for direct-buried conductors and cables emerging from grade, not for enclosures.

Enclosures or raceways are required to provide protection for conductors and cables.

Direct-buried cables and conductors

Copyright©IAEI 2007

Emerging from Grade
NEC, p. 132

Proposal 3-46
Log 2710
ROP, p. 263

Comment
None

REVISION!

Analysis and Effect

The changes to this section improve clarity and incorporate specific references to the columns of Table 300.5 to which these protection requirements apply. By changing the word "enclosures" to the word "cables," it is clear that the protection requirements apply to direct buried conductors and cables that emerge from grade, not to enclosures. This section has been revised to specifically indicate which columns of the table are required to meet this physical protection requirement. Columns 2 and 3 offer protection because of the wiring method addressed under each heading. Column 5 addresses control circuits of 30 volts or less. Circuits operating at 30 volts or less used for irrigation control and landscape lighting, for example, exhibit limited risk of electric shock in the event the conductors or cables become damaged. The operating characteristics of low-voltage circuits also subject the insulation of the conductors and cable to considerably less voltage stress than higher branch-circuit operating voltages of conductors and cables. These risks are limited enough for the column 5 conductors and cables not to require the extent of a 2.5 m (8 ft) raceway used for physical protection rising above finished grade to protect these conductors or cables from damage.

Change at a Glance

The protection required by 300.5(D)(1) is for conductors and cables, not for enclosures.

Code Language
300.5(D)(1)

Emerging from Grade

Direct-buried conductors and cables emerging from grade and specified in columns 1 and 4 of Table 300.5 shall be protected by enclosures or raceways extending from the minimum cover distance below grade required by 300.5(A) to a point at least 2.5 m (8 ft) above finished grade. In no case shall the protection be required to exceed 450 mm (18 in.) below finished grade.

Summary of Change

This section has been revised by removing the first instance of the word "enclosures" and replacing it with the word "cables." The first sentence of this rule has also been revised by adding the phrase "and specified in columns 1 and 4 of Table 300.5."

300.6(B)

Aluminum Metal Equipment
NEC, p. 134

Proposal 3-59, 3-60
Log 3396, 639
ROP, p. 266

Comment
None

Change at a Glance

Supplementary corrosion protection is required for aluminum metal conduits and equipment in concrete encasement and in direct contact with the earth.

300.6(B) Aluminum Metal Equipment

Aluminum raceways, cable trays, cablebus, auxiliary gutters, cable armor, boxes, cable sheathing, cabinets, elbows, couplings, nipples, fittings, supports, and support hardware embedded or encased in concrete or in direct contact with the earth shall be provided with supplementary corrosion protection.

Red brass (non-ferrous) conduit is suitable for use in direct contact with the earth or where encased in concrete.

Aluminum raceway or equipment embedded or encased in concrete or in direct contact with the earth requires supplementary corrosion protection.

Copyright©IAEI 2007

Analysis and Effect

This revision gives specific application of the requirements. Changing the word "non-ferrous" to the word "aluminum" clarifies that not all non-ferrous equipment requires supplementary corrosion protection. For example, red brass conduit is suitable for use embedded in concrete or in direct contact with the earth. This type of conduit is non-ferrous and the product standard (UL 6A) for red brass conduit clearly recognizes its use in these conditions. The UL Electrical Construction Equipment Directory includes limitations and special conditions of use for listed products. Under the product category "Conduit, Rigid Nonferrous Metallic (DYWV)," aluminum conduit is required to have supplementary corrosion protection when installed in concrete or in soil. Currently, the product standard does not require supplementary protection for red brass (non-ferrous) conduit. The revision to this section specifically requires supplementary corrosion protection only for aluminum materials and wiring methods that are embedded or encased in concrete or that are in direct contact with the earth.

Code Language
300.6(B)
Aluminum Metal Equipment
Aluminum raceways, cable trays, cablebus, auxiliary gutters, cable armor, boxes, cable sheathing, cabinets, elbows, couplings, nipples, fittings, supports, and support hardware embedded or encased in concrete or in direct contact with the earth shall be provided with supplementary corrosion protection.

Summary of Change
The word "non-ferrous" has been changed to the word "aluminum" in the title and the text of subdivision (B) to this section.

**Raceways in Wet
Locations Abovegrade**
NEC, p. 135

**Proposal 3-63
Log 2234**
ROP, p. 267

**Comment 3-52
Log 2257**
ROC, p. 166

Analysis and Effect

Action by CMP-3 on Comment 3-52 (Log. No. 2257) to Proposal 3-63 (Log. No. 2234) results in the creation of a new Section 300.9 that includes specific requirements for conductors and cables installed in raceways that are located in wet locations abovegrade level. CMP-3 accepted the concepts introduced by the submitter in this proposal that additional clarity in the *Code* requiring this requirement was warranted. One of the common methods of compliance with the raceway wet location rules is to install conductors and cables that are listed for wet locations; however, Section 310.8(C) provides additional methods by which the requirement can be met, therefore this new section provides that necessary correlation. The interior of raceways installed in wet locations are considered wet locations and conductors or cables installed in such raceways have to be suitable for use in wet locations by meeting any of the provisions in 310.8(C).

Change at a Glance

The conductors and cables installed in abovegrade raceways located in wet locations are required to be suitable for use in wet locations in accordance with 310.8(C).

Code Language

300.9
Raceways in Wet Locations Abovegrade

Where raceways are installed in wet locations abovegrade, the interior of these raceways shall be considered to be a wet location. Insulated conductors and cables installed in raceways in wet locations abovegrade shall comply with 310.8(C).

Summary of Change

A new section (300.9) that specifically addresses the requirements for conductors and cables installed within raceways located in wet locations abovegrade has been incorporated into Article 300.

3

300.11 (A)(2)

Non-Fire-Rated Assemblies
NEC, p. 136

Proposal 3-67a
Log CP300
ROP, p. 268

Comment
None

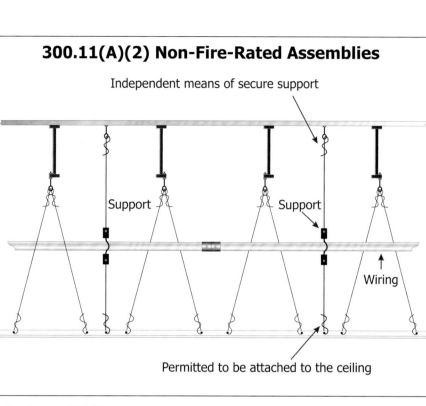

300.11(A)(2) Non-Fire-Rated Assemblies

Independent means of secure support

Support   Support

Wiring

Permitted to be attached to the ceiling

Copyright©IAEI 2007

Analysis and Effect

Section 300.11(A)(2) applies to securing and supporting wiring methods installed in non-fire-rated ceiling assemblies. This section addresses wiring located in the ceiling cavity and generally restricts such wiring from being secured to or supported by the ceiling assembly or the ceiling-assembly support wires. Wires that support the ceiling are not permitted as a means of securing or supporting wiring in these spaces, and the last sentence clearly requires that an independent means of secure support be provided. By adding the words "and shall be permitted to be attached to the assembly" to the last sentence of this rule, clarification and direction are provided for users as to what constitutes a secure means of support. In other words, if additional support wires are provided for the electrical wiring securing and supporting means, they are required to be attached to structure (usually at the top) and the ceiling assembly (usually at the bottom). The added text is permissive in nature and it is recognized that various types of securing and supporting means are not required to be attached to the ceiling assembly to provide secure support, such as strut-type trapezes, threaded rods, and so forth. A similar change was incorporated into Section 300.11(A)(1) in *NEC*-2005. This revision provides clarity for users and also correlates consistently with similar provisions in (A)(1) of this section.

Change at a Glance

Additional support wires in non-fire-rated ceilings are permitted to be attached to the ceiling grid assembly.

Code Language
300.11(A)(2)
Non-Fire-Rated Assemblies
...An independent means of secure support shall be provided and shall be permitted to be attached to the assembly.

Summary of Change

This section has been revised by adding the words "and shall be permitted to be attached to the assembly" to the end of the last sentence.

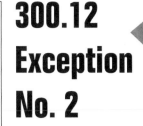
300.12 Exception No. 2

Exception No. 2 applies to open bottom equipment such as switchboards, motor control centers, and transformers.

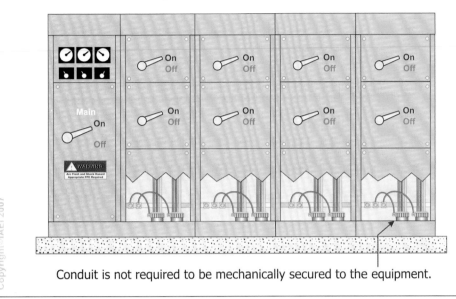

Conduit is not required to be mechanically secured to the equipment.

Copyright©IAEI 2007

**Mechanical Continuity —
Raceways & Cables**
NEC, p. 136

Proposal 3-65
Log 2228
ROP, p. 267

Comment 3-53
Log 1841
ROC, p. 166

Analysis and Effect

Action by CMP-3 results in the creation of a new Exception No. 2 to Section 300.12. The new exception relaxes the requirements for conduits to be mechanically secured to the enclosure, unless specifically required elsewhere in the *Code*. Large equipment such as switchboards, motor control centers, pad-mounted transformers, and so forth, are often supplied with open bottoms and are intended for conduit entry at the open bottom. There is no practical method to secure these open-bottom entry conduits to the equipment. This type of installation is fairly common practice in the field. The revision to this section provides consistency with commonly accepted practices in these types of installations by recognizing the required methods for installing conduit for open-bottom types of equipment that are manufactured in designs that facilitate these types of conduit and cable installations.

Change at a Glance

Conduits and cables installed with open-bottom equipment are not required to be mechanically secured to the equipment enclosures.

Code Language
300.12

Mechanical Continuity — Raceways and Cables
Exception No. 2: Raceways and cables installed into the bottom of open bottom equipment, such as switchboards, motor control centers, and floor or pad-mounted transformers, shall not be required to be mechanically secured to the equipment.

Summary of Change

A new Exception No. 2 has been added to Section 300.12.

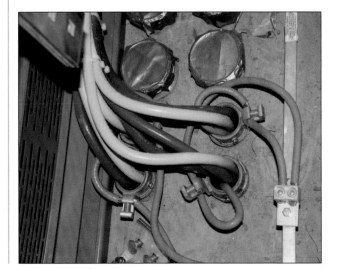

3

Table 300.50 Note 3 and Footnote d

Minimum Cover Requirements
NEC, p. 141

Proposal 3-105, 3-108
Log 3038, 679
ROP, p. 278

Comment
None

Change at a Glance

New provisions for depth reduction where concrete encasement is provided in industrial establishments. Warning ribbons must be used for UG direct-buried cables installed at 750 mm (30 in.) or greater depths.

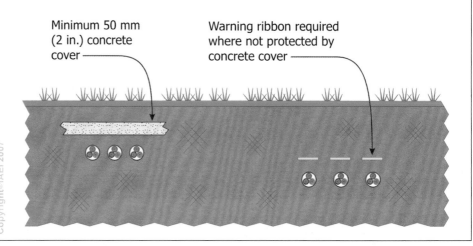

Table 300.50 Note 3 and Footnote d

New provisions for depth reduction where concrete encasement is provided in industrial establishments.

Warning ribbons must be used for UG direct-buried cables installed at 750 mm (30 in.) or greater depths.

Minimum 50 mm (2 in.) concrete cover

Warning ribbon required where not protected by concrete cover

Copyright©IAEI 2007

Analysis and Effect

These revisions include re-identifying the note and footnote identification scheme to improve usability by distinguishing between them. Notes apply to the whole table generally, and the footnotes have specific application but do not apply to the whole table. The notes to the table are numerical and the footnotes are small letters to meet the *NEC Style Manual* requirements. The technical changes to this table include adding a new Note 3 that relaxes the depth requirements in industrial establishments where conditions of maintenance and supervision ensure that qualified persons service the installation. Under these restrictive conditions, the burial depth for conduits other than rigid metal conduit and intermediate metal conduit is permitted to be reduced by 150 mm (2 in.) for each 50 mm (2 in.) of concrete or equivalent material placed in the trench entirely (from wall to wall) over the installed wiring method in the trench. The new footnote "d" incorporates a requirement for a warning ribbon to be placed in trenches not less than 300 mm (12 in.) over the top of direct buried cables that are buried at depths not less than 750 mm (30 in.) and are not encased or protected by concrete.

Code Language
Table 300.50
Note 3 and Footnote d

3. In industrial establishments, where conditions of maintenance and supervision ensure that qualified persons will service the installation, the minimum cover requirements, for other than rigid metal conduit and intermediate metal conduit, shall be permitted to be reduced 150 mm (6 in.) for each 50 mm (2 in.) of concrete or equivalent placed entirely within the trench over the underground installation.

d. Underground direct-buried cables that are not encased or protected by concrete and are buried 750 mm (30 in.) or more below grade shall have their location identified by a warning ribbon that is placed in the trench at least 300 mm (12 in.) above the cables.

Summary of Change

The notes to this table have been identified as Notes 1, 2, and 3. The previous footnotes 1, 2, and 3, have been re-identified as footnotes a, b, and c for usability. A new general Note 3 has been added to the general notes to Table 300.50 and a new footnote "d" has been added to this table.

Conductors in Parallel
NEC, p. 142

Proposal 6-7a
Log 601
ROP, p. 280

Comment 6-3
Log 1088
ROC, p. 172

REORGANIZE

Analysis and Effect

The revisions to Section 310.4 are in response to a number of proposals suggesting this section be revised and reorganized to improve clarity and usability. Action by CMP-6 results in this section being totally reorganized and structured in accordance with Section 2.1.5 of the *NEC Style Manual* to provide a more logical layout without impacting any of the existing technical requirements. Five subdivisions were created under 310.4 to provide placement of existing requirements, which cover the multiple conditions that apply to parallel conductor installations. Exception No. 1 was deleted because it was redundant with current requirements in Article 620. In fact, the inclusion of the exception added confusion because it implied that any item modified by chapters 5, 6, or 7 needs an exception in the general chapters. The deletion of the exception is consistent with the TCC direction to avoid redundancy with the provisions of 90.3. Since the rule in 620.12(A)(1) provides a specific exception to the text in 310.4, an exception is not needed. The remaining exceptions were renumbered accordingly.

> ### Change at a Glance
>
> Section 310.4 has been restructured to provide a more logical layout and improve clarity and usability.

Code Language

310.4

Conductors in Parallel

(A) General. [The existing first paragraph of the rule located here.]
Existing Exception Nos. 1, 2 and 3 to (A) General

(B) Conductor Characteristics. [The existing text in the second paragraph and items (1) through (5) located here in new subdivision (B).]

(C) Separate Cables or Raceways. [The existing third paragraph of the rule located here.]

(D) Ampacity Adjustment. Conductors installed in parallel shall comply with the provisions of 310.15(B)(2)(a).

(E) Equipment Grounding Conductors. [The existing fourth paragraph of the rule located here.]

See actual text of Section 310.4 in *NEC*-2008 including the exceptions.

Summary of Change

This section has been completely restructured, reorganized, and rewritten for *NEC*-2008. Existing Exception No. 1 has been deleted because it is redundant and the requirement is covered in Article 620.

3

310.6

Shielding
NEC, p. 143

Proposal 6-4
Log 1535
ROP, p. 279

Comment 6-9
Log 1235
ROC, p. 175

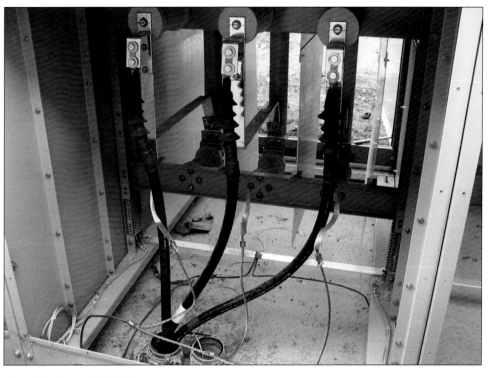

Change at a Glance

Medium-voltage shielding is required to be connected to a grounding electrode conductor, grounding busbar in equipment, or to a grounding electrode.

Analysis and Effect

These revisions are the result of the TCC assigned Task Group on Grounding and Bonding. The change provides more prescriptive language that gives specific direction as to where drain lead conductors from shielded cables that operate above 2000 volts are required to be connected. The previous text provided only references to Sections 250.4(A)(5) and 250.4(B)(4) that include performance criteria for effective ground-fault current paths that are intended to facilitate overcurrent device operation. The primary function of shielding on cables above 2000 volts is to provide an appropriate path (connection) to ground in order to drain any voltage stress at terminations of these cables. Equipment grounding conductors used with circuits are intended to provide equipment grounding functions and to facilitate overcurrent device operation. These performance requirements are appropriately addressed in 250.4. The revision provides prescriptive information about locations where the shielding drain leads are to be connected, with three options that include the common locations where such terminations of these shield leads are typically made. The three locations are to (1) a grounding conductor, (2) a grounding busbar, and (3) a grounding electrode. An example of where these shield drain leads are connected to a grounding conductor is at an outside pole-top installation where a grounding conductor provides the path to the electrode at the base of the pole. An example of a busbar connection would be where the shield leads terminate to the equipment grounding terminal bus within medium- or high-voltage equipment covered by Article 490. An example of connections to a grounding electrode could include direct connections to a ground rod (electrode) is located in the open bottom of a unit substation.

Code Language
310.6
Shielding

Solid dielectric insulated conductors operated above 2000 volts in permanent installations shall have ozone-resistant insulation and shall be shielded. All metallic insulation shields shall be connected to a grounding electrode conductor, grounding busbar, or a grounding electrode. Shielding shall be for the purpose of confining the voltage stresses to the insulation.

Summary of Change

The words "grounded through an effective grounding path meeting the requirements of 250.4(A)(5) or 250.4(B)(4)" have been deleted from the second sentence and replaced with the words "connected to a grounding electrode conductor, grounding busbar, or a grounding electrode."

Direct Burial Conductors
NEC, p. 143

Proposal 6-25
Log 2744
ROP, p. 285

Comment 6-36
Log 38
ROC, p. 181

Analysis and Effect

Action by CMP-6 on Comment 6-36 results in a new exception that relaxes the requirement for cable shielding on airfield runway cables rated up to 5,000 volts. Substantiation provided with the original proposal indicated that current practices and designs for airfield lighting installations are based on Federal Aviation Administration (FAA) Advisory Circulars (ACs). Advisory Circular AC 150/5340-30 A titled *Design and Installation Details for Airport Visual Aids* provides clear details and direction about the types of cables to be used. One such cable identified in this document is FAA Type L-824, 1C #8 AWG, 5 kV cable. This type of cable specified in this federal document is an unshielded cable. The FAA cites one advantage of such cables in the section of the document titled "System Design" — that an unintentional grounding condition will not result in the shutting down of the runway lighting system, which is an obvious safety concern for aircraft operations and air traffic controllers. The substantiation justified the use of non-shielded cable for these installations and was consistent with on-going industry practices for these airfield lighting circuits that are currently being installed and operated ungrounded. The new fine print note refers users to FAA documents with additional related information regarding airfield lighting systems and operations. Action by the TCC on Comment 6-27 results in a new exception to 310.6 to correlate with this exception for cable shielding for airfield lighting installations.

Code Language
310.7
Direct Burial Conductors

Exception No. 2: Airfield lighting cable used in series circuits that are rated up to 5000 volts and are powered by regulators shall be permitted to be nonshielded.

FPN to Exception No. 2: Federal Aviation Administration (FAA) Advisory Circulars (ACs) provide additional practices and methods for airport lighting.

Summary of Change

A new Exception No. 2 and FPN have been added to Section 310.7.

Change at a Glance

Airfield lighting cables rated at 5 kV or less are not required shielded type.

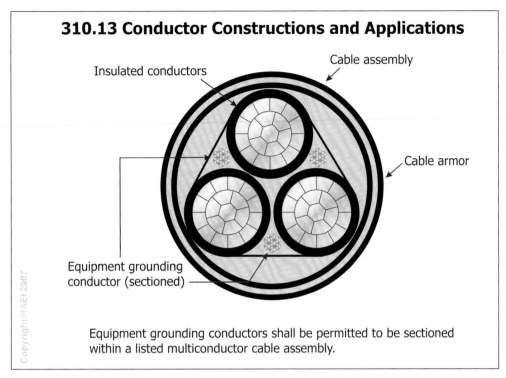

310.13 Conductor Constructions and Applications

Insulated conductors

Cable assembly

Cable armor

Equipment grounding conductor (sectioned)

Equipment grounding conductors shall be permitted to be sectioned within a listed multiconductor cable assembly.

Copyright © IAEI 2007

Conductor Constructions
and Applications
NEC, p. 145

Proposal 6-7
Log 1674
ROP, p. 280

Comment 6-41
Log 284
ROC, p. 182

REVISION

Analysis and Effect

The revision provides additional text in the *NEC* that recognizes sectioned equipment grounding conductors that are part of listed manufactured multiconductor assemblies. The original proposal was intended to revise 310.4 and allow smaller equipment grounding conductors that are installed in parallel configurations to be used with variable frequency drive equipment. This part of the proposal was not accepted. Substantiation provided with the proposal, however, did identify a need for a *Code* allowance of sectioned equipment grounding conductors to be consistent with the common application of various types of multiconductor cable assemblies manufactured with sectionalized equipment grounding conductors. As an example, metal-clad cables (Type MC), particularly in larger sizes, typically provide an equipment grounding conductor that is sectioned, but this is a cable assembly that is listed to meet the requirements of UL Standard 1569. Proposal 6-7 was accepted in part to recognize the need to address sectionalized equipment grounding conductors that are part of listed multiconductor cable assemblies, but it rejected the concept of allowing these types of cables where the contained equipment grounding conductors would not be sized to comply with 250.122. The panel action to relocate this provision to Section 310.13 clarifies that sectioned equipment grounding conductors will be recognized in the *NEC* for all installations, not just those of conductors in parallel. Input from CMP-5 in Comment 6-41 provided additional clarification that where such cables are installed

and used, whether they are in parallel or not, the contained equipment grounding conductor of sectioned equipment grounding conductor is required to meet the sizing rules in 250.122.

Code Language

310.13

Conductor Constructions and Applications

...Equipment grounding conductors shall be permitted to be sectioned within a listed multiconductor cable, provided the combined circular mil area in each cable complies with 250.122.

Summary of Change

A new sentence addressing sectioned equipment grounding conductors has been inserted after the fine print note in this section.

Change at a Glance

The equipment grounding conductor of multiconductor cable can be single conductor or sectioned.

3

310.15
(B)(2)(c)

Ampacities for Conductors Rated 0–2000 Volts
NEC, p. 150

Proposal 6-30, 6-51
Log 3150, 3151
ROP, p. 286, 295

Comment 6-45, 6-54
Log 1070, 1250
ROC, p. 183, 186

310.15(B)(2)(c) Conduits Exposed to Sunlight on Rooftops

Conductors or cables installed in conduit or tubing exposed to direct sunlight on rooftops require temperature adjustment factors in accordance with the values in Table 310.15(B)(2)(c).

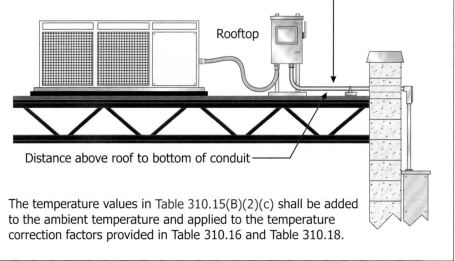

Distance above roof to bottom of conduit

The temperature values in Table 310.15(B)(2)(c) shall be added to the ambient temperature and applied to the temperature correction factors provided in Table 310.16 and Table 310.18.

Copyright©IAEI 2007

Analysis and Effect

This new requirement for ampacity correction due to ambient temperature results from extensive study, fact-finding efforts, and collected data that demonstrated valid concerns about excessive heat exposure for conductors and cables installed on rooftops in the sunlight. Full details are contained in the test report entitled *Effect of Rooftop Exposure on Ambient Temperatures Inside Conduits, November 2005*. The studies clearly warranted new requirements for ampacity correction factors for such installations. In electrical installations of conduit, tubing, and cables that are on rooftops and exposed to the sunlight, temperature value factors in accordance with new Table 310.15(B)(2)(c) are now required to be added; these factors vary based on the height the wiring method is installed above the roof surface. For example, if a conduit is installed 300 mm (12 in.) above a rooftop in an ambient temperature of 122°F, then 30° is required to be added to the anticipated maximum ambient temperature in which the conduit is installed. In this case, the value of 152°F must be used for temperature correction factor application adjustments from the applicable table in 310. Two new fine print notes were incorporated into this new section based on actions of CMP-6 on Comments 6-45 and 6-54. These two fine print notes refer users to essential and reliable documents that can assist in establishing maximum ambient temperatures for a given region in uniform and recognized methods provided by ASHRAE and the National Oceanographic and Atmospheric Administration (USNOM).

> ### Change at a Glance
> Raceways and cables installed on rooftops are subject to correction factors in Table 310.15(B)(2)(c) based on distance above the roof surface.

Table 310.15(B)(2)(c)

Table 310.15(B)(2)(c) Ambient Temperature Adjustment for Conduits Exposed to Sunlight On or Above Rooftops

Distance Above Roof to Bottom of Conduit	Temperature Added	
	°C	°F
0 - 13 mm (½ in.)	33	60
Above 13 mm (½ in.) - 90 mm (3½ in.)	22	40
Above 90 mm (3½ in.) - 300 mm (12 in.)	17	30
Above 300 mm (12 in.) - 900 mm (36 in.)	14	25

Reproduction of *NEC* Table 310.15(B)(2)(c)

Code Language
310.15(B)(2)(c)
Conduits Exposed to Sunlight on Rooftops
Where conductors or cables are installed in conduits exposed to direct sunlight on or above rooftops, the adjustments shown in Table 310.15(B)(2)(c) shall be added to the outdoor temperature to determine the applicable ambient temperature for application of the correction factors in Tables 310.16 and 310.18.

FPN: One source for the average ambient temperatures in various locations is the ASHRAE Handbook — *Fundamentals*.

FPN to Table 310.15(B)(2)(c): The temperature adders in Table 310.15(B)(2)(c) are based on the results of averaging the ambient temperatures.

Summary of Change

A new requirement in subdivision (c) has been added to Section 310.15(B)(2). In addition to the new text in subdivision (c), a new companion Table 310.15(B)(2)(c) has been added to this section. To correlate with this change, the existing FPN to Section 310.10 has been deleted in *NEC*-2008.

3

310.15 (B)(6)

Single-Phase Dwelling Services & Feeders
NEC, p. 151

Proposal 6-61, 9-7e, 6-66
Log 194, 903
ROP, p. 298, 297, 299

Comment 6-63
Log 1915
ROC, p. 188

Change at a Glance

A *main power feeder* supplies all branch circuits, feeders, or both, associated with the load profile of the dwelling unit.

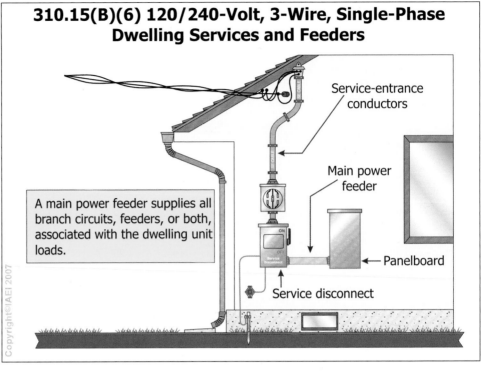

310.15(B)(6) 120/240-Volt, 3-Wire, Single-Phase Dwelling Services and Feeders

Service-entrance conductors

Main power feeder

A main power feeder supplies all branch circuits, feeders, or both, associated with the dwelling unit loads.

Panelboard

Service disconnect

Copyright©IAEI 2007

Analysis and Effect

There are no significant technical changes in the requirements of this section. The revisions clarify for users that the provisions in (B)(6) apply to a single-service feeder for the dwelling unit applications addressed in this section. As previously worded, it was contended that there could be more than one main power feeder in a dwelling that these ampacity allowances could be applied to. By removing the "(s)" after feeder and panelboard, it is clear that this section is permitted to be applied to the main power feeder for an individual dwelling of one-family, two-family, or multifamily dwelling unit installations. This action by CMP-6 clarifies that a dwelling could have a panelboard (subpanel) supplied by a feeder, as long as it is fed from the main panel so that the load diversity of the panel load is included within the loads of the main feeder from the service. The new wording also includes associated loads, as would be the case where there was a detached garage. The words "lighting and appliance branch circuit" before the word "panelboard" have been removed to correlate with the actions of CMP-9 to remove all references to "power panelboards" and "lighting and appliance branch circuit panelboards" from Article 408. The revisions to this section should provide needed clarification and result in more consistent and appropriate application of the conductor ampacity allowances covered and should identify which feeder of dwelling units qualify for application of the ampacities provided in Table 310.15(B)(6). As revised, a *main power feeder* is one that supplies all loads of the dwelling.

310.15(B)(6)

120/240-Volt, 3-Wire, Single-Phase Dwelling Services and Feeders

For individual dwelling units of one-family, two-family, and multifamily dwellings, conductors, as listed in Table 310.15(B)(6), shall be permitted as 120/240-volt, 3-wire, single-phase service-entrance conductors, service-lateral conductors, and feeder conductors that serve as the main power feeder to each dwelling unit and are installed in raceway or cable with or without an equipment grounding conductor. For application of this section, the main power feeder shall be the feeder between the main disconnect and the panelboard that supplies, either by branch circuits or by feeders, or both, all loads that are part or associated with the dwelling unit. The feeder conductors to a dwelling unit shall not be required to have an allowable ampacity rating greater than their service-entrance conductors. The grounded conductor shall be permitted to be smaller than the ungrounded conductors, provided the requirements of 215.2, 220.61, and 230.42 are met.

Summary of Change

The reference to "lighting and appliance branch circuit panelboard" has been deleted to correlate with changes in Article 408. Table 310.15(B)(6) has been rearranged to provide the ampacity values in the left column as a result of CMP-6 action on Proposal 6-66. The second sentence as revised now requires a main power feeder to supply all loads associated with the dwelling unit.

312.4

Repairing Noncombustible Surfaces
NEC, p. 161

Proposal 9-10
Log 1342
ROP, p. 301

Comment 9-5
Log 1073
ROC, p. 189

REVISION

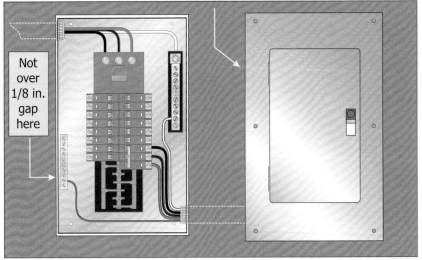

312.4 Repairing Noncombustible Surfaces

No gaps or open spaces greater than 3 mm (1/8 in.) at the edge of the cabinet or cutout box employing a flush-type cover.

Not over 1/8 in. gap here

Copyright©IAEI 2007

Surface repairs at cabinet or cutout boxes apply to all noncombustible surfaces including, but not limited to, plaster, drywall, and plasterboard surfaces.

Analysis and Effect

The revision to this section clarifies that where the gap or open space between the edge of a cabinet or cutout box and the surface material within which it is installed is greater than 3 mm (1/8 in.), the gap or open space requires repair. The previous requirement applied only to plaster, drywall, and plasterboard surface materials. Where cabinets and cutout boxes are installed in other surface materials such as tile, masonry, and other noncombustible products, the requirements of this section apply. The revision removes the list of specific noncombustible surface materials and expands the requirements to all noncombustible surfaces that qualify for repair under the provisions of this section.

Code Language
312.4

Repairing Noncombustible Surfaces

Noncombustible surfaces that are broken or incomplete shall be repaired so there will be no gaps or open spaces greater than 3 mm (1/ 8 in.) at the edge of the cabinet or cutout box employing a flush-type cover.

Summary of Change

The words "Plaster, drywall and plasterboard" have been replaced with the words "Noncombustible surfaces" in the title and text of this section.

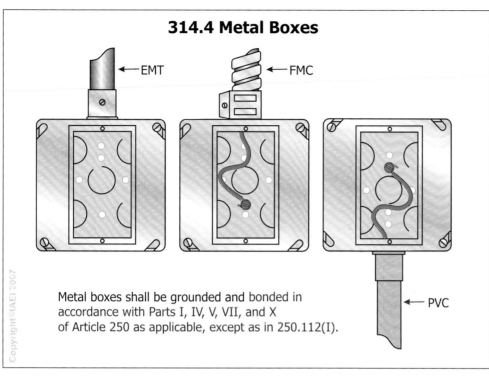

314.4 Metal Boxes

EMT

FMC

Metal boxes shall be grounded and bonded in accordance with Parts I, IV, V, VII, and X of Article 250 as applicable, except as in 250.112(I).

PVC

Copyright©IAEI 2007

314.4

Metal Boxes
NEC, p. 170

Proposal 9-18
Log 1538
ROP, p. 303

Comment 9-9
Log 1484
ROC, p. 190

Analysis and Effect

The revisions to this section clarify that metallic boxes are not only required to be grounded but also bonded, according to the applicable part(s) of Article 250. The previous requirements were too general in nature by referencing Article 250 in its entirety. This revision brings this section into conformance with the *NEC Style Manual*. The additional references provide users with more prescriptive language by referring to the parts of Article 250 that would apply to metal boxes covered by Article 314. Comment 9-9 and companion comments would have also resulted in all grounding and bonding requirements of Article 314 being located in this section; however, that concept in Comment 9-9 was not accepted because it was felt that the specific grounding and bonding requirements in separate sections within the article are still necessary and provide benefits for users.

Change at a Glance

Metal boxes are required to be grounded and bonded in accordance with the applicable parts of Article 250.

Code Language

314.4

Metal Boxes

Metal boxes shall be grounded and bonded in accordance with Parts I, IV, V, VI , VII, and X of Article 250 as applicable, except as permitted in 250.112(I).

Summary of Change

The words "and bonded" have been added to this section, and specific parts of Article 250 are now referenced from this requirement.

3

314.16
(B)(4)

**Equipment Grounding
Conductors**
NEC, p. 171

Proposal 9-31
Log 3398
ROP, p. 307

Comment 9-16
Log 1916
ROC, p. 191

Change at a Glance

A device requiring more than one gang opening in an outlet box requires double conductor volume allowances for each gang required.

314.16(B)(4) Device or Equipment Fill

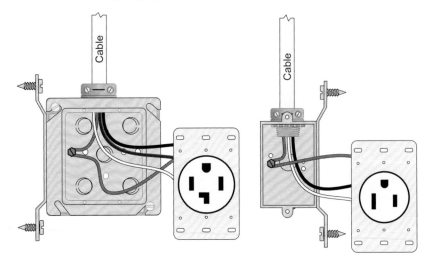

A device or utilization equipment wider than a single 50 mm (2 in.) device box as described in Table 314.16(A) shall have double volume allowances provided for each gang required for mounting.

(Copyright©IAEI 2007)

Analysis and Effect

This revision provides users with needed clarification that addresses devices that might require more than a single gang box to accommodate. A large device that cannot be mounted in a conventional single-gang box must be installed in a box with multiple gangs, even where conductor fill requirements have been met with a single gang box. The boxes used in these situations should carry the conductor allowances that multiple devices in adjacent gangs already carry. An example of this type of condition results where a typical single-phase dryer receptacle device is installed in a single-gang outlet box. The capacity to accommodate both the device and the conductors is reduced significantly. This revision is consistent with current industry practices and provides users with clear language that can be used by installers and enforcement to apply necessary volumes to these installations outlet boxes where additional room is necessary for larger devices or equipment and connected conductors.

Code Language
314.16(B)(4)

Device or Equipment Fill

For each yoke or strap containing one or more devices or equipment, a double volume allowance in accordance with Table 314.16(B) shall be made for each yoke or strap based on the largest conductor connected to a device(s) or equipment supported by that yoke or strap. A device or utilization equipment wider than a single 50 mm (2 in.) device box as described in Table 314.16(A) shall have double volume allowances provided for each gang required for mounting.

Summary of Change

A new second sentence has been added to Section 314.16(B)(4) as follows: A device or utilization equipment wider than a single 50 mm (2 in.) device box as described in Table 314.16(A) shall have double volume allowances provided for each gang required for mounting.

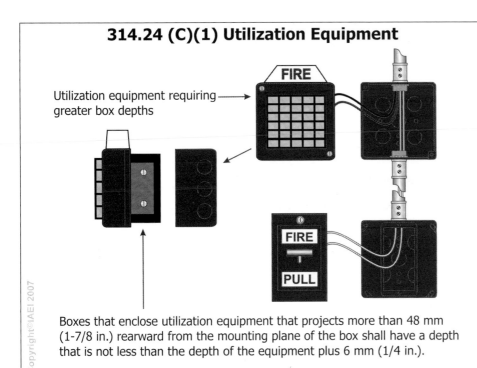

314.24 (C)(1) Utilization Equipment

Utilization equipment requiring greater box depths →

FIRE

FIRE
PULL

Boxes that enclose utilization equipment that projects more than 48 mm (1-7/8 in.) rearward from the mounting plane of the box shall have a depth that is not less than the depth of the equipment plus 6 mm (1/4 in.).

314.24

Minimum Depth of Boxes For Outlets, Devices and Utilization Equipment
NEC, p. 174

Proposal 9-52
Log 3322
ROP, p. 312, 313

Comment 9-20
Log 1414
ROC, p. 192

REVISION!

Analysis and Effect

The requirements of this section in previous editions of the *NEC* provided only general requirements that addressed the minimum depth of outlet boxes, but did not provide specific requirements applicable to various configurations of conductor sizes and required volumes. The restructuring and expansion of these requirements are the result of the efforts of a CMP-9 task group assembled to address issues raised in Proposal 9-34 (Log No. 2094) and Comment 9-62 (Log No. 1382). This section has been expanded to cover outlet and device boxes without enclosed devices in subdivision (A), and outlet boxes without enclosed devices in subdivision (B), and utilization equipment in subdivision (C). The expanded rules provide specific depth requirements for outlet and device boxes containing larger utilization equipment in (C)(1), conductors larger than 4 AWG in (C)(2), conductors in sizes 8, 6, or 4 AWG in (C)(3), conductors in sizes 12 and 10 AWG in (C)(4), and conductors 14 AWG and smaller in (C)(5). The new subdivision (A) applies only to outlet boxes that do not contain a device or utilization equipment and requires the minimum depth to be not less than 12.7 mm (1/2 in.) as it did in previous editions of the *Code*. The effect of this revision provides users with specific rules regarding the minimum sizes (specifically depths) required for outlet and device boxes used in field installations where larger devices or utilization equipment is installed and where larger conductors are connected to such devices or equipment. The basic objectives of the previous requirements

> ### Change at a Glance
>
> Minimum depths for outlet boxes containing utilization equipment or devices and minimum depths for boxes not containing either devices or utilization equipment have been clarified.

of this rule are retained, but specific depth dimensions are now provided for users to ensure adequate box capacity and compliance with minimum depths. It should be noted that CMP-9 used soft conversions in both Table 314.16(A) and in 314.24 (see Proposals 9-6 and 9-14 for the 2002 *NEC*) because hard conversions could have the effect of forcing the redesign of products built to current standards. Therefore, the dimensions in this revised section that describe the minimum depth of a box reflect soft conversions. Dimensions that describe the rearward projection of mounted equipment and that would likely be field-measured by installers or inspectors are provided in hard conversions.

3

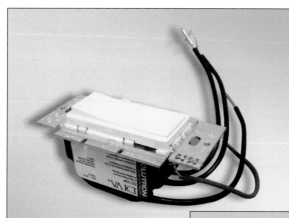

Code Language
314.24

Minimum Depth of Boxes For Outlets, Devices and Utilization Equipment

Outlet and device boxes shall have sufficient depth to allow equipment installed within them to be mounted properly and with sufficient clearance to prevent damage to conductors within the box.

(A) Outlet and Device Boxes Without Enclosed Devices or Utilization Equipment. No box shall have an internal depth of less than 12.7 mm (1/2 in.).

(B) Outlet and Device Boxes With Enclosed Devices. Boxes intended to enclose flush devices shall have an internal depth of not less than 23.8 mm (15/16 in.).

(C) Utilization Equipment. Outlet and device boxes that enclose utilization equipment shall have a minimum internal depth that accommodates the rearward projection of the equipment and the size of the conductors that supply the equipment. The internal depth shall include, where used, that of any extension boxes, plaster rings, or raised covers. The internal depth shall comply with all applicable provisions of (C)(1) through (C)(5).

  (1) Large Equipment. Boxes that enclose utilization equipment that projects more than 48 mm (1 7/8 in.) rearward from the mounting plane of the box shall have a depth that is not less than the depth of the equipment plus 6 mm (1/4 in.).

  (2) Conductors Larger Than 4 AWG. Boxes that enclose utilization equipment supplied by conductors larger than 4 AWG shall be identified for their specific function.

  (3) Conductors 8, 6, or 4 AWG. Boxes that enclose utilization equipment supplied by 8, 6, or 4 AWG conductors shall have an internal depth that is not less than 52.4 mm (2 1/16 in.).

  (4) Conductors 12 or 10 AWG. Boxes that enclose equipment supplied by 12 or 10 AWG conductors shall have an internal depth that is not less than 30.2 mm (1 3/16 in.). Where the equipment projects rearward from the mounting plane of the box by more than 25 mm (1 in.), the box shall have a depth not less than that of the equipment plus 6 mm (¼ in.).

  (5) Conductors 14 AWG and Smaller. Boxes that enclose equipment supplied by 14 AWG or smaller conductors shall have a depth that is not less than 23.8 mm (15/16 in.).

Exception to (C)(1) through (C)(5): Utilization equipment that is listed to be installed with specified boxes shall be permitted.

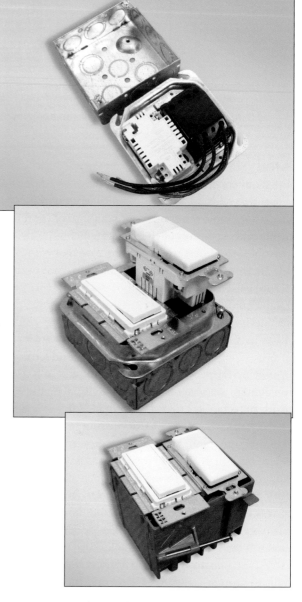

Summary of Change

This section has been restructured, reorganized and expanded to clarify the requirements for adequate space and to include various specific outlet and device box depths.

162

Analysis of Changes *NEC*-2008

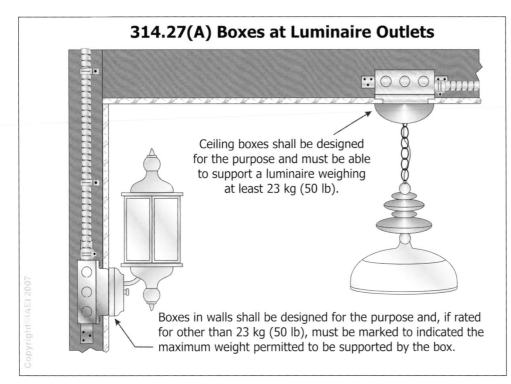

314.27(A) Boxes at Luminaire Outlets

Ceiling boxes shall be designed for the purpose and must be able to support a luminaire weighing at least 23 kg (50 lb).

Boxes in walls shall be designed for the purpose and, if rated for other than 23 kg (50 lb), must be marked to indicated the maximum weight permitted to be supported by the box.

Copyright©IAEI 2007

Listed Boxes Used for Luminaire Support
NEC, p. 175

Proposal 9-56
Log 2611
ROP, p. 315

Comment
None

Analysis and Effect

These revisions clarify the requirements for listed boxes used for luminaire support. Currently, there are outlet boxes that are listed and identified for supporting luminaires weighing between 3 kg (6 lb) and 23 kg (50 lb) for ceiling-mounted applications. Ceiling outlet boxes installed and used for luminaire support shall be required to provide adequate support of luminaires weighing 23 kg (50 lbs) or less. Markings for boxes between 3 kg (6 lb) and 23 kg (50 lb) were initially permitted for wall-mounted luminaires only and were not intended for ceiling-mounted luminaires. The revisions to both (A) and (B) provide needed clarification for strength requirements for the boxes addressed in both sections. The revision to (B) clarifies that not only must the box be adequate to support such weight, it is also required to be designed for the purpose of supporting luminaires. The revision to Section 314.27(B) clarifies that boxes listed for luminaires weighing more than 23 kg (50 lb) are not only required to be listed for the maximum weight, they must also be identified (marked) for such weights. Identification marks in boxes addressing luminaire support provide installers with indications that will reflect suitability where luminaires are installed or replaced on existing outlet boxes.

Change at a Glance

Boxes for luminaires are required to be listed for luminaire support and identified for the weight that must be supported.

Code Language
314.27(A) & (B)

See Sections 314.27(A) and (B) for actual *Code* text.

Summary of Change

The words "and shall be required to support a luminaire weighing a maximum of 23 kg (50 lb)" have been added to Section 314.27(A). The words "designed for the support of luminaires and" have been added in the first sentence of Section 314.27(B). References to *lighting fixtures* have been removed to leave only references to *luminaires* in this section as part of a global *NEC* change to remove these terms.

3

314.27(E) and Exception

Utilization Equipment
NEC, p. 175

Proposal 9-63
Log 3399
ROP, p. 317

Comment 9-34, 9-35
Log 59, 1918
ROC, p. 195

Change at a Glance

Ceiling-mounted boxes may support of utilization equipment other than paddle fans. By exception, equipment such as smoke alarms are permitted to be secured to such boxes with not less than two No. 6 machine screws.

314.27(E) and Exception

Boxes used for the support of utilization equipment other than ceiling-suspended (paddle) fans shall meet the requirements of 314.27(A) and (B) for the support of a luminaire that is the same size and weight.

By exception, utilization equipment weighing not more than 3 kg (6 lb) are permitted to be secured to boxes or plaster rings with not fewer than two No. 6 machine screws.

Unlike the exception for luminaires, this exception also applies to other ceiling-mounted equipment.

Copyright© IAEI 2007

Analysis and Effect

This new section results in a provision that clearly draws a distinction between boxes permitted for ceiling-suspended paddle fans and those that are installed to support luminaires. The new text directs that boxes used for utilization equipment, other than ceiling-suspended paddle fans, must meet the requirements in 314.27(A) and (B). The new exception relaxes this requirement when the box or box and plaster ring combination is used for other utilization equipment such as a smoke alarm, carbon monoxide alarm, and so forth. To qualify for the exception, the box is required to support equipment not more than 3 kg (6 lb) and be secured to the box or plaster ring with not less than two No. 6 or larger screws.

Code Language
314.27(E)
Utilization Equipment
Boxes used for the support of utilization equipment other than ceiling-suspended (paddle) fans shall meet the requirements of 314.27(A) and (B) for the support of a luminaire that is the same size and weight.

Exception: Utilization equipment weighing not more than 3 kg (6 lb) shall be permitted to be supported on other boxes or plaster rings that are secured to other boxes, provided the equipment or its supporting yoke is secured to the box with no fewer than two No. 6 or larger screws.

Summary of Change

A new subdivision (E) and associated exception have been added to Section 314.27.

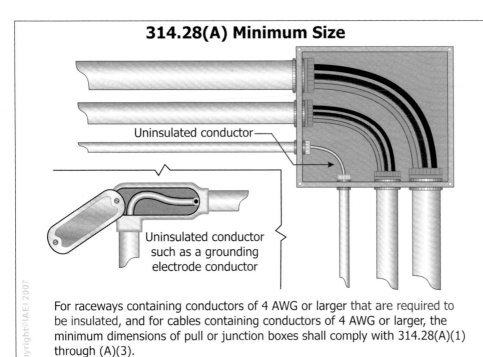

314.28(A) Minimum Size

Uninsulated conductor

Uninsulated conductor such as a grounding electrode conductor

Copyright©IAEI 2007

For raceways containing conductors of 4 AWG or larger that are required to be insulated, and for cables containing conductors of 4 AWG or larger, the minimum dimensions of pull or junction boxes shall comply with 314.28(A)(1) through (A)(3).

Minimum Dimensions of Pull or Junction Boxes
NEC, p. 175

Proposal 9-66
Log 3400
ROP, p. 318

Comment
None

Analysis and Effect

This revision clarifies that this section applies only to boxes and conduit bodies containing insulated conductors in sizes 4 AWG and larger. Since this section addresses concerns of protecting conductor insulation from abrasion, it is logical that the sizing requirements be relaxed for uninsulated conductors. This change will bring the *Code* into concert with installations of bare grounding electrode conductors that are often enclosed in raceways (metallic or nonmetallic) to meet physical damage concerns and requirements in the *NEC*. Where conduit bodies and pull boxes are used for enclosing bare grounding electrode conductors, the sizing requirements of this section need not be applied. From a practical perspective, conductors in sizes larger that 4 AWG (bare or insulated) are more difficult to install in pull boxes or conduit bodies due to physical size, and these pull boxes and conduit bodies should be sized adequately to meet the general requirements for practical ease of installation and electrical workmanship provided in Section 110.12.

Code Language
314.28[A]
Minimum Size

For raceways containing conductors of 4 AWG or larger that are required to be insulated, and for cables containing conductors of 4 AWG or larger, the minimum dimensions of pull or junction boxes installed in a raceway or cable run shall comply with (A)(1) through (A)(3).

Summary of Change

The words "that are required to be insulated" have been added to the first sentence of this section.

Change at a Glance

Junction and pull box sizing requirements in 314.28(A) apply to junction and pull boxes installed in conduit runs containing insulated conductors.

Courtesy of Fred Hartwell

3

314.28
(A)(2)

Angle or U Pulls or Splices
NEC, p. 176

Proposal 9-67
Log 2289
ROP, p. 318

Comment
None

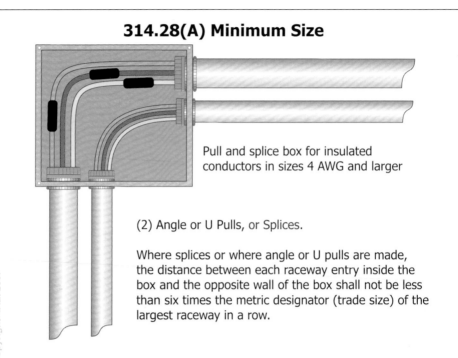

314.28(A) Minimum Size

Pull and splice box for insulated conductors in sizes 4 AWG and larger

(2) Angle or U Pulls, or Splices.

Where splices or where angle or U pulls are made, the distance between each raceway entry inside the box and the opposite wall of the box shall not be less than six times the metric designator (trade size) of the largest raceway in a row.

Copyright©IAEI 2007

Analysis and Effect

The changes to the title of this section incorporate the word "splices." Although "splices" appears in the requirement itself, adding the word to the title clarifies that these sizing requirements apply to boxes and conduit bodies that are provided for U pulls, angle pulls, and to boxes that contain splices for conductors in sizes 4 AWG and larger. Boxes meeting the sizing requirements for use as pull boxes should also provide adequate capacity for volume that is necessary where splices are made in conductors passing through such boxes.

Change at a Glance

Angle or U pull box sizing requirements in this section apply to boxes that contain splices as well as to boxes for conductors passing through without splices.

Code Language
314.28(A)(2)

Angle or U Pulls or Splices
Where splices or where angle or U pulls are made, the distance between each raceway entry inside the box and the opposite wall of the box shall not be less than six times the metric designator (trade size) of the largest raceway in a row. This distance shall be increased for additional entries by the amount of the sum of the diameters of all other raceway entries in the same row on the same wall of the box. Each row shall be calculated individually, and the single row that provides the maximum distance shall be used.

Summary of Change

The title of this section has been revised to include the word "splices" as follows: 314.28(A)(2) Angle or U Pulls, or Splices.

314.30(C) Enclosed Wiring

All enclosed conductors and any splices or terminations present shall be listed as suitable for wet locations.

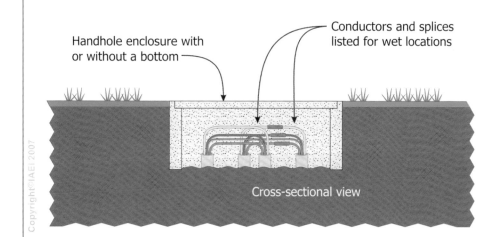

Handhole enclosure with or without a bottom

Conductors and splices listed for wet locations

Cross-sectional view

314.30[C]

Enclosed Wiring
NEC, p. 176

Proposal 9-77
Log 3402
ROP, p. 319

Comment
None

REVISION

Analysis and Effect

The current requirement addresses only handhole enclosures having no bottom, in spite of the fact that the enclosure will be located in a wet location as defined by Article 100. Under the terms of the Article 100 definitions that apply to locations, as well as the 2005 revision to Section 300.5(B), the interior of a handhole enclosure is classified as a wet location, regardless of whether it has a bottom or not. The revision to this rule clarifies that the conductors and splices or terminations contained in handhole enclosures are required to be listed as suitable for wet locations. The conductor and splicing means listing requirement applies whether the handhole enclosure has a bottom or not. This provision in *NEC*-2005 intended to address handhole enclosures with open bottoms that are often used for direct buried cable and conductor installations where complete enclosures are less practical. The crafting of the handhole requirements in *NEC*-2005 resulted in an inadvertent oversight that left enclosures with bottoms omitted from this section. This revision corrects the oversight and results in a requirement that is more complete and readily understood by installers and can be more easily applied by enforcement to these types of installations.

Change at a Glance

Conductors and splices in handhole enclosures are required to be listed for wet locations.

Code Language
314.30[C]
Enclosed Wiring

All enclosed conductors and any splices or terminations, if present, shall be listed as suitable for wet locations.

Summary of Change

Section 314.30 has been revised and reworded to simplify and clarify the rules and their application.

3

320.10(1)

Type AC Cable
NEC, p. 178

Proposal 7-2
Log 1495
ROP, p. 321

Comment
None

Change at a Glance

Armored clad cable (Type AC) is acceptable for branch-circuit and feeder wiring installations.

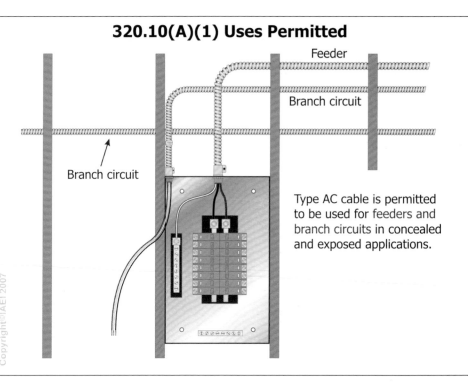

320.10(A)(1) Uses Permitted

Feeder

Branch circuit

Branch circuit

Copyright©IAEI 2007

Type AC cable is permitted to be used for feeders and branch circuits in concealed and exposed applications.

Analysis and Effect

Section 320.10 addresses the various uses permitted for Type AC cable (commonly referred to in the industry as BX). It should be noted that the FPN following this section clearly indicates that the "Uses Permitted" in Section 320.10 is not an all-inclusive list. The change to item (1) clarifies that Type AC cable is permitted to be used for both feeder and branch-circuit wiring. The UL General Information Directory for Electrical Equipment (White Book) under category AWEZ indicates aluminum sheathed Type AC cable is suitable for use in AC circuits only, which includes both feeders and branch circuits. While this change does not impact common industry practices that incorporate AC cable as the wiring method in designs and specifications, the revision does clarify that Type AC cable is permitted for such use. Section 230.43 does not permit Type AC cable for use as a wiring method for services.

Code Language
320.10
Uses Permitted
Type AC cable shall be permitted as follows:
(1) For feeders and branch circuits in both exposed and concealed work.

The remainder of this section is unchanged.

Summary of Change

The words "For feeders and branch circuits in" have been added to item (1) in Section 320.10.

320.108, 330.108, 332.108, 334.108, 340.108

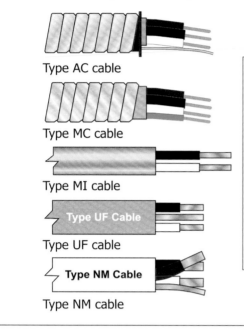

Type AC cable

Type MC cable

Type MI cable

Type UF Cable

Type UF cable

Type NM Cable

Type NM cable

Copyright©IAEI 2007

The titles to these sections have been revised to refer to equipment grounding conductors.

The .108 sections in these cable articles provide requirements for equipment grounding conductors in these cable assemblies, rather than general requirements for equipment grounding.

Note: Cable fittings not shown

Equipment Grounding Conductor
NEC, Various pages

Proposal 7-1
Log 1536
ROP, p. 320, 321

Comment
None

REVISION

Analysis and Effect

This revision is the result of the 2005 *NEC* cycle actions related to Proposal 5-1 and Comment 5-1 by the TCC Task Group on Grounding and Bonding. This is a companion proposal to the proposed revisions involving the terms *bonded, grounded,* and *equipment grounding conductor*. Revisions to the definitions of terms related to grounding and bonding in Article 100 resulted in this task group's recommendation to revise these terms for consistency and uniformity throughout the *NEC*. These revisions are not intended to change the technical meaning of the rules, but only to clarify the present requirement by using prescriptive language. The equipment grounding conductor performs two essential functions: (1) it establishes a connection to ground for equipment, and (2) it serves as an effective ground-fault current path for the circuit.

Change at a Glance

The .108 sections in these cable articles provide requirements for equipment grounding conductors in these cable assemblies rather than general requirements for equipment grounding.

The revisions to the .108 sections of these cable wiring method articles are now more prescriptive and include specific requirements for equipment grounding conductors associated with the particular wiring method rather than just generalized text that requires equipment grounding. These revisions are consistent with the revised term *equipment grounding conductor* and reference the specific conductor intended to perform the functions anticipated by these requirements.

Code Language

320.108
Equipment Grounding Conductor

Type AC cable shall provide an adequate path for fault current as required by 250.4(A)(5) or (B)(4) to act as an equipment grounding conductor.

330.108
Equipment Grounding Conductor

Where Type MC cable is used to provide an equipment grounding conductor, it shall comply with 250.118(10) and 250.122.

332.108
Equipment Grounding Conductor

Where the outer sheath is made of copper, it shall provide an adequate path to serve as an equipment grounding conductor. Where the outer sheath is made of steel, a separate equipment grounding conductor shall be provided.

334.108
Equipment Grounding Conductor

In addition to the insulated conductors, the cable shall have an insulated, covered, or bare equipment grounding conductor.

340.108
Equipment Grounding Conductor

In addition to the insulated conductors, the cable shall be permitted to have an insulated or bare equipment grounding conductor.

Summary of Change

The titles to these sections have been revised to refer to equipment grounding conductors. The general text has been revised specifically to refer to equipment grounding conductor requirements within section .108 of each respective article.

3

328.10, 328.12

Type MV Cable
NEC, p. 184

Proposal 7-20, 7-22
Log 2588, 199
ROP, p. 327, 328

Comment 7-9
Log 982
ROC, p. 198

Change at a Glance

Medium Voltage Cable: Type MV is permitted in cable trays under restricted conditions in accordance with Part II of Article 392.

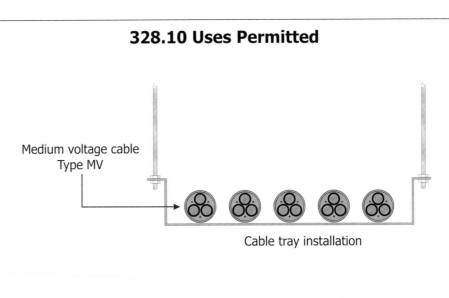

328.10 Uses Permitted

Medium voltage cable
Type MV

Cable tray installation

Medium voltage cable shall be permitted to be installed in cable trays where identified for the use and where the applicable requirements in Part II of Article 392 are met.

Copyright©IAEI 2007

Analysis and Effect

Sections 328.10 and 328.12 address the uses permitted and the uses not permitted for medium voltage (Type MV) cable. The revisions to this section clarify the uses permitted for this type of wiring. As revised, Section 328.10 states medium voltage cable is not generally permitted to be installed in cable trays. Only under restrictive conditions provided in *NEC*-2008, Section 328.10 is this wiring method acceptable. Section 328.10(3) previously referenced Section 392(3)(B)(2), which is not inclusive of all conditions necessary to comply with before this use is permitted by *NEC* provisions. Section 392.3(B) in *NEC*-2008 includes all such provisions. This revision clarifies that MV cable is only installable in cable trays unless the installation meets the conditions given in Part II of Article 392. This includes the industrial occupancy and qualified supervision provisions in the parent rule, and then the specific mention of Type MV cable. The existing reference was misleading to users because it did not refer to all of 392.3(B). This revision does not mean that Type MV cable is eligible for unprotected use in areas accessible to the public. The second revision to Section 328.10 includes adding a new item (6) that correlates the traditional permission for this type of wiring permitted by the rule in Section 300.37. Section 328.12 was revised by deleting list items (1) and (2) because they were incorporated into 328.10 as a result of action on Comment 7-9.

Code Language
328.10
Uses Permitted

Type MV cable shall be permitted....as follows:
(1) In wet or dry locations
(2) In raceways
(3) In cable trays, where identified for the use, in accordance with Part II of Article 392
(4) Direct buried in accordance with 300.50
(5) In messenger-supported wiring in accordance with Part II of Article 396
(6) As exposed runs in accordance with 300.37

328.12
Uses Not Permitted

Type MV cable shall not be used where exposed to direct sunlight, unless identified for the use.

Summary of Change

Section 328.10 has been revised to include cable trays where identified for the use in accordance Part II of Article 392. List items (1) and (2) have been removed from 328.12 and incorporated into 328.10 as positive text because of action by CMP-7 on Comment 7-9.

330.10
(A)(11)

Uses Permitted
NEC, p. 185

Proposal 7-23
Log 3297
ROP, p. 328

Comment
None

Analysis and Effect

This section has been revised to clarify the construction characteristics for Type MC cable that is suitable for use in wet locations. There are several concerns for MC cables installed in these locations. MC Cables installed in wet locations can become corrosive such as when installed in contact with concrete. Aluminum and galvanized steel in contact with concrete or mortar can result in corrosion to the uncovered metallic covering. For aluminum, a reaction that forms aluminum hydroxide and hydrogen gas may occur when in contact with wet concrete. For galvanized steel, a reaction may occur with moisture and chlorides in concrete or mortar

Change at a Glance

Type MC cable is permitted for use in wet locations where a corrosion-resistant jacket is provided over the metallic sheath.

to produce zinc oxide. The reaction rates increase with the dampness of the concrete. These reactions can deteriorate the metallic sheath or armor over time. For these reasons, this section has been revised to clarify that Type MC cable installed in wet locations must not only be listed for that specific application, but must be provided with a corrosion-resistant jacket over the metallic sheath of the cable assembly.

Code Language
330.10(A)
Uses Permitted

(11) In wet locations where any of the following conditions are met:

a. The metallic covering is impervious to moisture.

b. A lead sheath or moisture-impervious jacket is provided under the metal covering.

c. The insulated conductors under the metallic covering are listed for use in wet locations and a corrosion-resistant jacket is provided over the metallic sheath.

Summary of Change

The words "and a corrosion-resistant jacket is provided over the metallic sheath" have been added to item (11) in Section 330.10(A).

3

330.104

Conductors
NEC, p. 186

Proposal 7-37
Log 2989
ROP, p. 331

Comment
None

REVISION

Change at a Glance

Nickel or nickel-coated copper conductors are permitted in MC cable assemblies

330.104 Conductors

Conductors shall be of copper, aluminum, copper-clad aluminum, nickel, or nickel-coated copper, solid or stranded.

The minimum conductor size shall be 18 AWG copper, nickel or nickel-coated copper and 12 AWG aluminum or copper-clad aluminum.

Copyright©IAEI 2007

Analysis and Effect

Part III of Article 330 provides the construction criteria (specifications) for Type MC cable, and Section 330.104 specifically addresses the type of conductors permitted. This section has been revised to incorporate a reference to nickel or nickel-coated copper conductors as types of conductors with which the cable assembly could be manufactured. The change recognizes Type MC cables constructed to meet fire-resistant requirements that might utilize nickel conductors or nickel-coated copper conductors in the assembly. This revision provides manufacturers with additional alternatives to produce such cables while at the same time creating harmonization with the allowance of nickel and nickel-coated copper in 332.104 for MI cable.

Code Language
330.104
Conductors

Conductors shall be of copper, aluminum, copper-clad aluminum, nickel, or nickel-coated copper, solid or stranded. The minimum conductor size shall be 18 AWG copper, nickel or nickel-coated copper, and 12 AWG aluminum or copper-clad aluminum.

Summary of Change

The words "nickel, or nickel-coated copper" have been incorporated into the provision of this section.

Analysis of Changes *NEC*-2008

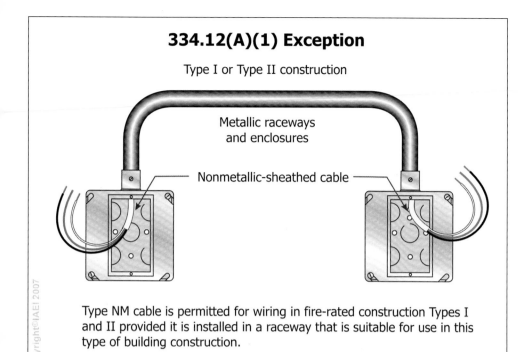

334.12(A)(1) Exception

Type I or Type II construction

Metallic raceways
and enclosures

Nonmetallic-sheathed cable

Type NM cable is permitted for wiring in fire-rated construction Types I and II provided it is installed in a raceway that is suitable for use in this type of building construction.

334.12

Types NM, NMC, and NMS Cables
NEC, p. 188

Proposal 7-51
Log 202
ROP, p. 334

Comment
None

Analysis and Effect

In the 2005 *NEC* development process, several revisions were accepted that recognize cables for installation in raceways where not prohibited by the respective cable article. The revision to this section provides a new exception that would allow Type NM cable to be used in wiring installations in fire-rated construction Types I and II, provided it is installed in a raceway that is suitable for use in this type of building construction. Typically, this includes metallic raceways. It is important to understand that this new allowance in Article 334 also must meet other requirements where so installed, such as conduit or tubing fill limitations, correction factors, and so forth. Incorporating this use in an exception under "uses not permitted" is appropriate because this type of wiring is strictly prohibited from use in these types of construction under general conditions.

Code Language
334.12

Exception: Type NM, NMC, and NMS cable shall be permitted in Type I and II construction when installed within raceways permitted to be installed in Type I and II construction.

Summary of Change

A new exception has been added to Section 334.12 addressing Types NM, NMC, and NMS cables installed in raceways in Types I and II construction.

Change at a Glance

Type NM cable is permitted for wiring in fire-rated construction Types I and II, provided it is installed in a raceway that is suitable for use in this type of building construction.

334.12 (B)(4)

Uses Not Permitted
NEC, p. 189

Proposal 7-50
Log 201
ROP, p. 334

Comment 7-24
Log 42
ROC, p. 202

Change at a Glance

Nonmetallic sheathed cable is not permitted in damp or wet locations.

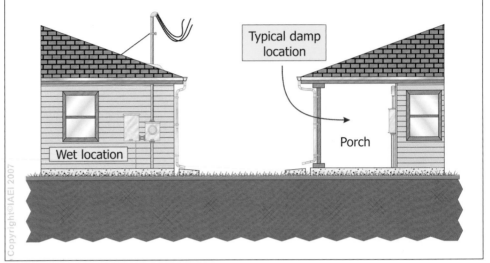

334.12(B)(4) Uses Not Permitted

Type NM and NMS shall not be permitted in wet or damp locations.

Article 100 defines damp, dry, and wet locations.

Typical damp location

Porch

Wet location

Copyright©IAEI 2007

Analysis and Effect

This section has been revised to clarify and remove the subjectivity of the previous language. As worded in *NEC*-2005, this section was vague and subject to varying interpretations by enforcement officials. These revisions remove the judgment factor required by the authority having jurisdiction and use terms related to locations that are defined in Article 100. Wet and damp locations are well-defined in the *Code* and the judgment applied should result in a determination that is more definitive. There are no parameters by which an inspector can reliably and consistently judge locations to be "subject to excessive moisture or dampness." Locations should be determined to be either wet or damp as defined. It is recognized that inspectors will still have to make these determinations about wet and damp locations, but they have definitions to help make better decisions. The revision to this section, although minimal in nature, should provide positive results in the way of more consistent and uniform application of this requirement to field installations.

Code Language
334.12(B)
Uses Not Permitted

(4) In wet or damp locations

Summary of Change

The text "Where exposed or subject to excessive moisture or dampness" has been replaced with the text "in wet or damp locations."

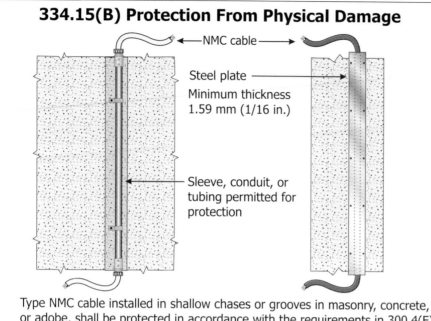

334.15(B) Protection From Physical Damage

← NMC cable →

Steel plate
Minimum thickness
1.59 mm (1/16 in.)

Sleeve, conduit, or
tubing permitted for
protection

Type NMC cable installed in shallow chases or grooves in masonry, concrete, or adobe, shall be protected in accordance with the requirements in 300.4(F) and covered with plaster, adobe, or similar finish.

334.15(B)

Protection from
Physical Damage
NEC, p. 189

Proposal 7-61
Log 1905
ROP, p. 336

Comment 7-33, 7-34
Log 602, 1209
ROC, p. 204

Analysis and Effect

The revision to this section expands the physical protection options to more that just a steel plate not less than 1.59 mm (1/16 in.) thick and then covered with plaster, adobe, or similar finish. Section 300.4(F) adequately addresses this type of installation and what is permitted generally for protecting cables from physical damage where installed in shallow chases or grooves in plaster, adobe, or similar finishes. Adding the words "or grooves" provides consistency between the requirements in 334.15(B) that are specific to NM cable installation, and the protection requirements in 300.4(F) which apply to protecting cable or raceway-type wiring methods installed in

Change at a Glance

Protection as specified in 300.4(F) is required where NM cable is installed in shallow chases or grooves in masonry, concrete, or adobe.

such a manner. This revision removes the conflict between these two sections that address the same issue of providing protection from physical damage, and at the same time opens up the options for installers to select a 1.6 mm (1/16 in.) steel plate, a listed steel plate less than 1.6 mm (1/16 in.), or equivalent as provided in 300.4(F). It should also be noted that Exception No. 1 to 300.4(F) relaxes the requirements for a steel plate where rigid metal conduit, intermediate metal conduit, rigid non-metallic conduit, or electrical metallic tubing are used to provide such protection.

Code Language
334.15(B)

Protection from Physical Damage
Cable shall be protected from physical damage...above the floor.

Type NMC cable installed in shallow chases or grooves in masonry, concrete, or adobe, shall be protected in accordance with the requirements in 300.4(F) and covered with plaster, adobe, or similar finish.

Summary of Change

The last sentence of Section 334.15(B) has been revised to provide a reference to Section 300.4(F). The words "or grooves" have been inserted after the words "in shallow chases."

3

334.15[C]

Exposed Work
NEC, p. 189

Proposal 7-58, 7-63, 7-67
Log 2399, 344, 2916
ROP, p. 336–338

Comment 7-35
Log 43
ROC, p. 204

Change at a Glance

The provisions of 334.15(C) apply to unfinished basements and crawl spaces. Prescriptive installation criteria similar to 312.5(C) Exception are now included in this rule.

334.15(C) Exposed Work

(C) In Unfinished Basements and Crawl Spaces

Conduit or tubing shall be provided with a suitable insulating bushing or adapter at the point the cable enters the raceway.

The NM cable sheath shall extend through the conduit or tubing and into the outlet or device box not less than 6 mm (1/4 in.).

The cable shall be secured within 300 mm (12 in.) of the point where the cable enters the conduit or tubing.

Metal conduit, tubing, and metal outlet boxes shall be connected to an equipment grounding conductor.

Copyright©IAEI 2007

Analysis and Effect

This section provides requirements for installing nonmetallic-sheathed cables on the lower edge of joists in basements and addresses the concerns of damage to cables in smaller sizes installed in unfinished basements. These provisions apply to nonmetallic-sheathed cable assemblies containing two conductors not smaller than 6 AWG or cable assemblies containing three conductors not smaller than 8 AWG. In previous editions of the *NEC,* this requirement applied only to installations on the lower edges of joists in unfinished basements. This section has been revised to clarify that the requirements apply not only to unfinished basements, but also to crawl spaces. It is logical that equivalent protection be afforded to cables in these sizes that are installed to meet the requirements of this section whether they are installed in unfinished basements or crawl spaces. Additional revisions incorporate prescriptive requirements for nonmetallic-sheathed cable installations on unfinished basement walls. The new requirements address securing the cable before it enters the conduit or tubing, the length of the sheath in the conduit or tubing, and references the protection means now provided in 300.4.

Code Language
334.15[C]

In Unfinished Basements and Crawl Spaces. Where cable is run at angles with joists in unfinished basements and crawl spaces, it shall be permissible to secure cables not smaller than two 6 AWG or three 8 AWG conductors directly to the lower edges of the joists. Smaller cables shall be run either through bored holes in joists or on running boards. NM cable installed on the wall of an unfinished basement shall be permitted to be installed in a listed conduit or tubing or shall be protected in accordance with 300.4. Conduit or tubing shall be provided with a suitable insulating bushing or adapter at the point the cable enters the raceway. The NM cable sheath shall extend through the conduit or tubing and into the outlet or device box not less than 6 mm (1/4 in.). The cable shall be secured within 300 mm (12 in.) of the point where the cable enters the conduit or tubing. Metal conduit, tubing, and metal outlet boxes shall be connected to an equipment grounding conductor.

Summary of Change

The words "and crawl spaces" have been added to this section. Additional text has been added to provide prescriptive requirements where nonmetallic-sheathed cable is installed on walls of unfinished basements and crawl spaces. The revisions include requirements that are consistent with those in 312.5(C) Exception as appropriate.

Analysis of Changes *NEC-2008*

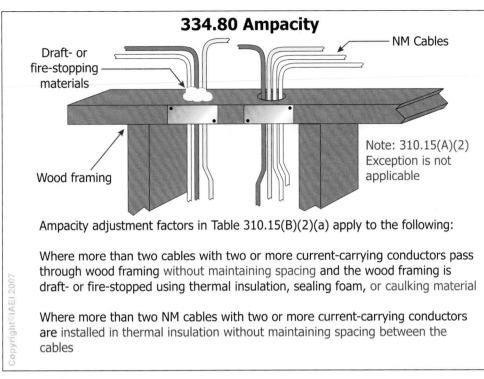

334.80 Ampacity

Draft- or fire-stopping materials

NM Cables

Wood framing

Note: 310.15(A)(2) Exception is not applicable

Ampacity adjustment factors in Table 310.15(B)(2)(a) apply to the following:

Where more than two cables with two or more current-carrying conductors pass through wood framing without maintaining spacing and the wood framing is draft- or fire-stopped using thermal insulation, sealing foam, or caulking material

Where more than two NM cables with two or more current-carrying conductors are installed in thermal insulation without maintaining spacing between the cables

Copyright©IAEI 2007

334.80

Ampacity
NEC, p. 190

Proposal 7-70, 7-72, 7-73, 7-74
Log 880, 1770, 2737, 3152
ROP, p. 338–339

Comment 7-41
Log 1255
ROC, p. 205

Analysis and Effect

Three significant revisions were accepted and incorporated into this section. The second paragraph was revised by removing the word "bundled." The proposal indicated that currently there is no definition of the word *bundled* in Article 100 of the *NEC*. Additional revisions provide more specifics about common types of fire- or draft-stopping materials used. These requirements are related to the restriction of heat dissipation by the fire- or draft-stopping materials, whatever material is used. The revisions also clarify that the provisions of 310.15(A)(2) Exception are not permitted to be applied to installations meeting the criteria covered in this section. The new last paragraph resulted from case studies and research data that supports the need to apply ampacity adjustment factors to NM cables that are installed in contact with thermal insulation without spacing maintained between them. Where NM cables containing two or more current-carrying conductors are installed in contact with thermal insulation, the allowable ampacity of the conductors in the cables must be adjusted in accordance with the values in Table 310.15(B)(2)(a).

Change at a Glance

Specific types of fire-stopping or draft-stopping materials are now included in these requirements. NM cables installed in contact with thermal insulation and without maintaining spacing are subject to ampacity adjustment factors in Table 310.15(B)(2)(a). The exception to 310.15(A)(2) is not applicable in this section.

Code Language
334.80
Ampacity

The ampacity of Types NM, NMC, and NMS cable...determined in accordance with 392.11.

Where more than two NM cables containing two or more current-carrying conductors are installed, without maintaining spacing between the cables, through the same opening in wood framing that is to be fire- or draft-stopped using thermal insulation, caulk, or sealing foam, the allowable ampacity of each conductor shall be adjusted in accordance with Table 310.15(B)(2)(a) and the provisions of 310.15(A)(2), Exception, shall not apply.

Where more than two NM cables containing two or more current-carrying conductors are installed in contact with thermal insulation without maintaining spacing between cables, the allowable ampacity of each conductor shall be adjusted in accordance with Table 310.15(B)(2)(a).

Summary of Change

The second paragraph has been revised to remove the word "bundled" and the words "using thermal insulation, caulk, or sealing foam" have been added after the words "fire- or draft-stopped." The words "and the provisions of 315.15(A)(2), Exception, shall not apply" were added to the last sentence of the second paragraph. A new third paragraph has been added that addresses installations of NM cable in contact with thermal insulation.

Analysis of Changes *NEC*-2008

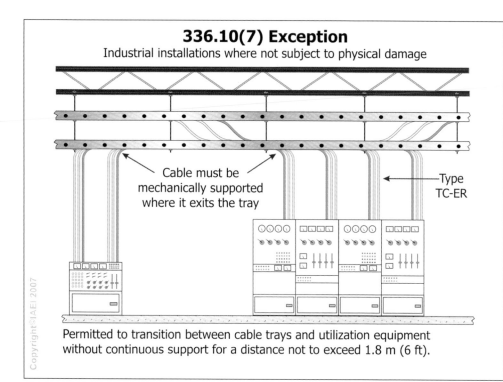

336.10(7) Exception
Industrial installations where not subject to physical damage

Cable must be mechanically supported where it exits the tray

Type TC-ER

Permitted to transition between cable trays and utilization equipment without continuous support for a distance not to exceed 1.8 m (6 ft).

Copyright©IAEI 2007

Uses Permitted
NEC, p. 191

Proposal 7-80
Log 1720
ROP, p. 341

Comment
None

Analysis and Effect

The new exception relaxes the support requirements provided in item (7) and specifically addresses the allowable method of securing and supporting the cable when all the conditions of the exception are met. The conditions of the exception include installations of Type TC-ER cable at transition points in lengths up to 1.8 m (6 ft) without continuous support where not subject to physical damage. Another qualifier in this allowance is that the cable is mechanically supported where it exits the tray in a manner that the minimum bending radius of the cable is not exceeded.

Change at a Glance

Type TC-ER cable is permitted at transition points in lengths up to 1.8 m (6 ft) without continuous support where mechanically supported and not subject to physical damage.

Code Language
336.10
Uses Permitted

Type TC cable shall be permitted to be used as follows:

(7) In industrial establishments where conditions of…identified as an equipment grounding conductor in accordance with 250.119(B).

Exception: Where not subject to physical damage, Type TC-ER shall be permitted to transition between cable trays and utilization equipment or devices for a distance not to exceed 1.8 m (6 ft) without continuous support. The cable shall be mechanically supported where exiting the cable tray to ensure that the minimum bending radius is not exceeded.

Summary of Change

A new exception has been added to Section 336.10(7).

3

338.10, 338.12

Uses Not Permitted
NEC, p. 192

Proposal 7-84, 7-88, 7-89, 7-93
Log 2636, 2639, 3124, 3486
ROP, p. 342, 343

Comment
None

Change at a Glance

Uses not permitted for service-entrance (Type SE) cable are differentiated clearly from uses not permitted for underground service-entrance (Type USE) cable.

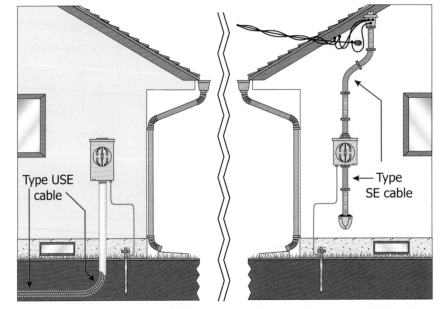

338.12(A) and (B) Uses Not Permitted

Type USE cable

Type SE cable

Uses not permitted clearly differentiated between USE cable and SE cable

Copyright©IAEI 2007

Analysis and Effect

Action by a CMP-7 assigned task group results in a new Section 338.12 Uses Not Permitted for Type SE Cable. The revisions to 338.10 include the removal of specific existing provisions that relate more appropriately to installations or conditions where Type SE cable is not permitted and, therefore, belong in the newly created Section 338.12. The addition of Section 338.12 was considered necessary to add uniformity to all of the cable articles for which Panel 7 is responsible. The reference to Part I of Article 334 has been removed from 338.10(B)(4)(a) since it is not applicable for Type SE and USE cables. Section 338.12(A)(2) incorporates the concepts in Proposal 7-93 to clarify that Type SE cable is not permitted to be used in underground installations, with or without a raceway. The text that excluded 334.80 was deleted from Section 338.10 (B)(4)(a) because the ampacity requirements apply to both types of cable installed.

Summary of Change

Section 338.10 has been revised by removing text that relates to where service-entrance cable is not permitted to be installed. A new Section 338.12 has been created to incorporate the revisions in 338.10. The reference to excluding 334.80 has been removed from Section 338.10(B)(4). Section 338.12(A)(2) has been inserted to clarify underground uses are not permitted.

Code Language
338.12
Uses Not Permitted

(A) Service-Entrance Cable. Service-entrance cable (SE) shall not be used under the following conditions or in the following locations.
(1) Where subject to physical damage unless protected in accordance with 230.50(A)
(2) Underground with or without a raceway
(3) For exterior branch circuits and feeder wiring unless the installation complies with the provisions of Part I of Article 225 and is supported in accordance with 334.30 or is used as messenger-supported wiring as permitted in Part II of Article 396.

(B) Underground Service-Entrance Cable. Underground service-entrance cable (USE) shall not be used under the following conditions or in the following locations:
(1) For interior wiring
(2) For aboveground installations except where USE cable emerges from the ground and is terminated in an enclosure at an outdoor location and the cable is protected in accordance with 300.5(D)
(3) As aerial cable unless it is a multiconductor cable identified for use aboveground and installed as messenger-supported wiring in accordance with 225.10 and Part II of Article 396.

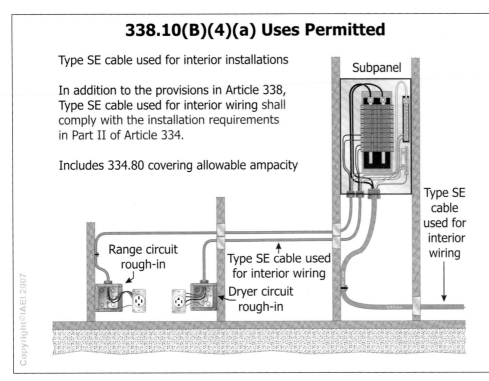

338.10(B)(4)(a) Uses Permitted

Type SE cable used for interior installations

In addition to the provisions in Article 338, Type SE cable used for interior wiring shall comply with the installation requirements in Part II of Article 334.

Includes 334.80 covering allowable ampacity

Subpanel

Type SE cable used for interior wiring

Range circuit rough-in

Type SE cable used for interior wiring

Dryer circuit rough-in

Copyright©IAEI 2007

338.10(B) (4)(a)

Installation Methods for Branch Circuits and Feeders
NEC, p. 192

Proposal 7-88, 7-89, 7-90
Log 2639, 3124, 3399
ROP, p. 343

Comment
None

Analysis and Effect

Nothing in Part I of Article 334 is applicable to service-entrance (Type SE) cable installations. For this reason, the reference to Part I of Article 334 has been removed. This exclusion of 334.80 results in requirements for the same ampacity rules to be applied to nonmetallic-sheathed cable (Types NM, NMC, and NMS) and service-entrance cable (Type SE) alike. When Type SE conductors are used for interior wiring, as a replacement for Type NM cable, the ampacity of the conductors should be the same as permitted for NM cable since the method of installation affects the allowable ampacity of the cables. This revision clarifies that ampacity requirements for NM, NMC, and NMS cables are consistent with those required for SE cables installed as interior wiring.

Change at a Glance

Part II of Article 334 applies to SE cables installed as interior wiring and Section 334.80 governing allowable ampacity applies to SE cable applications.

Code Language
338.10(B)(4)

Installation Methods for Branch Circuits and Feeders.

(a) *Interior Installations.* In addition to the provisions of this article, Type SE service-entrance cable used for interior wiring shall comply with the installation requirements of Part II of Article 334.

Summary of Change

The reference to Part I of Article 334 has been removed, and the words "excluding 334.80" have been removed from Section 338.10(B)(4)(a).

342.30(C),
344.30(C),
352.30(C),
355.30(C),
358.30(C)

Unsupported Raceways
NEC, Various pages

Proposal 8-9, 8-23, 8-65, 8-78,
8-104
Log 1345, 1346, 1348, 1920,
1349
ROP, p. Various

Comment 8-7, 8-8, 8-20, 8-21,
8-38, 8-39, 8-57, 8-58
Log 781, 983, 782, 966, 785,
967, 784, 968
ROC, Various

342.30(C) Unsupported Raceways

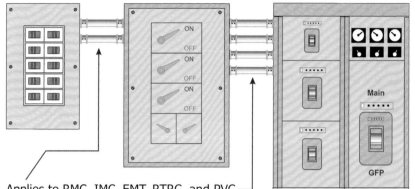

Applies to RMC, IMC, EMT, RTRC, and PVC ⎯

Where oversized, concentric or eccentric knockouts are not encountered, Type IMC shall be permitted to be unsupported in lengths up to 450 mm (18 in.).

The conduit must be unbroken (without couplings) and be terminated in a box or enclosure at the end of the raceway.

Copyright©IAEI 2007

Analysis and Effect

This change applies to the supporting and securing requirements for intermediate metal conduit, electrical metallic tubing, rigid metal conduit, and rigid polyvinyl chloride conduit: Type PVC, and reinforced thermosetting resin conduit. The new subdivision (C) to these sections incorporates a new provision that relaxes the securing and supporting requirements for lengths of conduit or tubing that do not exceed 450 mm (18 in.). The conditions under which the conduit or tubing is not required to be supported are that it must be a continuous, unbroken length without a coupling or other fitting, no oversized, concentric or eccentric knockouts are encountered, and it must be securely fastened to a box, cabinet or other enclosure termination. This revision reflects many installations that have been completed using this practice with no evidence of related problems or failures. This revision provides a specific dimension in the *Code* that users can apply to installations reflecting securing practices for short lengths of conduit or tubing where no such *Code* provisions or guidance previously existed.

Change at a Glance

Conduit and tubing covered by Articles 342, 344, 352, 355, and 358 are permitted without supports in lengths not exceeding 450 mm (18 in.).

Code Language
342.30(C)
Unsupported Raceways

Where oversized, concentric or eccentric knockouts are not encountered, Type _____ shall be permitted to be unsupported where the raceway is not more than 450 mm (18 in.) in length and remains in unbroken lengths (without coupling). Such raceway shall terminate in an outlet box, junction box, device box, cabinet, or other termination at each end of the raceway.

Summary of Change
A new subdivision (C) has been added to the .30 section in Articles 342, 344, 352, 355, and 358.

3

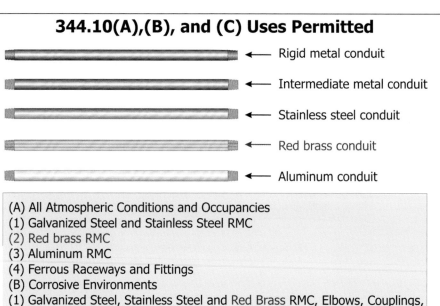

344.10(A),(B), and (C) Uses Permitted

← Rigid metal conduit

← Intermediate metal conduit

← Stainless steel conduit

← Red brass conduit

← Aluminum conduit

Copyright©IAEI 2007

(A) All Atmospheric Conditions and Occupancies
(1) Galvanized Steel and Stainless Steel RMC
(2) Red brass RMC
(3) Aluminum RMC
(4) Ferrous Raceways and Fittings
(B) Corrosive Environments
(1) Galvanized Steel, Stainless Steel and Red Brass RMC, Elbows, Couplings, and Fittings
(2) Supplementary Protection of Aluminum RMC
(C) Cinder Fill. Galvanized steel, stainless steel and red brass RMC...

344.10
(A)(B)(C)

Uses Permitted
NEC, p. 195, 196

Proposal 8-15
Log 3456
ROP, p. 346

Comment 8-14
Log 984
ROC, p. 210

Change at a Glance

Red brass conduit is now included in 344.10, and the corrosion protection rules for all types of rigid metal conduit have been clarified.

Analysis and Effect

This section has been reorganized to provide a more logical layout, improving clarity and usability. Significant revisions include adding red brass RMC to the *Code* as a listed wiring method, and clarifying where corrosion protection is required to be applied to rigid metal conduit. Titles were added to the sub-divisions, and the former fine print note (FPN) that referred to Section 300.6 and corrosion protection requirements following subdivision (D) was deleted. These changes were consistent with the requirements in the *NEC Style Manual*. These changes will improve usability for installers and inspectors, and give more specifics as to which types of RMC require corrosion protection, and the locations where protection will be required.

Code Language
344. 10
Uses Permitted
(A) Atmospheric Conditions and Occupancies.
  (1) Galvanized Steel and Stainless Steel RMC
  (2) Red Brass RMC
  (3) Aluminum RMC
  (4) Ferrous Raceways and Fittings

(B) Corrosive Environments.
  (1) Galvanized Steel, Stainless Steel, and Red Brass RMC, Elbows, Couplings, and Fittings
  (2) Supplementary Protection of Aluminum RMC

Note: See Section 344.10 of *NEC*-2008 for full text of this section.

(C) Cinder Fill. Galvanized steel, stainless steel, and red brass RMC shall be permitted to be installed in or under cinder fill where subject to permanent moisture where protected on all sides by a layer of noncinder concrete not less than 50 mm (2 in.) thick; where the conduit is not less than 450 mm (18 in.) under the fill; or where protected by corrosion protection and judged suitable for the condition.

(D) Wet Locations. (The text remains unchanged).

Summary of Change

Major changes were made to the uses permitted of RMC, clarifying requirements for corrosion protection, and adding a new type of RMC.

Analysis of Changes *NEC*-2008

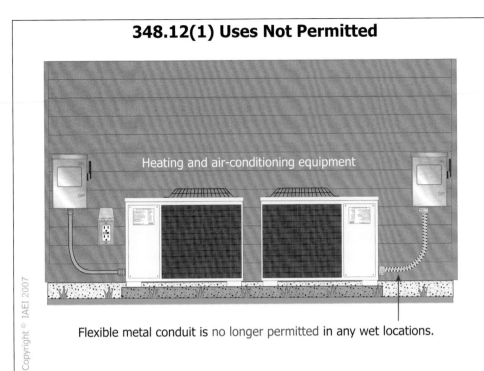

348.12(1) Uses Not Permitted

Heating and air-conditioning equipment

Flexible metal conduit is no longer permitted in any wet locations.

Copyright © IAEI 2007

348.12(1)

Uses Not Permitted
NEC, p. 197

Proposal 8-26, 8-27, 8-28
Log 641, 2613, 3355
ROP, p. 349

Comment
None

REVISION

Analysis and Effect

Section 348.12 provides a list of uses not permitted for flexible metal conduit. Item (1) in that list has generally prohibited use of this wiring method in wet locations unless the conductors are approved for the specific conditions and the installation is such that liquid is not likely to enter raceways or enclosures to which the conduit is connected. It is practical to comply with the first part of that condition that requires conductors to be suitable for wet locations because wet location conductors are available and this requirement already exists in the *NEC* for conductors installed in wet locations. The second condition in the previous item (1) was much more difficult to

> ### Change at a Glance
>
> Flexible metal conduit is not permitted for use in wet locations, regardless of any conditions.

comply with, and often did not result in reasonable assurances that water would not enter raceways or enclosures where flexible metal conduit was used in wet locations. The revision to this section removes the allowance of flexible metal conduit in wet locations all together, which provides users with a requirement that is not subjective. There are other flexible wiring methods and fittings included in chapter 3 of the *NEC* that are listed for use in wet locations and provide the level of protection from the wetness anticipated where flexible wiring is installed. From both the installer and inspector perspectives, this change provides clarity and will result in more uniform and consistent application of this rule, and, at the same time, will help reduce possibilities of wetness entering raceways or enclosures, which can ultimately lead to other safety concerns.

Code Language
348.12

Uses Not Permitted
FMC shall not be used in the following:
(1) In wet locations

Summary of Change

The words "unless the conductors are approved for the specific conditions and the installation is such that liquid is not likely to enter raceways or enclosures to which the conduit is connected" have been removed from 348.12(1).

3

348.30(A) Exc. No. 1 and 350.30(A) Exc. No. 1

Uses Not Permitted
NEC, p. 198, 200

Proposal 8-33, 8-46
Log 3331, 3330
ROP, p. 350, 352

Comment
None

Change at a Glance
Securing and supporting fished flexible metal conduit is not necessary where it is impractical.

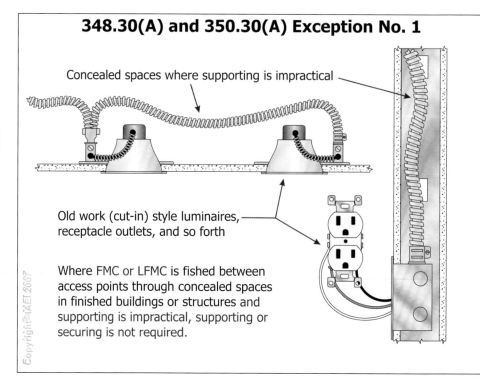

348.30(A) and 350.30(A) Exception No. 1

Concealed spaces where supporting is impractical

Old work (cut-in) style luminaires, receptacle outlets, and so forth

Where FMC or LFMC is fished between access points through concealed spaces in finished buildings or structures and supporting is impractical, supporting or securing is not required.

Copyright © IAEI 2007

Analysis and Effect
The revision to these exceptions clarifies the conditions necessary before flexible metal conduit and liquidtight flexible metal conduit is permitted to be installed without securing or supporting in fished installations. The previous allowance literally permitted these wiring types to be unsupported and not secured where fished, whether access or means by which it could be supported was available. The revision to these exceptions tighten the provision for installers and results in application of this exception that is more limited to installations where it is not practical, or even possible in many cases, to secure or support flexible metal conduit or liquidtight flexible metal conduit that is fished in hollow spaces of buildings or structures. Although the objective (intent) of these exceptions is fairly evident, the additional wording provides a condition that inspectors can use to apply judgment when applying these exceptions to field installations of flexible metal conduit and liquidtight flexible metal conduit where fishing is not only desired for the installation, but necessary because of impracticability.

Code Language
348.30(A)
Securely Fastened
Exception No. 1: Where FMC is fished between access points through concealed spaces in finished buildings or structures and supporting is impractical.

350.30(A)
Securely Fastened
Exception No. 1: Where LFMC is fished between access points through concealed spaces in finished buildings or structures and supporting is impractical.

Summary of Change
The words "between access points through concealed spaces in finished buildings or structures and supporting is impractical" have been added to 348.30(A) Exception No. 1 and 350.30(A) Exception No. 1.

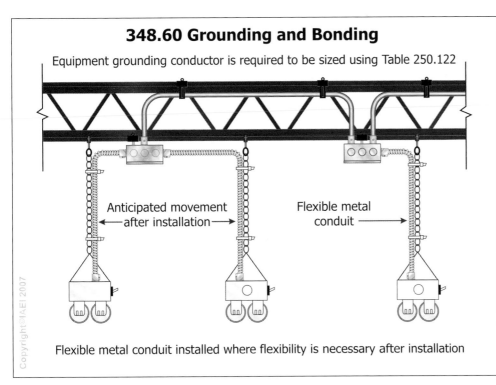

348.60 Grounding and Bonding

Equipment grounding conductor is required to be sized using Table 250.122

Anticipated movement
← after installation →

Flexible metal
conduit →

Flexible metal conduit installed where flexibility is necessary after installation

Copyright©IAEI 2007

348.60

Grounding & Bonding
NEC, p. 199

Proposal 8-40, 8-41
Log 882, 1482
ROP, p. 351

Comment 8-27
Log 1079
ROC, p. 213

Analysis and Effect

This section has been revised to clarify the requirements for users and to correlate with similar requirements presently provided in Section 250.118(5). The concerns of the effective ground-fault current path integrity being maintained are the primary concepts behind this revision, as they were when Sections 250.118(5) and (6) were revised in *NEC*-2005. By adding the words "after installation" to this requirement, it is now clear that where there is anticipated movement or vibration that could compromise the integrity of the effective ground-fault current path where flexible metal conduit is used as an equipment grounding conductor allowed by 250.118(5), an equipment grounding conductor of the wire type that is sized in accordance with 250.122 must be installed. It should be noted that not all installations of flexible metal conduit require flexibility after it is installed. For example, where it is installed under drywall from outlet to outlet, once the wall covering is in place, flexibility is not necessary. Where the reasons this wiring method is selected for the installation involve anticipated movement, which in some cases could include vibration during normal operation, the *Code* is now clear that an equipment grounding conductor must be installed for equipment grounding purposes and to ensure an effective ground-fault current path is in place and remains effective to facilitate overcurrent device operation in ground-fault conditions.

Change at a Glance

Flexible metal conduit that is installed because there is anticipated movement or where flexibility is required after installation requires an equipment grounding conductor.

Code Language
348.60

Grounding and Bonding

Where used to connect equipment where flexibility is required after installation, an equipment grounding conductor shall be installed.

Where flexibility is not required after installation, FMC shall be permitted to be... (remainder unchanged).

Summary of Change

The words "after installation" have been inserted in two places in Section 348.60.

3

350.30(A)
Exc. No. 2

Flexibility at Terminals
NEC, p. 200

Proposal 8-44, 8-48
Log 1347, 3438
ROP, p. 352, 353

Comment 8-29
Log 2044
ROC, p. 213

Change at a Glance

Securing distance requirements for liquidtight flexible metal conduit are permitted to increase incrementally based on sizes provided in the new exception.

350.30(A) Exception No. 2

Securing and supporting liquidtight flexible metal conduit

Copyright©IAEI 2007

Where flexibility is necessary after installation, lengths shall not exceed:

(1) 900 mm (3 ft) for trade sizes 1/2 through 1-1/4
(2) 1200 mm (4 ft) for trade sizes 1 1/2 through 2
(3) 1500 mm (5 ft) for trade size 2 1/2 and larger

Analysis and Effect

In the 2005 *NEC* development process, substantiation was provided with Proposal 8-43 (Log No. 225) that clearly indicated a need to expand the provisions of Exception No. 2 to 348.30(A) for practicality and consistency of its application. It was emphasized that the 900 mm (3 ft) length of flexible metal conduit provided in the exception is not sufficient in all cases to make connections to equipment, specifically in the larger sizes. While shorter lengths of smaller sizes can meet the 900 mm (3 ft) securing and supporting requirement, larger sizes present problems from a practical standpoint. The same conditions are encountered where liquidtight flexible metal conduit is installed in larger sizes. The revisions to this exception in *NEC*-2008 are consistent with the revisions to 348.30(A) Exception No. 2 accepted by CMP-8 in the 2005 *NEC* cycle. The changes to this exception provide uniform allowances for relaxing the securing distances to lengths based on the conduit sizes to provide users with *Code* what not only reflects current industry practices but provides a requirement that is more reasonable and easily satisfied when larger sizes of liquidtight flexible metal conduit are used.

Code Language
350.30(A)

Exception No. 2: Where flexibility is necessary after installation, lengths shall not exceed the following:

(1) 900 mm (3 ft) for metric designators 16 through 35 (trade sizes 1/2 through 1 1/4)

(2) 1200 mm (4 ft) for metric designators 41 through 53 (trade sizes 1 1/2 through 2)

(3) 1500 mm (5 ft) for metric designators 63 (trade size 2 1/2) and larger.

Summary of Change

Exception No. 2 to Section 350.30(A) has been revised and expanded.

350.60

Grounding & Bonding
NEC, p. 200

Proposal 8-49, 8-50
Log 883, 1481
ROP, p. 353

Comment 8-30
Log 1080
ROC, p. 213

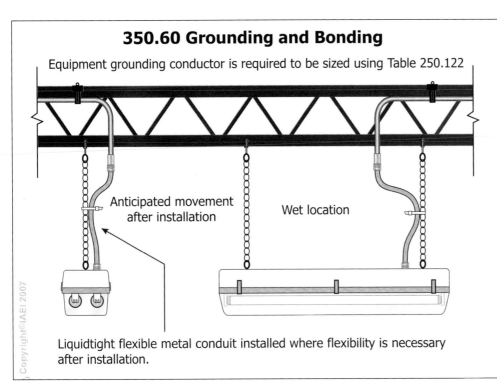

350.60 Grounding and Bonding

Equipment grounding conductor is required to be sized using Table 250.122

Anticipated movement after installation

Wet location

Liquidtight flexible metal conduit installed where flexibility is necessary after installation.

Copyright©IAEI 2007

Analysis and Effect

This revision provides needed clarification and correlates with similar requirements in Section 250.118(6). The concerns of the effective ground-fault current path integrity being maintained are the primary concepts behind this revision, as they were when Sections 250.118(5) and (6) were revised in the 2005 *NEC*. Adding the words "after installation" to this requirement, clarifies that where there is anticipated movement or vibration that could compromise the integrity of the effective ground-fault current path where liquidtight flexible metal conduit is used as an equipment grounding conductor as allowed by 250.118(6), an equipment grounding conductor of the wire type that is sized in accordance with 250.122 must be installed. Not all installations of liquidtight flexible metal conduit require flexibility after it is installed. For example, where it is installed in a wet location to connect a weatherproof neon transformer enclosure and securely fastened in place, flexibility is not necessary. Where the reasons this wiring method is selected for the installation involve anticipated movement, which in some cases could include vibration during normal operation, the *Code* is now clear that an equipment grounding conductor must be installed for equipment grounding purposes and to ensure an effective ground-fault current path is in place and remains effective to facilitate overcurrent device operation in ground-fault conditions.

Change at a Glance

Liquidtight flexible metal conduit that is installed because there is anticipated movement or where flexibility is required after installation requires an equipment grounding conductor.

Code Language

350.60

Grounding and Bonding

Where used to connect equipment where flexibility is required after installation, an equipment grounding conductor shall be installed.

Where flexibility is not required after installation, LFMC shall be permitted to be... (remainder unchanged).

Summary of Change

The words "after installation" have been inserted in two places in Section 350.60.

Article 352

Rigid Polyvinyl Chloride Conduit: Type PVC
NEC, Various pages

Proposal 8-53
Log 1919
ROP, p. 354

Comment 8-32
Log 1378
ROC, p. 214

Change at a Glance

Article 352 covers requirements for Schedules 40 and 80 rigid polyvinyl chloride conduit: Type PVC, installation, construction specifications and associated fittings.

Courtesy of Carlon, Lamson and Sessions

Analysis and Effect

In *NEC*-2002, Article 352 Rigid Nonmetallic Conduit (RNC) included PVC, RTRC, and HDPE products. In *NEC*-2005, Type HDPE was separated from the other products and placed in its own new Article 353, because its composition and permitted uses are quite different from PVC and RTRC. The revision left two very dissimilar products grouped together as RNC in Article 352, and technically eliminated HDPE as an acceptable wiring method in all applications where rigid nonmetallic conduit was specified. Type RTRC (fiberglass) conduit has different physical properties and dimensions than PVC conduit. The separation of these products into distinct articles now corrects the situation by better defining the installation and construction specifications for each conduit type. Existing references to rigid nonmetallic conduit code-wide will need to be clarified as to which specific type of rigid nonmetallic conduit is being referred to, and additional references will need to be incorporated in the *Code*. Separation of these three different products provides a better distinction as to their individual installation practices, application and use, and makes it easier for *Code* users. The change correlates with Proposal 8-78, Log 1920, which created new Article 355, Reinforced Thermosetting Resin Conduit: Type RTRC. Article 352 has been revised and renamed to include PVC conduit and associated fittings only, and to remove Reinforced Thermosetting Resin Conduit Type RTRC from Article 352 to new Article 355.

Code Language
Article 352
Rigid Polyvinyl Chloride Conduit: Type PVC
Part I General

352.1
Scope. This article covers the use, installation, and construction specifications for rigid polyvinyl chloride conduit (PVC) and associated fittings.

FPN: Refer to Article 353 for High Density Polyethylene Conduit: Type HDPE and Article 355 for Reinforced Thermosetting Resin Conduit: Type RTRC.

352.2
Rigid Polyvinyl Chloride Conduit (PVC). A rigid nonmetallic conduit (RNC) of circular cross section, with integral or associated couplings, connectors, and fittings for the installation of electrical conductors and cables.

(See *NEC*-2008 for the remainder of Article 352).

Summary of Change
The title of Article 352 has been changed to include only those requirements associated with PVC conduit. Requirements for Type RTRC conduit have been removed from Article 352, and placed in new Article 355.

Exposed
NEC, p. 201

Proposal 8-57
Log 2614
ROP, p. 360

Comment
None

Analysis and Effect

This revision clarifies that Schedules 40 and 80 Type PVC conduits are approved for both concealed and exposed work. If Type PVC conduit is installed in a location where it will be exposed to physical damage, it is required to be identified for that use. These revisions clearly state that Schedule 80 Type PVC conduit is identified for the use when exposed to physical damage. This change gives installers and inspection authorities improved guidance for the use of Type PVC conduit, and correlates with Proposal 8-53, which removed Type RTRC conduit from Article 352.

> ### Change at a Glance
>
> PVC conduit is permitted for exposed installations, but where subject to physical damage it has to be identified for that use.

Code Language
352.10(F)
Exposed

PVC conduit shall be permitted for exposed work. PVC conduit used exposed in areas of physical damage shall be identified for the use.

FPN: PVC Conduit, Type Schedule 80, is identified for areas of physical damage.

Summary of Change

New text and FPN has been added to 352.10(F) to clarify the permitted uses of Type PVC conduit.

3

352.10(G)

Underground Installations
NEC, p. 201

Proposal 8-53, 8-68
Log 1919, 2616
ROP, p. 354, 362

Comment 8-45a
Log CC801
ROC, p. 214

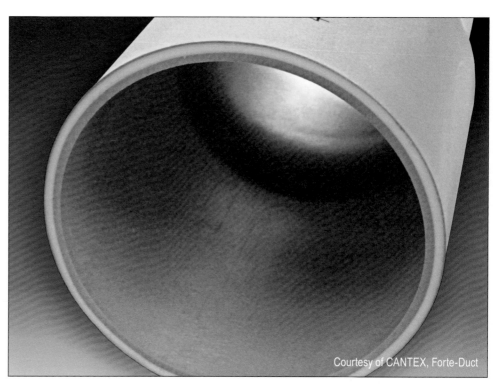

Courtesy of CANTEX, Forte-Duct

Analysis and Effect

This revision introduces a new type of PVC conduit that is manufactured using closed-cell technology to form a rigid core. The revision to 352.10(G) results in recognition of both homogenous and nonhomogenous types of rigid PVC conduit in direct burial applications or underground concrete encasement. The new foam-core PVC conduit has recently been evaluated as sunlight-resistant, which expands its use to those provided within Article 352. Concerns about bending methods were expressed at a recent meeting of the UL Electrical Council. Where bends are necessary, they must be accomplished using factory bends or by bending the conduit according to the manufacturer's requirements and the product's evaluation and listing.

Code Language
352.10(G)
Underground Installations
For underground installations, homogenous and nonhomogenous PVC shall be permitted for direct burial and underground encased in concrete. See 300.5 and 300.50.

Summary of Change

The words "homogenous and nonhomogenous PVC shall be permitted for direct burial and underground encased in concrete" have been incorporated into this section.

Change at a Glance

Nonhomogenous (foam core) PVC is permitted for use in direct burial applications or where encased in concrete underground.

Analysis of Changes *NEC*-2008

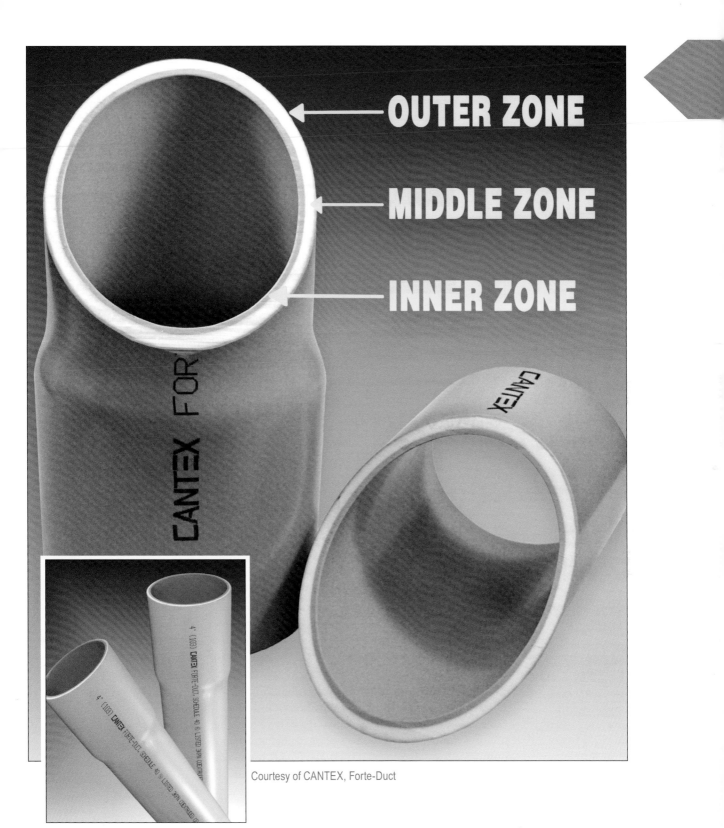

OUTER ZONE

MIDDLE ZONE

INNER ZONE

Courtesy of CANTEX, Forte-Duct

352.12[A],
353.12[3],
354.12[3],
355.12[A]
[1] and [2],
356.12[5],
and
362.12[1]

Uses Not Permitted
NEC, Various pages

**Proposal 8-59, 8-70, 8-76,
8-78, 8-53, 8-84, 8-113
Log 1974, 1967, 1968, 1920,
1919, 1969, 1963**
ROP, p. 360, 364, 365, 354,
368,373

**Comment 8-34
Log 2504**
ROC, p. 214

352.12(A) Uses Not Permitted

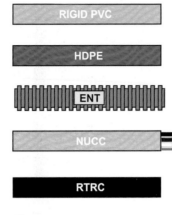

(A) Hazardous (Classified) Locations

Nonmetallic wiring methods are not permitted in any hazardous (classified) location unless specifically permitted in other articles of the *NEC*.

Applies to:

Rigid PVC conduit
High density polyethylene conduit
Electrical nonmetallic tubing
Nonmetallic underground conduit with conductors
Reinforced thermosetting resin conduit
Liquititght flexible nonmetallic conduit

Copyright©IAEI 2007

Analysis and Effect

This sweeping change affects many articles, such as PVC conduit, HDPE conduit, NUCC conduit, HDPE conduit, LFNC conduit and ENT tubing. Type NUCC is a factory assembly that includes conductors or cables inside a smooth wall conduit intended for use underground, or aboveground with concrete encasement under certain conditions. Previous *Code* references specific to a few classified (hazardous) location *Code* sections that permitted very limited use of nonmetallic conduits in those locations have been removed because they were considered by some as too restrictive to the use of non-metallic raceways. The revisions to these sections permit these types of nonmetallic raceways to be installed in classified (hazardous) locations only where allowed in the *Code* article specific to that location. An example would be a classified location where conditions corrosive to metal raceways exist, and possible combustion of explosive mixtures may be lessened to a point where the use of a nonmetallic raceway system would not compromise safety. Section 501.10(B)(1)(7) was revised to allow Types PVC Schedule 80 and RTRC conduits to be installed in Class 1 Division 2 industrial locations with restricted public access and qualified persons servicing the installation, and where metallic conduit does not provide sufficient corrosion resistance. This change to nonmetallic conduit (PVC) also correlates with Proposals 8-53, 8-59, 8-76, 8-78, 8-84 and 8-113. Similar changes occurred in Article 378 regarding the use of nonmetallic wireways in classified (hazardous) locations, as well as other nonmetallic raceway articles in the *Code*.

Code Language

One example from one article as follows:

352.12
Uses Not Permitted
PVC conduit shall not be used under the conditions specified in 352.12(A) through (F).

(A) Hazardous (Classified) Locations. In any hazardous (classified) locations, except as permitted by other articles of this *Code*.

Summary of Change

Revision of Articles 352, 353, 354, 356, 362, and inclusion in new Article 355 to clarify that Type PVC, HDPE, NUCC, HDPE, LFNC and ENT conduits and tubing are not permitted in hazardous (classified) locations unless specifically permitted within other articles of the *Code*.

Change at a Glance

Nonmetallic raceways are permitted in hazardous (classified) locations only where specifically permitted by other articles in the *Code*.

353.10(5) Uses Permitted

Courtesy of Carlon, Lamson and Sessions

High density polyethylene conduit is permitted to be used in aboveground installations where in a concrete encasement not less than 50 mm (2 in.).

Uses Permitted
NEC, p. 203

Proposal 8-69
Log 2617
ROP, p. 364

Comment
None

Analysis and Effect

This revision clarifies that Type HDPE conduit is now permitted for use aboveground under certain conditions: if encased in not less than 50 mm (2 in.) of concrete, installed per the product listing, and except as prohibited by 353.12. Type HDPE conduit has been listed by a third party nationally recognized electrical testing laboratory for use aboveground with concrete encasement.

Type HDPE conduit is designed for joining by threaded couplings, drive-on couplings, or a butt-fusing process. The basic product standard for testing of this type of nonmetallic conduit is ANSI/UL 651A. The phrase "except as prohibited in Section 352.12" was added by Code Panel 8 to clarify that HDPE conduit is not permitted in buildings.

Change at a Glance

HDPE conduit is permitted to be used aboveground where encased in concrete and in conformance with the limits of its listing unless prohibited by 353.12.

Code Language

Part II
Installation

353.10
Uses Permitted

The use of HDPE conduit shall be permitted under the following conditions:

(5) Above ground, except as prohibited in 353.12, where encased in not less than 50 mm (2 in.) of concrete.

Summary of Change

New wording has been added to Section 353.10 to clarify that Type HDPE conduit is permitted for use aboveground, under certain conditions.

3

353.20(B)

Size
NEC, p. 203

Proposal 8-72
Log 2618
ROP, p. 364

Comment
None

353.20(B) Maximum Size

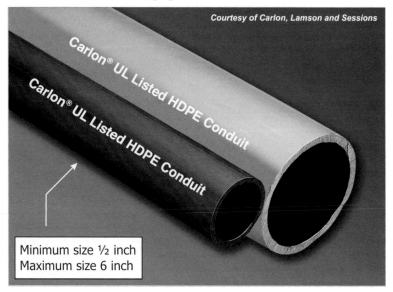

Courtesy of Carlon, Lamson and Sessions

Carlon® UL Listed HDPE Conduit

Carlon® UL Listed HDPE Conduit

Minimum size ½ inch
Maximum size 6 inch

High density polyethylene conduit larger than metric designator 155 (trade size 6) shall not be used.

Analysis and Effect

This revision clarifies that Type HDPE conduit is now listed by a third party nationally recognized electrical testing laboratory for use in the maximum metric designator 155 mm (6-in. trade size). Wiring methods 155 mm (6-in. trade size) are the largest permitted by *Code*.

Change at a Glance

Listed HDPE conduit is recognized by the *NEC* in sizes up to MD 155 (6-in. trade size).

This change brings the maximum permitted size of Type HDPE conduit into alignment with other wiring methods in the *NEC*.

Code Language
353.20
Size
(B) Maximum. HDPE conduit larger than metric designator 155 (trade size 6) shall not be used.

Summary of Change

A revision to 353.20(B) clarifies that Type HDPE conduit is now listed in a maximum metric designator 155 (6-in. trade size).

353.48 FPN

HDPE conduit can be joined using either heat fusion, electrofusion, or mechanical fittings.

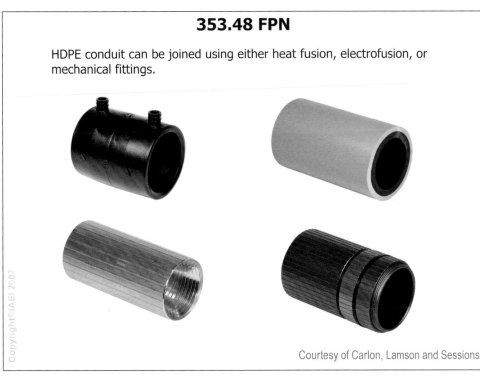

Courtesy of Carlon, Lamson and Sessions

353.48 FPN

Joints
NEC, p. 204

Proposal 8-74
Log 2619
ROP, p. 364

Comment
None

Analysis and Effect

This new fine print note clarifies that Type HDPE conduit may be joined together by using heat fusion, electrofusion, or mechanical fittings. This has been a common and safe practice for years by gas utility companies for joining two sections of yellow HDPE gas pipe. Electrical and telephone contractors use this established method to join two pieces of conduit. This type of joining creates a joint that is both air- and watertight. The joint is usually stronger than the conduit itself. It should be noted that Type HDPE conduit is intended primarily for use underground, and therefore is placed in rugged environments; yet standard PVC cement is not permitted to be used on type HDPE conduit, because of possible damage to the raceway by the solvents contained in the cement. Authorities have the responsibility for approving the type of conduit joint used based on the current language in this section. This fine print note provides users and enforcement with clear guidelines for acceptable methods of joining sections of high-density polyethylene conduit.

Change at a Glance

User guidelines for joining high-density polyethylene conduit are provided in a new fine print note. PVC solvents and cement are not suitable for this purpose.

Code Language
353.48
Joints

All joints between lengths of conduit, and between conduit and couplings, fittings, and boxes, shall be made by an approved method.

FPN: HDPE conduit can be joined using either heat fusion, electrofusion, or mechanical fittings.

Summary of Change

A revision to 353.48 added a new fine print note indicating several common methods to join Type HDPE conduit together.

Courtesy of Carlon, Lamson and Sessions

354.10(5) Uses Permitted

Listed nonmetallic underground conduit with conductors and fittings are permitted to be used aboveground where encased in concrete and not prohibited by 354.12.

Concrete-encasement not less than 50 mm (2 in.) ——

354.10(5)

Type NUCC Conduit
NEC, p. 204

Proposal 8-75
Log 2620
ROP, p. 364

Comment
None

Change at a Glance

Nonmetallic underground conduit with conductors (NUCC) is permitted for aboveground use where listed for this use, encased in concrete, and not prohibited by 354.12.

Analysis and Effect

This revision clarifies that Type NUCC conduit is now permitted for use aboveground under certain conditions: if encased in not less than 50 mm (2 in.) of concrete, per the product listing, and except as prohibited by 354.12. Type NUCC conduit is listed for use aboveground with concrete encasement by qualified electrical testing laboratories. Substantiation with the proposal indicated that it has been an accepted use of the product to be installed concrete-encased in barrier walls. The phrase "except as prohibited in 354.12" was added by CMP-8 to clarify that NUCC conduit is not permitted in buildings, with the exception that the conductor or cable portion of the assembly is permitted to extend within the building for termination purposes where suitable and in accordance with Section 300.3.

Code Language
Part II
Installation

354.10
Uses Permitted
The use of NUCC and fittings shall be permitted in the following:

(5) Aboveground, except as prohibited in 354.12, where encased in not less than 50 mm (2 in.) of concrete.

Summary of Change

A new list item (5) has been added to Section 354.10 to clarify that Type NUCC conduit is permitted for use aboveground under certain conditions.

Article 355 Reinforced Thermosetting Resin Conduit

Part I General
Part II Installation
Part III Construction Specifications

Photo courtesy of FRE Composites

A new Article 355 Reinforced Thermosetting Resin Conduit: Type RTRC has been added to Chapter 3. The article includes three parts.

Article 355

Type RTRC Conduit
NEC, Various pages

Proposal 8-78
Log 1920
ROP, p. 365

Comment 8-49b
Log CC800
ROC, p. 219

Analysis and Effect

In *NEC*-2002, Article 352, Rigid Nonmetallic Conduit (RNC), included PVC, RTRC, and HDPE products. However, for *NEC*-2005, High Density Polyethylene Conduit: Type HDPE was separated from these other conduit types and located in new Article 353. This action left two very dissimilar products grouped together as rigid nonmetallic conduit under Article 352 and technically eliminated HDPE as an acceptable wiring method in all applications where rigid nonmetallic conduit was specified. The separation of the PVC and RTRC conduit, and the change in title to Article 352 and new definition of rigid polyvinyl chloride conduit in Article 352 are specific to PVC conduit and fittings. Types HDPE and RTRC are covered under separate articles, correcting this situation by better defining the installation and construction specifications for each nonmetallic conduit type. The new Article 355 includes three parts as follows: Part I General, Part II Installation, Part III Construction Specifications.

> ### Change at a Glance
>
> New Article 355 provides rules pertaining to reinforced thermosetting resin conduit: Type RTRC.

Code Language

See actual *Code* text for the complete article. Article 355 is arranged as follows:

Summary of Change

A new article covering requirements for Reinforced Thermosetting Resin Conduit: Type RTRC has been included in the *Code* as Article 355.

356.10(7)

Type LFNC Conduit
NEC, p. 209

Proposal 8-82
Log 2622
ROP, p. 368

Comment
None

Change at a Glance

Liquidtight flexible nonmetallic conduit Type LFNC is permitted to be encased in concrete under certain conditions.

356.10(7) Uses Permitted

Copyright©IAEI 2007

LFNC is permitted to be used where encased in concrete provided it is listed for direct burial use and meets the requirements in 356.42.

Straight fittings are permitted to be used in direct-burial or concrete-encased applications of LFNC (356.42).

Analysis and Effect

This revision clarifies that liquidtight flexible nonmetallic conduit Type LFNC is permitted to be encased in concrete where it is listed for direct burial, and installed in compliance with 356.42. Section 356.42 requires that straight LFNC fittings be used when LFNC is installed encased in concrete or direct buried in soil. Fittings for use with liquidtight flexible nonmetallic conduit are covered under UL Product Category (DWTT) Conduit Fittings, and are suitable for only the type of conduit indicated by the marking on the fitting. The Product Standard for LFNC is ANSI/UL 1660. The minimum radius of bends is covered in the manufacturer's technical information for each size of raceway manufactured. The manufacturer's product information must be consulted before use, as some sizes of LFNC may have limitations to their use underground or encased in concrete.

Code Language
Part II
Installation

356.10
Uses Permitted
LFNC shall be permitted to be used in exposed or concealed locations for the following purposes:

(7) For encasement in concrete where listed for direct burial and installed in compliance with 356.42.

Summary of Change

A new list item (7) has been added to Section 356.10 covering permitted uses.

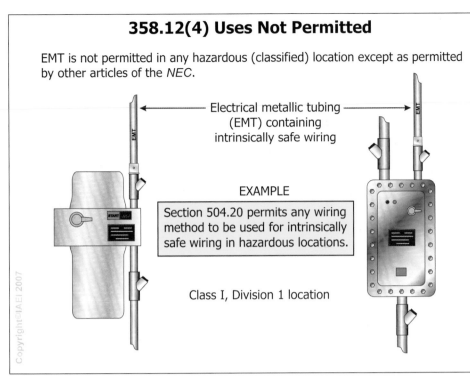

358.12(4) Uses Not Permitted

EMT is not permitted in any hazardous (classified) location except as permitted by other articles of the *NEC*.

Electrical metallic tubing (EMT) containing intrinsically safe wiring

EXAMPLE

Section 504.20 permits any wiring method to be used for intrinsically safe wiring in hazardous locations.

Class I, Division 1 location

Copyright©IAEI 2007

Uses Not Permitted
NEC, p. 210

Proposal 8-101
Log 642
ROP, p. 371

Comment
None

Analysis and Effect

Previous *Code* references specific to a limited few classified (hazardous) location *Code* sections that permitted very limited use of EMT in those locations have been removed because they were considered by some as too restrictive to the use of EMT. There are installations such as wiring intrinsically safe apparatus, nonincendive field wiring, and other classified (hazardous) locations where the use of EMT is permitted. The substantiation included with the proposal stated that the current *Code* text limits the use of EMT to only three classified (hazardous) locations, and that the change will actually loosen the restrictions of use of the product in those locations. The change will now allow the use of EMT in classified (hazardous) locations if permitted in the hazardous location *Code* article that addresses that specific type of installation. This change correlates with similar revisions in other articles of the *Code*, such as PVC conduit, HDPE conduit, NUCC conduit, HDPE conduit, LFNC conduit, and nonmetallic wireways, Articles 352, 353, 354, 355, 356, and 378 respectively. See CMP-8 actions on Proposals #8-53, 8-59, 8-76, 8-78, and 8-84.

Change at a Glance

Electrical Metal Tubing (EMT) is not permitted in hazardous (classified) locations unless specifically permitted within other articles of the *Code*.

Code Language
358.12

Uses Not Permitted

EMT shall not be used under the following conditions:

(4) In any hazardous (classified) location except as permitted by other articles in this *Code*.

Summary of Change

List item (4) in 358.12 has been revised and clarified to correlate with other *Code* articles that permit EMT in hazardous (classified) locations.

3

360.20(A) Exception No. 2

Size of FMT
NEC, p. 212

Proposal 8-107
Log 505
ROP, p. 372

Comment
None

Change at a Glance

The 1.8 m (6 ft) luminaire whip assemblies in sizes MD 12 (trade size ³/₈) covered by Exception No. 2 are required to be listed.

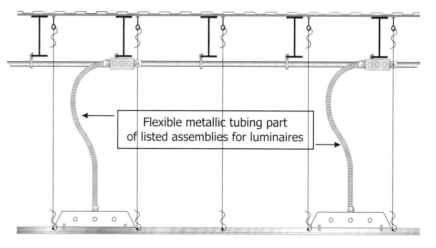

360.20(A) Exception No. 2

The word *listed* replaces the word *approved* in the exception.

Flexible metallic tubing part of listed assemblies for luminaires

FMT in metric designator 12 (trade size 3/8) is permitted to be used where part of a listed assembly for luminaires.

Analysis and Effect

Exception No. 2 has been revised by changing the word *approved* to *listed*. The purpose of the change is to promote consistency in the *Code* with the use of the terms *approved*, *listed* and *identified*. In accordance with Sections 110.2 and 90.4, the general requirements for approvals of conductors and equipment fall under the responsibilities of the authority having jurisdiction. Under this authority, inspectors can approve a ceiling fixture and whip assembly whether it is listed or not. Inspectors typically rely on listing as a basis for approvals of wiring methods, devices, and equipment. Manufacturers produce luminaire whips as listed assemblies. These listed assemblies are commonly used in electrical installations, as required by inspection authorities. It should be noted that the use of Type FMT tubing in sizes metric designator 12 (trade size ³/₈) is limited to 1.8 m (6 ft) length because of concerns with physical damage. This wiring method is very flexible and rarely affected by vibration or other movement, and therefore is often used as a wiring method in ducts, plenums, and other air-handling spaces per 300.22(B). It is important to use listed fittings for termination with this wiring method, because the fittings are required to close effectively any openings in the connections to boxes, luminaires and the like. The revision in Exception No. 2 requiring listing provides installers and manufacturers with greater degrees of assurance that installations incorporating these listed assemblies will attain desired approval.

Code Language

360.20
Size

360.20(A)
Minimum
FMT smaller than metric designator 16 (trade size ½) shall not be used.

Exception No. 1: FMT of metric designator 12 (trade size ³/₈) shall be permitted to be installed in accordance with 300.22(B) and (C).

Exception No. 2: FMT of metric designator 12 (trade size ³/₈) shall be permitted in lengths not in excess of 1.8 m (6 ft) as a part of a listed assembly or for luminaires. See 410.117(C).

Summary of Change

The word *approved* has been replaced by the word *listed* in Exception No. 2.

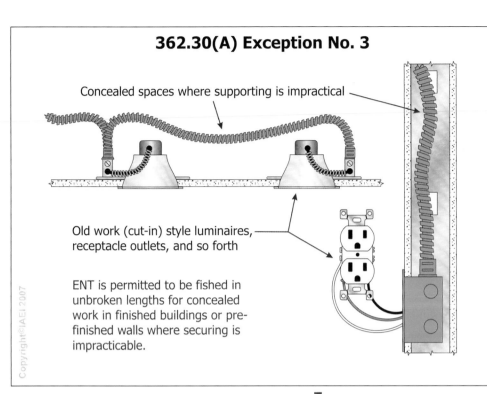

362.30(A) Exception No. 3

Concealed spaces where supporting is impractical

Old work (cut-in) style luminaires, receptacle outlets, and so forth

ENT is permitted to be fished in unbroken lengths for concealed work in finished buildings or pre-finished walls where securing is impracticable.

Copyright©IAEI 2007

Securing & Supporting ENT
NEC, p. 214

Proposal 8-119, 8-117, 8-118
Log 2623, 837, 1156
ROP, p. 375

Comment
None

Analysis and Effect

A new Exception No. 3 has been added to Section 362.30(A) to permit ENT to be installed in concealed locations without requirements for the tubing being secured and supported. The exception relaxes requirements for securing and supporting of ENT when fished into walls, for example, of existing buildings or prefinished wall panels. Substantiation provided in the proposal stated that fishing ENT into walls of existing buildings is a common practice. The flexibility of ENT makes it easy to be fished and a viable alternative for concealed wiring installations that are fished. It should be noted that the change is consistent with Section 300.4(D) Exception No. 2, which permits cables and raceways to be fished in concealed work of finished buildings, and in prefabricated buildings where support is impracticable. It should also be noted that proper care must be taken when installing ENT to protect it from physical damage.

Change at a Glance

Electrical nonmetallic tubing is permitted to be fished in unbroken lengths and unsecured where securing is impractical.

Code Language
362.30
Securing and Supporting
ENT shall be installed as a complete system in accordance with 300.18 and shall be securely fastened in place and supported in accordance with 362.30(A) and (B).

(A) Securely Fastened. ENT shall be securely fastened... (remainder unchanged).

Exception No. 1 (Unchanged)

Exception No. 2 (Unchanged)

Exception No. 3: For concealed work in finished buildings or prefinished wall panels where such securing is impracticable, unbroken lengths (without coupling) of ENT shall be permitted to be fished.

Summary of Change
A new exception has been added to Section 362.30(A).

366.2

Metallic and Nonmetallic Auxiliary Gutters
NEC, p. 215

Proposal 8-124, 8-125
Log 3403, 3611
ROP, p. 376

Comment
None

Change at a Glance

The definitions of *metallic* and *nonmetallic auxiliary gutters* have been revised to clarify their difference from wireways.

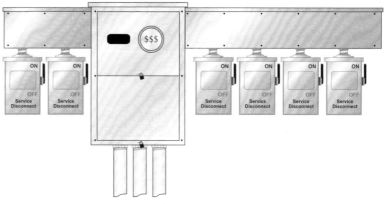

366.2 Definitions

Service equipment with auxiliary gutters

The definitions of *nonmetallic auxiliary gutter* and *metallic auxiliary gutter* have been revised.

The word *wireway* has been removed to help differentiate between wireways and auxiliary gutters.

Copyright©IAEi 2007

Analysis and Effect

The revisions of these definitions were made to remove the term *wireway*, and to differentiate between wireways and auxiliary gutters. There are differences in the requirements for auxiliary gutters and wireways. For example, wireways do not enclose busbars and have unlimited length. Auxiliary gutters do enclose busbars, and are limited to 30 feet maximum length, unless used in an elevator installation. Auxiliary gutters may include busbars or conductors; and they are often used to augment the wiring spaces of switchboards, distribution equipment, and so forth. This change provides clarity and improves usability of the *Code*, but does not change technical requirements as to the application of the article. This change will assist installers and inspectors in applying the appropriate *Code* rules to auxiliary gutters and wireways, and will clarify the differences in their application and use.

Code Language
366.2

Metallic Auxiliary Gutter
A sheet metal enclosure used to supplement wiring spaces at meter centers, distribution centers, switchboards, and similar points of wiring systems. The enclosure has hinged or removable covers for housing and protecting electric wires, cables, and busbars. The enclosure is designed for conductors to be laid or set in place after the enclosures have been installed as a complete system.

Nonmetallic Auxiliary Gutter. A flame retardant, non-metallic enclosure used to supplement wiring spaces at meter centers, distribution centers, switchboards, and similar points of wiring systems. The enclosure has hinged or removable covers for housing and protecting electric wires, cables, and busbars. The enclosure is designed for conductors to be laid or set in place after the enclosures have been installed as a complete system.

Summary of Change
The word "wireway" has been removed from the existing definitions.

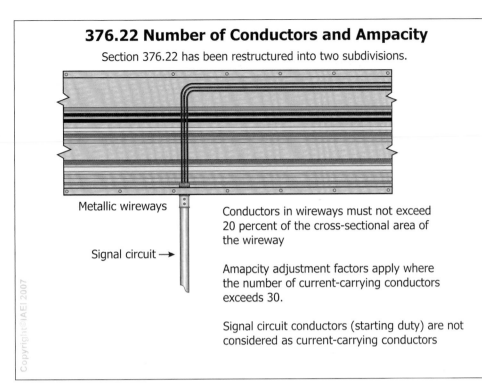

376.22 Number of Conductors and Ampacity

Section 376.22 has been restructured into two subdivisions.

Metallic wireways

Signal circuit →

Conductors in wireways must not exceed 20 percent of the cross-sectional area of the wireway

Amapcity adjustment factors apply where the number of current-carrying conductors exceeds 30.

Signal circuit conductors (starting duty) are not considered as current-carrying conductors

Copyright©IAEI 2007

Number of Conductors and Ampacity
NEC, p. 223

Proposal 8-157
Log 2754
ROP, p. 381

Comment 8-73
Log 969
ROC, p. 223

Analysis and Effect

Action by CMP-8 on Proposal 8-157 results in the restructuring of this section into two separate subdivisions, to provide a more logical layout of two separate requirements formerly contained in a single paragraph. Section 376.22 in the 2005 *NEC* provided two separate requirements dealing with number of conductors. As reworked, the two subdivisions provide two different requirements, each under its own separate subdivision. This revision does not change any of the current requirements, but serves to clarify and improve usability.

Change at a Glance

Conductors in wireways must not exceed 20 percent of the cross-sectional area, and ampacity adjustment factors apply where the number of current-carrying conductors exceeds 30.

Summary of Change

This section has been restructured into two subdivisions. The title has been revised by adding the words "and ampacity." Subdivision (A) provides the maximum percentage of fill, and subdivision (B) provides requirements for ampacity adjustment factors where the number of current-carrying conductors at a wireway crosssection exceeds 30.

Code Language
376.22

Number of Conductors and Ampacity

The number of conductors and their ampacity shall comply with 376.22(A) and (B).

(A) Cross-Sectional Areas of Wireway. The sum of the cross-sectional areas of all contained conductors at any cross section of a wireway shall not exceed 20 percent of the interior cross-sectional area of the wireway.

(B) Adjustment Factors. The adjustment factors in 310.15(B)(2)(a) shall be applied only where the number of current-carrying conductors, including neutral conductors classified as current-carrying under the provisions of 310.15(B)(4), exceeds 30. Conductors for signaling circuits or controller conductors between a motor and its starter and used only for starting duty shall not be considered as current-carrying conductors.

3

376.56 (B)(4)

Splices, Taps, and Power Distribution Blocks
NEC, p. 223

Proposal 8-155
Log 3405
ROP, p. 381

Comment
None

REVISION

POWER
DIST.
BLOCK

L1

L2

L3

Analysis and Effect

This revision clarifies that all uninsulated live parts of listed power distribution blocks installed in wireways are required to be covered to prevent contact from persons or other conductors, regardless of whether or not the wireway cover is installed. The requirement makes it clear that these uninsulated live parts are to be covered with the proper power distribution block cover that is listed for such use, and that the wireway cover by itself does not provide the protection meeting *Code* requirements. It should be noted that energized insulated conductors are live parts, yet they are insulated from contact. Safe working practices must always be employed when working on or around energized electrical circuits or systems. NFPA 70E provides the important information regarding requirements for electrical workplace safety and safe work practices.

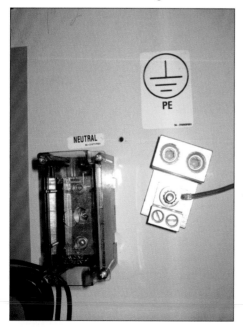

Change at a Glance

Power distribution blocks installed in a wireway shall not have uninsulated live parts exposed, whether or not the wireway cover is installed.

Code Language
376.56

Splices, Taps, and Power Distribution Blocks

(B) Power Distribution Blocks

(4) Live Parts. Power distribution blocks shall not have uninsulated live parts exposed within a wireway, whether or not the wireway cover is installed.

Summary of Change

The words "whether or not the wireway cover is installed" have been added to list item (4).

Construction
NEC, p. 224

Proposal 8-157a, 8-151
Log CP802, 673
ROP, p. 381, 380

Comment
None

Analysis and Effect

Because of this change, there are now construction requirements for metal wireways in the *Code*. Metal wireways, auxiliary gutters, and their associated fittings are manufactured to ANSI/UL Product Standard 870. Many products are already listed to applicable product standards, which promotes many of the construction requirements addressed in this new section. Since wireways have not been required to be listed, it is logical to include construction specifications for these products. This revision provides users with information for wireways that are not listed and evaluated to meet the requirements of applicable product standards. The addition of 376.100 provides *Code* enforcement with criteria by which to issue approvals for wireways that are not certified to applicable product safety standards.

Change at a Glance

Wireway construction specifications addressing continuity, construction, smooth edges, and covers have been added to Article 376.

Code Language
376.100
Construction

(A) Electrical and Mechanical Continuity. Wireways shall be constructed and installed so that adequate electrical and mechanical continuity of the complete system is secured.

(B) Substantial Construction. Wireways shall be of substantial construction and shall provide a complete enclosure for the contained conductors. All surfaces, both interior and exterior, shall be suitably protected from corrosion. Corner joints shall be made tight, and where the assembly is held together with rivets, bolts, or screws, such fasteners shall be spaced not more than 300 mm (12 in.) apart.

(C) Smooth Rounded Edges. Suitable bushings, shields, or fittings having smooth, rounded edges shall be provided where conductors pass between wireways, through partitions, around bends, between wireways and cabinets or junction boxes, and at all other locations where necessary to prevent abrasion of the insulation of the conductors.

(D) Covers. Covers shall be securely fastened to the wireway.

Summary of Change

A new section 376.100 covering construction specifications has been incorporated into Article 376.

378.12(2)

Nonmetallic Wireways in Hazardous Locations
NEC, p. 224

Proposal 8-160
Log 1966
ROP, p. 382

Comment
None

Change at a Glance

Nonmetallic wireways are generally not permitted in hazardous (classified) locations unless specifically recognized for this use by other *Code* articles.

378.12(2) Uses Not Permitted

Nonmetallic wireways are generally not permitted in any hazardous (classified) location except as permitted by other *NEC* articles.

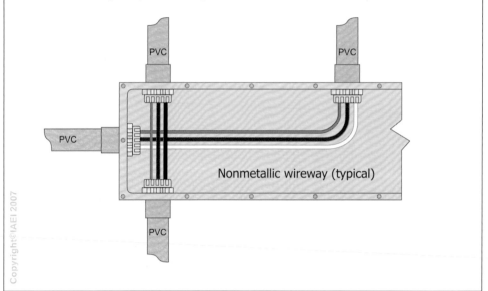

Nonmetallic wireway (typical)

Copyright©IAEI 2007

Analysis and Effect

This change will now allow the use of nonmetallic wireways in classified (hazardous) locations if permitted in a classified (hazardous) locations *Code* article. The change eliminates the former wording found in the article, which restricted the use of nonmetallic wireways in a classified (hazardous) location to intrinsically safe locations only. Nonmetallic wireways are installed in many classified (hazardous) locations where corrosive conditions exist which would have deteriorating effects on metallic wireways, and where possible combustion of explosive mixtures may be lessened to a point where the use of nonmetallic wireways would not compromise safety. The effect of the change will actually allow more use of this wiring method in classified (hazardous) locations if allowed elsewhere in the *Code* for that location. The change to this article is part of a sweeping change that has affected several articles of the *Code,* such as Type PVC, HDPE, NUCC, HDPE and LFNC conduits. The change correlates with Proposals 8-53, 8-59, 8-76, and 8-78.

Code Language
378.12
Uses Not Permitted.

(2) In any hazardous (classified) location, except as permitted by other articles in this *Code*.

Summary of Change

Section 378.12(2) was revised to clarify that nonmetallic wireways are not permitted in hazardous (classified) locations unless specifically permitted within other articles of the *Code*.

Analysis of Changes *NEC*-2008

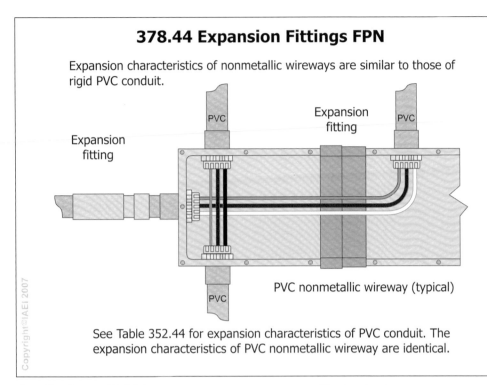

378.44 Expansion Fittings FPN

Expansion characteristics of nonmetallic wireways are similar to those of rigid PVC conduit.

Expansion fitting

Expansion fitting

PVC

PVC

PVC

PVC nonmetallic wireway (typical)

Copyright©IAEI 2007

See Table 352.44 for expansion characteristics of PVC conduit. The expansion characteristics of PVC nonmetallic wireway are identical.

Expansion Fittings
NEC, p. 225

Proposal 8-161
Log 1924
ROP, p. 382

Comment
None

Analysis and Effect

Article 378 provides the rules for nonmetallic wireways. The revision to 378.44, FPN occurred because of changes to nonmetallic raceways elsewhere in the *Code*. Article 352 in *NEC*-2005 was titled Rigid Nonmetallic Conduit: Type RNC, and included Types PVC, HDPE, and RTRC conduits. Article 352 has been revised for *NEC*-2008 to include only requirements applicable to rigid polyvinyl chloride conduit: Type PVC. Section 378.44 FPN has therefore been revised to clarify that nonmetallic wireways respond to expansion in the

> **Change at a Glance**
>
> Expansion characteristics for nonmetallic wireways are similar to those of rigid PVC conduit: Type PVC covered in Article 352.

same manner as Type PVC conduit, not Types HDPE or RTRC, and the correct table to reference for expansion of nonmetallic wireways is Table 352.44. Nonmetallic wireways and fittings are investigated per ANSI/UL Standards 870 and UL 5A as to their suitability to sunlight exposure and other weather and temperature related conditions. It is important that installers and inspectors consider the probable ambient temperature conditions where nonmetallic wireways are installed, and account, where necessary, for expansion characteristics inherent in these products.

Code Language
378.44
Expansion Fittings

Expansion fittings for nonmetallic wireway shall be provided to compensate for thermal expansion and contraction where the length change is expected to be 6 mm (0.25 in.) or greater in a straight run.

FPN: See Table 352.44 for expansion characteristics of PVC conduit. The expansion characteristics of PVC nonmetallic wireway are identical.

Summary of Change

A revision to existing Section 378.44, fine print note, clarifies that the same expansion characteristics inherent in PVC conduit are found in nonmetallic wireways.

Article 382

Nonmetallic Extensions
NEC, Various pages

Proposal 7-98
Log 3450
ROP, p. 383

Comment 7-56
Log 2231
ROP, p. 224

Change at a Glance

Nonmetallic extensions are permitted to be concealed under certain conditions.

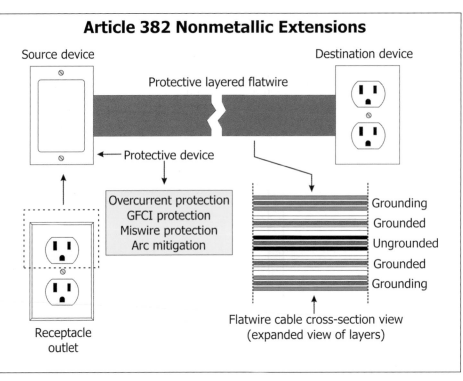

Article 382 Nonmetallic Extensions

Source device — Protective layered flatwire — Destination device

Protective device →

Overcurrent protection
GFCI protection
Miswire protection
Arc mitigation

Receptacle outlet

Grounding
Grounded
Ungrounded
Grounded
Grounding

Flatwire cable cross-section view
(expanded view of layers)

Copyright©IAEI 2007

Analysis and Effect

Nonmetallic extensions addressed in Article 382 traditionally have been the exposed types and the rules contained in the article addressed those methods accordingly. Article 382 has been revised and expanded to provide requirements for a new type of *concealable nonmetallic extension* wiring method suitable for use on existing walls and ceilings of offices and residential occupancies. New technologies, consumer electronics devices such as flat panel televisions and custom audio systems, along with ever-changing lifestyles have increased the need for additional power outlets and the desire to place power or lighting outlets where needed to obtain an functionality as well as an aesthetically pleasing environment. Often these changes are poorly accommodated by using extension cords that are easily damaged, misused and can lead to electrical hazards. This new type of concealable nonmetallic extension incorporated into Article 382 provides a safe and reliable alternative for existing occupancies that can reduce the misuse of extension cords, overload power taps, and so forth. Concealable nonmetallic extensions are inherently safe because of their design and construction features, which are detailed in the new Part III of the article. Because the concealable wire nonmetallic extension is inherently safe, requirements for mechanical protection are not necessary to insure the practical safeguarding of persons and property in the event of physical damage to the cable. Section 382.6 requires a multiple protection features as follows:

The starting/source tap device for the extension shall contain and provide the following protection for all load-side extensions and devices:

(1) Supplementary overcurrent protection
(2) Level of protection equivalent to a Class A GFCI
(3) Level of protection equivalent to a portable GFCI
(4) Line and load-side miswire protection
(5) Effects of arc faults

The conductors of the concealable wire nonmetallic extension are flat and layered in a manner that insures practical safeguarding of persons or property. The flat wire cable is a multi-layer flat conductor design consisting of a center ungrounded conductor enclosed by a sectioned grounded conductor, and an overall equipment grounding conductor. The cable itself is a symmetrical design providing two levels of protection on both sides of the flat wire cable via the outer equipment grounding conductor layers and inner-grounded (neutral) conductor layers. This design insures that if the cable is damaged, punctured or penetrated, it will trip the overcurrent protection device (OCPD) and safely open the circuit. If the OCPD is reset, the circuit will trip and continue to do so upon subsequent resets. Evaluation and fact-finding studies by Underwriters Laboratories have been performed to ensure product safety.

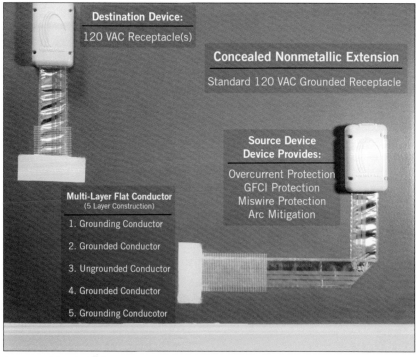

Courtesy of Southwire Company, Inc.

Summary of Change

Article 382 has been revised to incorporate provisions for concealed nonmetallic extensions. A new definition of this type of *concealable nonmetallic extension* has been added in 382.2. The article has been expanded to include specific product listing requirements in 382.6. Section 382.10 and 382.12 covering Uses Permitted and Uses Not Permitted have been revised and expanded to incorporate requirements and restrictions for concealable nonmetallic extensions. A new Part III has been added to provide specific construction specifications for concealable nonmetallic extensions.

392.8(A)

Cable Installation
NEC, p. 234

Proposal 8-192a
Log P800
ROP, p. 391

Comment P8-86
Log 2158
ROC, p. 239

Analysis and Effect

This revision provides users with guidance regarding splices in cable trays. Action by CMP-8 on Proposal 8-192a and Comment 8-86 result in text that recognizes splices in cable tray installations and provides restrictions where the splice is subject to physical damage. Cable splices of conductors in cable trays are now permitted to project above the side rails only where they are not subject to physical damage. When the splice is subject to physical damage, the splice cannot project above the side of the cable tray.

Change at a Glance

Cable splices of conductors in cable trays are now permitted to project above the side rails where not subject to physical damage.

Code Language
392.8

Cable Installation
(A) Cable Splices. Cable splices made and insulated by approved methods shall be permitted to be located within a cable tray, provided they are accessible. Splices shall be permitted to project above the side rails where not subject to physical damage.

Summary of Change

Revised wording to permit splices above side rails in cable trays.

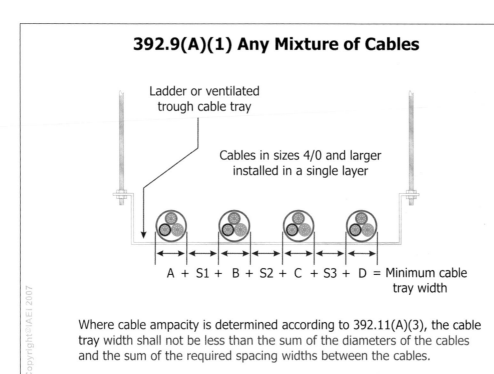

392.9(A)(1) Any Mixture of Cables

Ladder or ventilated trough cable tray

Cables in sizes 4/0 and larger installed in a single layer

A + S1 + B + S2 + C + S3 + D = Minimum cable tray width

Where cable ampacity is determined according to 392.11(A)(3), the cable tray width shall not be less than the sum of the diameters of the cables and the sum of the required spacing widths between the cables.

392.9 (A)(1)

Cable Tray Installations
NEC, p. 235

Proposal 8-194
Log 3129
ROP, p. 391

Comment
None

REVISION!

Analysis and Effect

Section 392.11(A) addresses cable ampacity and spacing between multiconductor cables installed in single layers in an uncovered cable tray. Information submitted with the proposal indicated that there is a problem at times in the field with cables being added to cable trays during remodeling, or when re-working or adding conductors or cables to the tray. Installers need to be aware of cable-tray-width requirements, as well as the conductor ampacity and *Code*-required spacing between cables and single conductors. Concerns were raised that the cable tray needs to be the proper width for all conductors or cables installed, and that proper spacing between conductors must be maintained. With this new language, it now should be clear to installers that cable trays must be wide enough for the installed conductors and cables to meet *Code* ampacity and spacing requirements. Users will benefit by the improved clarity in this section, and the *Code* enforcement community will now have improved wording to apply these requirements to cable tray installations.

Change at a Glance

Cable trays must be wide enough for the installed conductors and cables to meet *Code* ampacity and spacing requirements.

Code Language
392.9(A)(1)

Where all of the cables are 4/0 AWG or larger, the sum of the diameters of all cables shall not exceed the cable tray width, and the cables shall be installed in a single layer. Where the cable ampacity is determined according to 392.11(A)(3), the cable tray width shall not be less than the sum of the diameters of the cables and the sum of the required spacing widths between the cables.

Summary of Change

A new second sentence has been added to 392.9(A)(1).

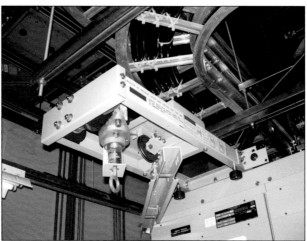

396.30

Messenger
NEC, p. 240

Proposal 7-106
Log 3361
ROP, p. 393

Comment 7-76
Log 1517
ROC, p. 243

Change at a Glance

Where messengers are used as neutral conductors or equipment grounding conductors, they must comply with other applicable rules in Articles 225 and 250 as noted in subdivisions (B) and (C).

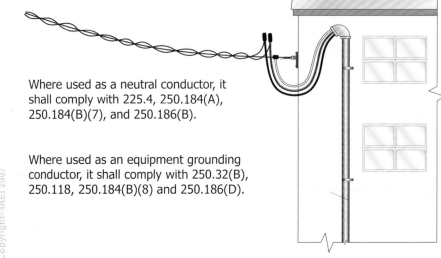

396.30 Messenger

This section has been arranged into three subdivisions providing rules for messengers used as support, neutral conductors, or equipment grounding conductors.

Where used as a neutral conductor, it shall comply with 225.4, 250.184(A), 250.184(B)(7), and 250.186(B).

Where used as an equipment grounding conductor, it shall comply with 250.32(B), 250.118, 250.184(B)(8) and 250.186(D).

Copyright IAEI 2007

Analysis and Effect

This change is consistent with changes in past cycles of the *Code*, which have been modified to restrict the use of grounded circuit or feeder conductors that supply power to separate buildings or structures and are used as a fault-current return path. In recent *Code* cycles, there has been a progressive move away from the use of the grounded neutral feeder or circuit conductor for grounding of separate structures and to require that a separate equipment grounding conductor be included with the feeder or circuit wiring method. The revisions to this section provide a more logical layout of the provisions for messengers and include appropriate references where the messenger is used as either a neutral conductor or equipment grounding conductor. These revisions recognize that messenger wires are commonly used as equipment grounding conductors and under some other provisions of the *Code* are used as neutral conductors. Action by CMP-7 on Comment 7-106 results in 396.60 remaining as it read in *NEC*-2005, and incorporates the concepts introduced by Proposal 7-106 that recognize the messenger does serve as a current-carrying conductor under some restrictive conditions addressed in the *NEC*.

Code Language
396.30
Messenger
(A) Support. The messenger shall be supported at dead ends and at intermediate locations so as to eliminate tension on the conductors. The conductors shall not be permitted to come into contact with the messenger supports or any structural members, walls, or pipes.
(B) Neutral Conductor. Where the messenger is used as a neutral conductor, it shall comply with the requirements of 225.4, 250.184(A), 250.184(B)(7), and 250.186(B).
(C) Equipment Grounding Conductor. Where the messenger is used as an equipment grounding conductor, it shall comply with the requirements of 250.32(B), 250.118, 250.184(B)(8), and 250.186(D).

Summary of Change

Section 396.30 has been revised to include three subdivisions, and new wording has been added to 396.30(B) and (C) regarding the use of the messenger cable as a neutral conductor and as an equipment grounding conductor.

Analysis of Changes *NEC*-2008

Chapter

4

Selected Changes

Article 400

Chapters 4, 5, and 6

Adding Locks to Disconnecting Means
NEC, Various

Proposal Multiple
Log Multiple
ROP, Various

Comment Multiple
Log Multiple
ROC, Various

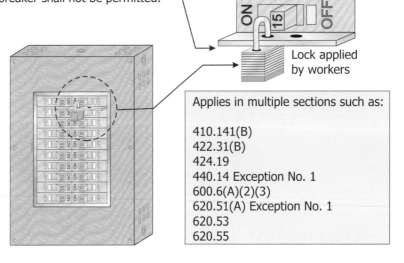

Disconnects Capable of Being Locked Open

The provisions for locking or adding a lock to the disconnecting means shall remain in place at the switch or circuit breaker whether the lock is installed or not. Portable means for adding a lock to the switch or circuit breaker shall not be permitted.

ON 15 OFF

Lock applied by workers

Copyright © IAEI 2007

Applies in multiple sections such as:

410.141(B)
422.31(B)
424.19
440.14 Exception No. 1
600.6(A)(2)(3)
620.51(A) Exception No. 1
620.53
620.55

Analysis and Effect

The phrase "capable of being locked in the open position" appears in at least 27 locations throughout chapters 4, 5, and 6 of the *NEC*. In each case, the fundamental purpose of this locking characteristic is driven by the concern for worker safety. Substantiation provided with these proposals identified a need to use common language where this phrase is used to promote uniformity and consistency in its application. Where the disconnects are not provided within sight from the equipment it supplies, the switch or circuit breaker must include provisions for adding a lock, and these provisions must remain with the equipment. These locking provisions have to be part of the equipment, either inherent to the equipment design or as an accessory feature that can be installed on the equipment. The *Code* does not recognize portable locking devices that must be carried to and then attached to the equipment so a portable lock could be installed. The *NEC* covers installations and does not cover such portable locking provisions that could satisfy requirements in NFPA 70E, more specifically, the provisions in Article 120. This is one of the primary reasons for the changes to these *NEC* sections referencing disconnecting means that are capable of being locked in the off position. Generally, the *NEC* requires equipment disconnects to be in sight from the supplied equipment; only by specific allowances are these disconnects permitted to be remote and out of sight from the equipment. The changes to these sections provide installers and inspectors with clear requirements for locking provisions where equipment disconnecting means (switches or circuit breakers) are located out of sight from the equipment supplied by addressing installed equipment which is covered by the *NEC*, whereas portable locking means that have to be carried by workers and applied in the field are not covered.

Change at a Glance

Where a disconnecting means is not located within sight from the equipment it serves, it is required to be capable of being locked in the open (off) position and the means for adding the lock must remain with the equipment whether the lock is installed or not.

Code Language

[See specific *NEC* section] The following Code sections are examples of where this revision occurred (non-inclusive).

410.141(B)
422.31(B)
424.19
440.14 Exception No. 1
600.6(A)(2)(3)
620.51(A) Exception No. 1
620.53
620.55

Summary of Change

The text in various sections has been either revised or new text has been added as follows: The provision for locking or adding a lock to the disconnecting means shall be installed on or at the switch or circuit breaker used as the disconnecting means and shall remain in place with or without the lock installed. (See *NEC*-2008 for actual text in each section affected by these revisions.)

Table 400.4, Table 400.4 Superscript Note 8

Flexible Cords and Cables
NEC, p. 243–249

Proposal 6-4, 6-75
Log 1535, 816
ROP, p. 279, 394

Comment
None

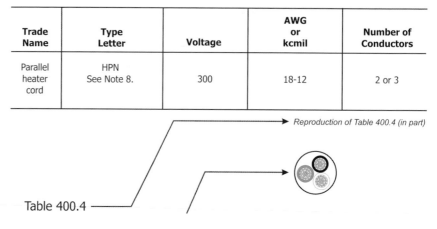

Table 400.4 Superscript Note 8 (in part)

Trade Name	Type Letter	Voltage	AWG or kcmil	Number of Conductors
Parallel heater cord	HPN See Note 8.	300	18-12	2 or 3

Reproduction of Table 400.4 (in part)

Table 400.4

Superscript Note 8. The third conductor in Type HPN shall be used as an equipment grounding conductor only.

Analysis and Effect

New wording has been added to superscript note 8 to Table 400.4 to clarify that the third conductor in Type HPN heater cord is to be used for equipment grounding purposes only. Information in the proposal indicated that the ANSI/UL product standard for flexible cords used for vacuum cleaners, also covered by superscript note 8, permits a 3-wire non-grounding version of these cords. Table 400.4 must be consulted for more information on the usage: whether portable, appliance, and so forth; type and mil thickness of insulation; size of the conductors; and types of locations, whether dry, damp, and so forth that the cords are listed for use in. UL product category code ZJCZ covers these types of stranded copper cords, which have a maximum 300-volt rating.

Change at a Glance

The first sentence of superscript note 8 to Table 400.4 applies only to Type HPN cords.

Code Language
Table 400.4
Superscript Note 8.
The third conductor in Type HPN shall be used as an equipment grounding conductor only.

Summary of Change

New wording has been added to Table 400.4 and to note 8 of the table to clarify that the third conductor in Type HPN heater cord is to be used for equipment grounding purposes only.

Table 400.5(A) (in part)

Table 400.5(A) Allowable Ampacity for Flexible Cords and Cables [Based on Ambient Temperature of 30°C (86°F). See 400.13 and Table 400.4.]

Size (AWG)	Thermoplastic Types TPT, TST	Thermoset Types C, E, EO, PD, S, SJ, SJO, SJOW, SJOO, SJOOW, SO, SOW, SOO, SOOW, SP-1, SP-2, SP-3, SRD, SV, SVO, SVOO / Thermoset Types ET, ETLB, ETP, ETT, SE, SEW, SEO, SEOW, SEOOW, SJE, SJEW, SJEO, SJEOW, SJEOOW, SJT, SJTW, SJTO, SJTOW, SJTOO, SJTOOW, SPE-1, SPE-2, SPE-3, SPT-1, SPT-1W, SPT-2, SPT-2W, SPT-3, ST, SRDE, SVEO, SVT, SVTO, SVTOO		Types HDP, HPN, HSJ, HSJO, HSJOO
		Column A*	Column B*	
27*	0.5	—	—	—
20	—	5**	***	—
18	—	7	10	10
17	—	9	12	13
16	—	10	13	15
15	—	12	16	17
14	—	15	18	20
12	—	20	25	30
10	—	25	30	35
8	—	35	40	—
6	—	45	55	—
4	—	60	70	—
2	—	80	95	—

No changes to table notes

Reproduction of NEC Table 400.5(A) less notes

Table 400.5(A)

Allowable Ampacity for Flexible Cords and Cables
NEC, p. 251

Proposal 6-76
Log 2281
ROP, p. 394

Comment
None

Analysis and Effect

Sizes 15 and 17 AWG flexible cords have appeared in Table 400.5 since *NEC*-1959. Substantiation with the proposal identified that previously only one of the four ampacity values possible were placed in the *Code* for these sizes of cord conductors, because there were no companies manufacturing these types of cords or cables. Now, however, manufacturers are producing cord sets and power supply cords in these sizes. The ampacity values are consistent with those provided in UL 1659 *Standard for Attachment Plug Blades for Use in Cord Sets and Power Supply Cords*. The revision to this table provides maximum ampacities permitted for two-conductor and three-conductor configurations of flexible cords and cables that are manufactured in 17 AWG and 15 AWG sizes.

Change at a Glance

Flexible cords and cables in sizes 17 AWG and 15 AWG have allowable ampacities assigned by columns A and B of Table 400.5(A).

Code Language

Ampere values added to table

Summary of Change

The ampacities 9 (column A) for 17 AWG, and 12 (column A) and 16 (column B) for 15 AWG have been added to Table 400.5(A).

402.11

Fixture Wires
Uses Not Permitted
NEC, p. 258

Proposal 6-92
Log 997
ROP, p. 401

Comment
None

Change at a Glance

Fixture wires are only permitted to be used as branch-circuit conductors where recognized by other *NEC* rules.

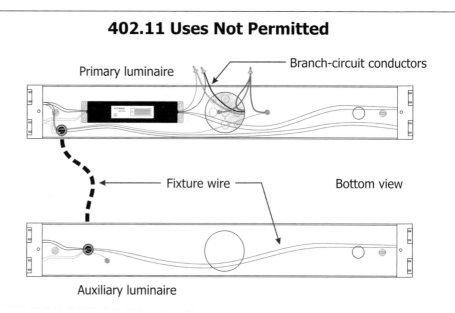

402.11 Uses Not Permitted

Primary luminaire — Branch-circuit conductors

Fixture wire — Bottom view

Auxiliary luminaire

Fixture wire shall not be used as branch-circuit conductors except as permitted elsewhere in the *Code*.

Copyright©IAEI 2007

Analysis and Effect

This revision clears up an inconsistency between Sections 402.11 and former Section 725.27(B) [now Section 725.49(B)]. Section 402.11 now clearly indicates that fixture wires may be used as branch-circuit conductors, but only under the provisions of 725.49(B). This revision recognizes the common practice of control circuits being tapped from the secondary of a motor branch-circuit short-circuit ground-fault protective device, which is typically rated at larger amperage than that for which the conductor is rated, yet permissible under the provisions of 430.72 and 725.49(B). These conductors serve motor-control circuit devices, thus qualifying as branch-circuit conductors. This change clarifies the permitted use of fixture wires and improves the usability of the *Code* for installers and inspectors.

Code Language
402.11
Uses Not Permitted
Fixture wires shall not be used as branch-circuit conductors except as permitted elsewhere in the *Code*.

Summary of Change

The words "except as permitted elsewhere in the *Code*" have been added to 402.11.

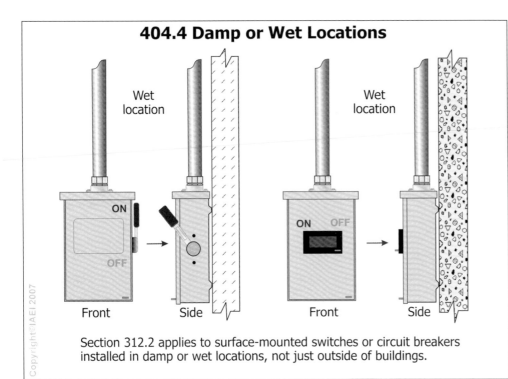

404.4 Damp or Wet Locations

Wet location

Front Side

Wet location

Front Side

Section 312.2 applies to surface-mounted switches or circuit breakers installed in damp or wet locations, not just outside of buildings.

404.4

Switches
Damp or Wet Locations
NEC, p. 259

Proposal 9-88, 9-89
Log 974, 1029
ROP, p. 403

Comment
None

Analysis and Effect

Wet location is defined in Article 100 as a "location subject to saturation with water or other liquids ... and in unprotected locations exposed to weather." The words "outside of a building" were removed from the article to clarify that not all switches or circuit breakers installed outside of a building are placed in wet locations. Some are installed in damp locations, such as under a porch or canopy. New wording has been added to indicate that flush- or surface-mounted switches installed in damp locations require a weatherproof cover. Weatherproof covers were not previously required for a switch installed in a damp location. This revision makes it clear that flush- or surface-mounted switches or circuit breakers installed in damp or wet locations must have a weatherproof cover installed. This section now correlates with the wording in Section 406.8(A), which requires weatherproof covers for receptacles installed in damp or wet locations.

Substantiation in the proposal indicated that not all switches or circuit breakers installed outdoors are placed on or outside a building. Some may be installed remotely from a building and attached to a structure such as a pole, post or other types of supporting framework or surfaces, such as a concrete wall, for example. Therefore, the phrase "outside a building" was removed from this section to improve applicability.

Change at a Glance

Surface-mounted switches or circuit breakers installed in damp or wet locations must have a weatherproof cover installed.

Code Language
404.4

Damp or Wet Locations
A surface-mounted switch or circuit breaker in a damp or wet location shall be enclosed in a weatherproof enclosure or cabinet that shall comply with 312.2. A flush-mounted switch or circuit breaker in a damp or wet location shall be equipped with a weatherproof cover. Switches shall not be installed within wet locations in tub or shower spaces unless installed as part of a listed tub or shower assembly.

Summary of Change

The words "or outside a building" have been removed, and a new second sentence covering flush-mounted switches or circuit breakers has been added.

404.8(C)

Multipole Snap Switches
NEC, p. 260

Proposal 9-92
Log 3406
ROP, p. 404

Comment
None

Change at a Glance

Multipole snap switches are not permitted to control more than a single circuit unless they are listed and marked for the use, or their voltage ratings are not less than the applied voltage of the connected circuits.

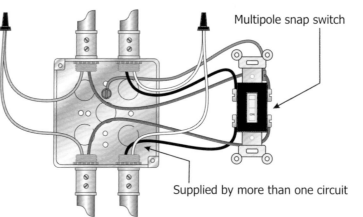

404.8(C) Multipole Snap Switches

Multipole snap switch

Supplied by more than one circuit

General-use multipole snap switches are not permitted to be fed from more than a single circuit unless listed and marked as a two-circuit or a three-circuit switch.

Switches are permitted in these applications where the rating is not less than the nominal line-to-line voltage of the system supplying the circuits.

Copyright©IAEI 2007

Analysis and Effect

A new subdivision (C) has been added to Section 404.8 that brings new requirements for multipole snap switches. Snap switch devices that are supplied by two or three circuits will now be required to be listed and marked as a two-circuit or three-circuit switch, or have a voltage rating not less than the nominal line voltage of the system supplying the circuits. Switches will therefore have to be manufactured in accordance with applicable product standards and marked as to their specific use. The Guide Information for Electrical Equipment (UL White Book) under product category (WJQR) indicates that multipole, general-use snap switches have not been investigated for more than single-circuit operation unless marked "2-circuit" or "3-circuit." Installers will be required to install switches that are listed for the use or have a marked voltage rating not less than the nominal line voltage of the system supplying the circuits. Workers (qualified persons) will now have improved means to verify that the switch is properly rated for the intended use when installed in multiple circuit configurations or designs.

Code Language
404.8(C)

Multipole Snap Switches
A multipole, general-use snap switch shall not be permitted to be fed from more than a single circuit unless it is listed and marked as a two-circuit or three-circuit switch, or unless its voltage rating is not less than the nominal line-to-line voltage of the system supplying the circuits.

Summary of Change

A new subdivision (C) has been added to Section 404.8 regarding requirements for multipole snap switches.

404.9(B) Grounding

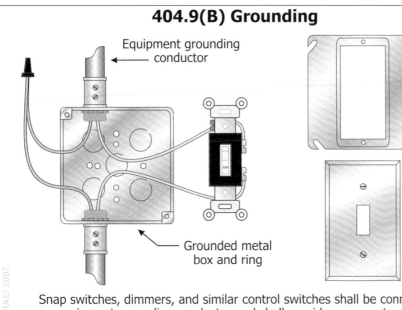

Equipment grounding conductor

Grounded metal box and ring

Snap switches, dimmers, and similar control switches shall be connected to an equipment grounding conductor and shall provide a means to connect metal faceplates to the equipment grounding conductor, whether or not a metal faceplate is installed.

Copyright©IAEI 2007

404.9(B)

Switches
Grounding
NEC, p. 260

Proposal 9-94, 9-18, 9-96
Log 1541, 1538, 2248
ROP, p. 404, 303, 404

Comment
None

Analysis and Effect

Language was revised in subdivision (B) of this section due to code-wide changes as a result of work done by the TCC assigned Task Group on Grounding and Bonding. Wording was changed to clarify that metal switch yokes and metal covers or faceplates for switches are required to be connected to an equipment grounding conductor for safety. Where means exists in the switch enclosure to connect the enclosure, metal switch yokes, and metal faceplates to an equipment grounding conductor, all of these metal parts shall be so connected. The term *effectively grounded* has been removed from this section because it is ambiguous and difficult to define. These revisions prescriptively guide users as to how to accomplish the equipment grounding requirements in this rule. *Code* language in this section correlates with revised definitions of grounding and bonding terms in Article 100.

Change at a Glance

Language that is more specific requires connection of an equipment grounding conductor to the devices listed in this section, rather than just a general requirement for grounding.

Code Language
404.9(B)

Grounding

Snap switches, including dimmer and similar control switches, shall be connected to an equipment grounding conductor and shall provide a means to connect metal faceplates to the equipment grounding conductor, whether or not a metal faceplate is installed. Snap switches shall be considered to be part of an effective ground-fault current path if either of the following conditions is met: ...

Summary of Change

The words "connected to an equipment grounding conductor" have replaced the phrase "effectively grounded" in 404.9.

404.9
(B)(1)

Provisions for General-Use Snap Switches
NEC, p. 260

Proposal 9-96 , 9-18
Log 2248, 1538
ROP, p. 405, 303

Comment
None

Change at a Glance

Metal box covers that provide mounting for switches and are attached by #8/32 screws to a wiring box are recognized for grounding switches that are installed in the raised cover.

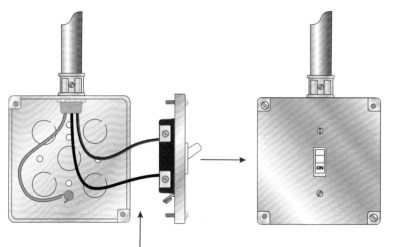

404.9(B)(1) Grounding

Applies to snap switches, dimmers, and similar control devices

Bonding jumper is not required for raised switch covers that are securely fastened to grounded metal boxes.

Analysis and Effect

A metal wiring box with raised surface cover that provides mounting for a snap switch (or switches) will now be permitted to be grounded by the screws that attach the raised cover to the wiring box, without being required to install an equipment bonding conductor to any metal switch yokes mounted on the box cover. A typical installation utilizes two #8/32 in. machine screws to electrically connect and mechanically secure the extension or raised cover to the metal box, which is required to be connected to an equipment grounding conductor. Substantiation with the proposal stated that a 4-inch square blank cover is not required to have a bonding jumper installed to ground it to the box because it is considered grounded by being secured with two #8/32 in. screws, thereby having metal-to-metal contact between the box and the cover. The panel action on this proposal was to clarify that these types of surface covers for switches are permitted to be grounded by securing them to a grounded metal box. As a result of the change, equipment bonding jumpers to metal switch yokes installed in these types of covers are not required where metal-to-metal contact for equipment grounding purposes is achieved through the connection between the metal box switch cover and the grounded metal box.

Code Language
404.9
Provisions for General-Use Snap Switches

404.9(B)
Grounding
(1) The switch is mounted with metal screws to a metal box or metal cover that is connected to an equipment grounding conductor or to a nonmetallic box with integral means for connecting to an equipment grounding conductor.

Summary of Change

The words "or metal cover that is connected to an equipment grounding conductor" have been added to this section.

Analysis of Changes *NEC*-2008

Voltage Between Adjacent Devices
NEC, p. 263

Proposal 18-24
Log 2129
ROP, p. 415

Comment 18-13
Log 216
ROC, p. 251

Analysis and Effect

Action by CMP-18 on Comment 18-13 (Log No. 216) results in a rule that parallels the requirements for switches where the voltage exceeds 300 between adjacent devices. The proposal identified similar hazards that are present with ganged receptacles at higher voltage levels. The revision results in similar language that applies to receptacles in ganged enclosures where the voltage between adjacent devices exceeds 300 volts. An example is where two 480-volt, 3-phase, 4-wire receptacles are installed in an appropriately sized two-gang outlet box. Box manufacturers provide identified accessory features to accomplish readily the barrier requirement. Remaining consistent with the provisions of 404.8(B), this new requirement for receptacles also calls for the barriers to be identified and securely fastened to the outlet box in which they are installed. It should be noted that certain box and plaster ring combinations are available for this use, but the correct box and cover combination must be installed during the rough-in stages of a project in order to accept an identified barrier to meet the requirements of this section.

Code Language
406.4(G)

Voltage Between Adjacent Devices
A receptacle shall not be grouped or ganged in enclosures with other receptacles, snap switches, or similar devices, unless they are arranged so that the voltage between adjacent devices does not exceed 300 volts, or unless they are installed in enclosures equipped with identified, securely installed barriers between adjacent devices.

Summary of Change

A new subdivision (G) covering voltage between adjacent receptacles has been added to 406.4.

Change at a Glance

Where voltages between adjacent receptacles in ganged enclosures exceed 300, identified and securely fastened barriers are required between the devices.

4

406.8
[A] and [B]

Receptacles in Damp or Wet Locations
NEC, p. 264

Proposal 18-28, 18-33
Log 3639, 3641
ROP, p. 415, 416

Comment 18-16, 18-18
Log 1424, 1426
ROC, p. 252, 253

Change at a Glance

Standard nonlocking straight-blade receptacles in 120- and 250-volt configurations are required to be listed weather-resistant type.

Analysis and Effect

Action by CMP-18 responded to substantiation that demonstrated a need for nonlocking receptacles installed in these locations to be suitable for the elements to which they are subjected over time. Substantiation indicated that deterioration and other detrimental conditions have a negative effect on receptacles, often resulting in receptacle faces becoming brittle and breaking. Even though the *NEC* has made significant progress in the cover requirements for receptacles installed in wet and damp locations, receptacles are often still exposed to varying degrees of moisture, UV, and impact under detrimental conditions (low and high temperatures). These products have not been constructed or evaluated for such exposure to these conditions. An appropriately listed weather-resistant receptacle (able to withstand the elements) addresses the associated safety hazards and concerns of suitability of electrical products for outdoor use. Statistical data has substantiated the need for a more weather-resilient device, in spite of the use of protective covers. The inclusion of the proposed additional text in conjunction with the existing code language would address this dangerous condition and noted failure rates. A new fine print note has been included to provide users with guidance to the applicable ANSI/NEMA Standard WD 6-2002 for additional information about attachment plugs and receptacles.

Code Language
406.8(A)
Damp Locations

A receptacle...and will not be subjected to a beating rain or water runoff. All nonlocking 15- and 20-ampere, 125- and 250-volt receptacles shall be a listed weather-resistant type.

FPN: The types of receptacles covered by this requirement are identified as 5-15, 5-20, 6-15, and 6-20 in ANSI/NEMA WD 6-2002, National Electrical Manufacturers Association *Standard for Dimensions of Attachment Plugs and Receptacles*.

(B)
Wet Locations
(1) 15- and 20-Ampere Receptacles in a Wet Location. 15- and 20-ampere, 125- and 250-volt receptacles installed in a wet location shall have an enclosure that is weatherproof whether or not the attachment plug cap is inserted. All 15- and 20-ampere, 125- and 250-volt nonlocking receptacles shall be listed weather-resistant type.

FPN: The types of receptacles covered by this requirement are identified as 5-15, 5-20, 6-15, and 6-20 in ANSI/NEMA WD 6-2002, National Electrical Manufacturers Association *Standard for Dimensions of Attachment Plugs and Receptacles*.

Summary of Change

A new last sentence and new FPN have been added to 406.8(A) and (B).

Analysis of Changes *NEC-2008*

406.11 Tamper-Resistant Receptacles in Dwelling Units

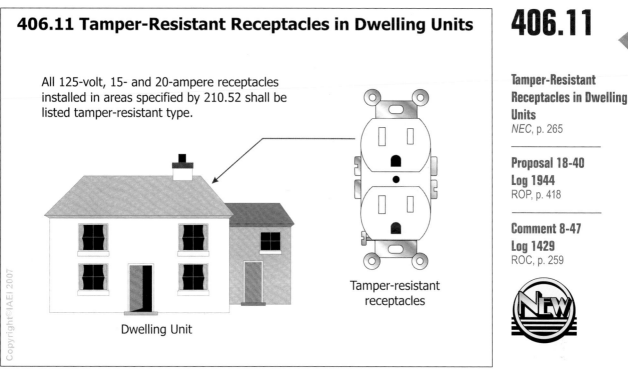

All 125-volt, 15- and 20-ampere receptacles installed in areas specified by 210.52 shall be listed tamper-resistant type.

Tamper-resistant receptacles

Dwelling Unit

Copyright© IAEI 2007

Tamper-Resistant Receptacles in Dwelling Units
NEC, p. 265

Proposal 18-40
Log 1944
ROP, p. 418

Comment 8-47
Log 1429
ROC, p. 259

Analysis and Effect

CMP-18 action on Proposal 18-40 results in a new requirement in Article 406 addressing receptacles installed in dwelling units. The definition of *dwelling unit* clarifies that all 15- and 20-ampere receptacles installed in outlets required under Section 210.52 for dwelling units be a listed tamper-resistant type. Substantiation clearly identified concerns about the number of child injuries and electrocutions when foreign objects are inserted into receptacles. The U.S. Consumer Product Safety Commission's (CPSC) National Electronic Injury Surveillance System (NEISS), indicated that from 1991 to 2001 over 24,000 children were injured when they inserted foreign objects into electrical receptacles. This means an average of 2,400 children are injured each year by tampering with energized electrical receptacles. Patient information is collected from each participating NEISS hospital for every emergency visit involving an injury associated with consumer products. From this sample, the total number of product-related injuries treated in hospital emergency rooms nationwide can be estimated. Injuries related to the insertion of foreign objects into electrical receptacles are significant and demonstrate the need for more protection. This change extends the tamper-resistant receptacle requirement to all 125-volt, 15- and 20-ampere receptacles in all areas specified in 210.52 for dwelling units.

Change at a Glance

Listed tamper-resistant receptacles are required for 125-volt, 15- and 20-ampere receptacles in dwelling units in areas specified in 210.52.

Code Language
406.11

Tamper-Resistant Receptacles in Dwelling Units
In all areas specified in 210.52, all 125-volt, 15- and 20-ampere receptacles shall be listed tamper-resistant receptacles.

Summary of Change

Section 406.11 was added to provide a requirment that all 125-volt, 15- and 20-ampere receptacles required under 210.52 be listed as tamper-resistant.

Courtesy of Pass and Seymour Legrand

408.3(F)

High-Leg Identification
NEC, p. 266

Proposal 9-109
Log 674
ROP, p. 421

Comment 9-63
Log 265
ROC, p. 263

Change at a Glance

Switchboards and panelboards containing high-leg systems are required to be field marked on the outside of the enclosure(s).

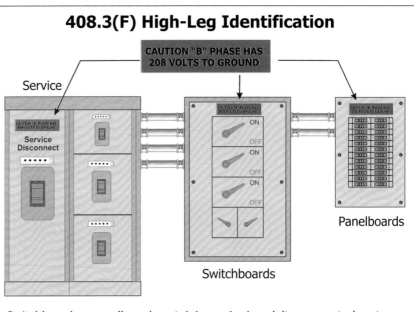

408.3(F) High-Leg Identification

CAUTION "B" PHASE HAS 208 VOLTS TO GROUND

Service

CAUTION "B" PHASE HAS 208 VOLTS TO GROUND

Service Disconnect

CAUTION "B" PHASE HAS 208 VOLTS TO GROUND

ON
OFF
ON
OFF
ON
OFF

CAUTION "B" PHASE HAS 208 VOLTS TO GROUND

Panelboards

Switchboards

Switchboard or panelboard containing a 4-wire, delta-connected system where the midpoint of one phase winding is grounded shall be marked CAUTION_____PHASE HAS_____VOLTS TO GROUND

Analysis and Effect

This revision provides users with a new specific marking requirement for equipment that contains a phase conductor or busbar with a higher voltage to ground. The new marking rule also calls for the voltage of the high-leg. Previous editions of the *Code* provided users with direction only as to which phase should be used as the high-leg, and to which terminal or bus within equipment it should be connected. Having the switchboard or panelboard clearly marked to indicate which phase has the higher voltage to ground and what that voltage is, should increase safety levels for workers. Labeling requirements are never intended to replace safe work practices, which should include testing before working on any circuit. This new requirement enhances the high-leg identification rules already provided in 110.15 and 408.3(E) and serves as valuable information to installers, maintenance personnel, inspectors, and so forth, as to the particular voltage and phase arrangement before they access the enclosure.

Code Language
408.3(F)

High-Leg Identification

A switchboard or panelboard containing a 4-wire, delta-connected system where the midpoint of one phase winding is grounded shall be legibly and permanently field marked as follows:

"Caution _____ Phase Has _____ _Volts to Ground"

Change existing 408.3(F) to 408.3(G).

Summary of Change

A new subdivision (F) has been included in this section, and former subdivision (F) has been re-identified as subdivision (G).

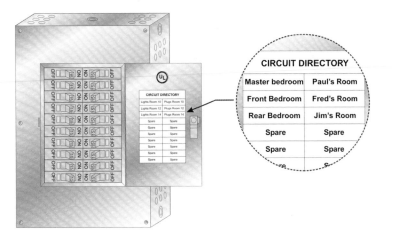

408.4 Circuit Directory or Circuit Identification

CIRCUIT DIRECTORY

Master bedroom	Paul's Room
Front Bedroom	Fred's Room
Rear Bedroom	Jim's Room
Spare	Spare
Spare	Spare

Spare positions containing unused overcurrent devices or switches shall be marked accordingly.

Circuits shall not be marked in a manner that depends on transient conditions of occupancy.

408.4

Circuit Directory or
Circuit Identification
NEC, p. 266

Proposal 9-101, 9-105
Log 362, 3407
ROP, p. 419, 420

Comment 9-56
Log 61
ROC, p. 262

Analysis and Effect

This revision requires identification of spare switches or circuit breakers installed in equipment. Current practices are to identify unused switches or circuit breakers as spares, even without any set requirement in the *Code* to do so. The *Code* currently requires circuits to be identified as to their purpose and to be clearly distinguished one from another. Section 110.22 requires the disconnecting means to be identified as to its purpose. *Disconnecting means*, by definition, can be devices other than overcurrent devices. A rule that requires additional or redundant fused switches or circuit breakers that are unused and installed in panelboards or switchboards will provide additional guidance and safety for occupants and workers. Unused switches or circuit breakers that are put into service after the initial installation would be required to meet the identification requirements of this section. The purpose for additional spaces for circuit breakers or switches in such equipment is typically self-evident, and those breakers or switches require no additional identification. The fourth sentence clearly requires circuit identification to be functional, without referring to transitory occupants of buildings, which would have a negative impact on the accuracy of the circuit identification directories.

Change at a Glance

Spare overcurrent devices in panelboards must be identified as spares, and circuits cannot be identified in a manner that depends on transient occupancy.

Code Language
408.4

Circuit Directory or Circuit Identification

Every circuit and circuit modification shall be legibly identified as to its clear, evident, and specific purpose or use. The identification shall include sufficient detail to allow each circuit to be distinguished from all others. Spare positions that contain unused overcurrent devices or switches shall be described accordingly. The identification shall be included in a circuit directory that is located on the face or inside of the panel door in the case of a panelboard, and located at each switch on a switchboard. No circuit shall be described in a manner that depends on transient conditions of occupancy.

Summary of Change

Two new sentences have been added—a third and a fourth. The third sentence reads: "Spare positions that contain unused overcurrent devices or switches shall be described accordingly." The fourth sentence reads: "No circuit shall be described in a manner that depends on transient conditions of occupancy."

408.36

Overcurrent Protection
NEC, p. 267

Proposal 9-117
Log 2643
ROP, p. 422

Comment 9-70
Log 2268
ROC, p. 265

408.36 Overcurrent Protection

Overcurrent protection for panelboards is required within or at any point on the supply side feeder for the panelboard.

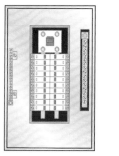 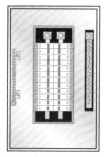 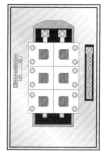

Copyright©IAEI 2007

The definitions of *power panelboard* and a *lighting and appliance branch circuit panelboard* have been removed.

Section 408.35 has been deleted, removing the general limitation of not more than 42 overcurrent devices other than what is required by Exception No. 2.

Section 408.54 requires physical means to prevent the installation of more overcurrent devices than the panelboard is designed, rated, and listed for.

Analysis and Effect

These revisions essentially remove the 42-overcurrent-devices limitation for panelboards and result in requirements that now address power panelboards and lighting and appliance panelboards as simply panelboards. Part of the substantiation for this proposal indicates that the original intent (around 1933) of the circuit limitation was to prevent overheating caused from installing too many rubber-insulated conductors in the panelboard, which resulted in crowding and heating conditions. Since that time, revisions to UL 67 *Standard for Panelboards'* construction requirements and thermal test requirements eliminate the original concerns. A CMP-9 Task Group for *NEC*-1996 studied this topic; this change reflects much of the task group's efforts and objectives of that time. Among them was the belief that these panelboards would be safer with a main overcurrent protective device. The newly created Exception No. 1 is based on the 2005 exception to 408.36(B) which is intended to recognize a longstanding practice of allowing a small panel to be used as service equipment, with large line-to-line loads leaving at this point and a smaller feeder entering the building to supply what formerly was called a *lighting and appliance branch circuit panelboard*. The limitations now contained in this exception prevent the extension of this limited practice to what could otherwise become a split-bus panelboard with an unlimited number of overcurrent devices in the future. The six-circuit limit correlates with the

Change at a Glance

There is no longer a differentiation between lighting and appliance branch-circuit panelboards and power panelboards. The general limit of 42 overcurrent devices in a panelboard has been relaxed.

customary service limitation contained in 230.71. Exception No. 2 corresponds to the 2005 language of 408.36(A). Prior practice effectively limited these panelboards to 42 overcurrent devices; action by CMP-9 carries that limitation forward, but only for these panelboards formerly referred to as *lighting and appliance branch-circuit panelboards*. Exception No. 3 corresponds to the 2005 language of 408.36(A) Exception No. 2, and is carried forward to *NEC*-2008 without change. The substantiation pointed out that where a panelboard was classified as a *power panelboard*, the 42-circuit limitation was not a concern. Additionally, most domestic panelboard manufacturers produce panelboards for use in Canada, where there is currently no circuit restriction for any panelboard application. These revisions also bring the *NEC* into closer harmony with similar rules in the CE *Code* Part I covering panelboards.

Code Language
408.36
Overcurrent Protection

In addition to the requirements of 408.30, a panelboard shall be protected by an overcurrent protective device having a rating not greater than that of the panelboard. This overcurrent protective device shall be located within or at any point on the supply side of the panelboard.

Exception No. 1: Individual protection shall not be required for a panelboard used as service equipment with multiple disconnecting means in accordance with 230.71. In panelboards protected by three or more main circuit breakers or sets of fuses, the circuit breakers or sets of fuses shall not supply a second bus structure within the same panelboard assembly.

Exception No. 2: Individual protection shall not be required for a panelboard protected on its supply side by two main circuit breakers or two sets of fuses having a combined rating not greater than that of the panelboard. A panelboard constructed or wired under this exception shall not contain more than 42 overcurrent devices. For the purposes of determining the maximum of 42 overcurrent devices, a 2-pole or a 3-pole circuit breaker shall be considered as two or three overcurrent devices, respectively.

Exception No. 3: For existing panelboards, individual protection shall not be required for a panelboard used as service equipment for an individual residential occupancy.

Summary of Change

Sections 408.36(A) and (B) and the associated exceptions have been restructured into one section with three exceptions. Under this revision the differentiation between power panelboards and lighting and appliance branch-circuit panelboards has been removed. Existing subdivisions (C), (D), (E), and (F) of this section have been re-identified as subdivisions (A), (B), (C), and (D) respectively. Sections 408.34 and 408.35, which included definitions of the terms *power panelboard* and *lighting and appliance branch-circuit panelboard,* have been deleted as a result of these revisions to Section 408.36.

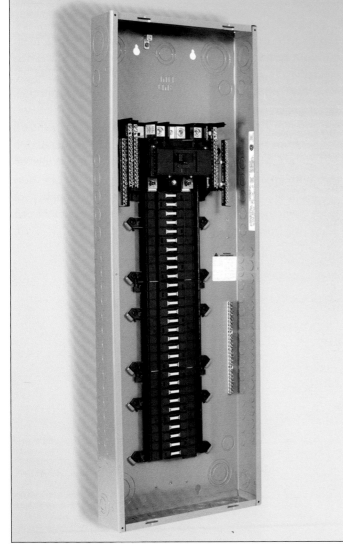

Courtesy of Schneider Electric/Square D Company

408.36, Exc. No 1

Overcurrent Protection
NEC, p. 267

Proposal 9-117
Log 2643
ROP, p. 422

Comment 9-70
Log 2268
ROC, p. 265

408.36 Exception No. 1

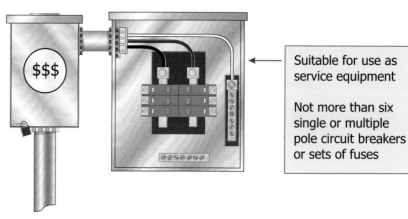

Suitable for use as service equipment

Not more than six single or multiple pole circuit breakers or sets of fuses

Individual protection shall not be required for a panelboard used as service equipment with multiple disconnecting means in accordance with 230.71.

In panelboards protected by three or more main circuit breakers or sets of fuses, the circuit breakers or sets of fuses shall not supply a second bus structure within the same panelboard assembly.

Copyright©IAEI 2007

Analysis and Effect

This exception addresses smaller panelboards that are suitable for use as service equipment and that are arranged with multiple service disconnects in accordance with 230.71. The calculated load connected to such panelboards is an important aspect of these panelboards installed with inherent limitations of number of branch circuits and loads connected. The exception recognizes these arrangements and retains similar concepts that were also provided in 408.36(B) Exception [*NEC*-2005] while restricting a split-bus panelboard from being used in this type of arrangement. Action by CMP-9 results in the broadening of this exception to apply to all panelboards that are installed in these limited-service applications where the number of switches or circuit breakers installed does not exceed six, meeting the allowances in 230.71.

Change at a Glance

A service-rated panelboard with service disconnect arrangements in accordance with 230.71 does not require individual protection, and a second separate bus structure is not permitted within this panelboard enclosure.

Code Language
408.36
Overcurrent Protection

Exception No. 1: Individual protection shall not be required for a panelboard used as service equipment with multiple disconnecting means in accordance with 230.71. In panelboards protected by three or more main circuit breakers or sets of fuses, the circuit breakers or sets of fuses shall not supply a second bus structure within the same panelboard assembly.

Summary of Change
The Exception to 408.36(B) [*NEC-2005*] has been relocated and renumbered as Exception No. 1 to 408.36(A). The revision includes an additional sentence that restricts breakers or fuses in this panelboard from supplying a second bus within the same enclosures assembly.

4

409.21(B)

Overcurrent Protection
NEC, p. 270

Proposal 11-4, 11-5, 11-6
Log 646, 1688, 1689
ROP, p. 426, 427

Comment
None

Change at a Glance

More than one circuit is permitted to supply industrial control panels, and compliance with 409.21(B)(1) or (2) is required for each supply circuit.

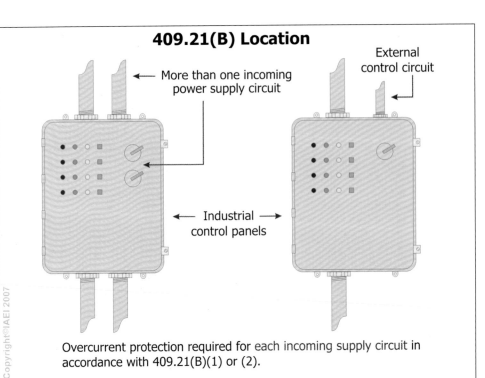

409.21(B) Location

More than one incoming power supply circuit

External control circuit

Industrial control panels

Overcurrent protection required for each incoming supply circuit in accordance with 409.21(B)(1) or (2).

Analysis and Effect

The revision of this section retains the general overcurrent protective device requirements from the previous edition found in Article 240, and it provides users with an option as to where those devices may be located. This change recognizes that multiple circuits or power sources could be installed to an individual industrial control panel. Section 409.21(B) has been revised to clarify that more than one overcurrent device is permitted to supply power to an industrial control panel. Previous *Code* language limited the incoming power supply to an "overcurrent device" or a "single overcurrent device." In some installations, control circuits may be supplied by a 120-volt circuit, and power may be supplied by a 480-volt 3-phase supply. For more elaborate equipment, multiple three-phase power supplies could be required—such as where two supply voltages are necessary to supply commercial cooling equipment for supermarket chillers. The supply conductors could be either protected feeders or tap conductors per 240.21.

Code Language
409.21
Overcurrent Protection

(B)
Location
This protection shall be provided for each incoming supply circuit by either of the following:
(1) An overcurrent protective device located ahead of the industrial control panel.
(2) A single main overcurrent protective device located within the industrial control panel. Where overcurrent protection is provided as part of the industrial control panel, the supply conductors shall be considered as either feeders or taps as covered by 240.21.

Summary of Change

This section has been revised to permit more than one power supply source to an industrial control panel.

Wire Bending Space
NEC, p. 270

Proposal 11-8
Log 643
ROP, p. 427

Comment 11-1
Log 2325
ROC, p. 266

Analysis and Effect

The existing reference to 312.6 for the wire bending space for the main supply terminals has been removed. Section 430.10(B) will now be the only reference for wire bending space for all terminals within the industrial control panel. *NEC* 312.6 offered two wire bending options with a number of exceptions, which necessitated knowing where the field-connected conductors would enter the enclosure. This is seldom known at the time of the placement of the components in an industrial control panel, unless it is field-assembled at the installation site. A panel assembler remote from the installation site could comply with the requirements of 312.6(A) by placing the components in a panel suitable for conductor entry at 90 degrees to the component terminals, effectively allowing a smaller wire bending space than that required by 312.6(B) for a straight-in entry, which might be needed at the installation. Such a misapplication cannot happen with the wire bending space according to Table 430.10(B) since its spacing requirements account for the worst-case installation. This change will allow the panel assembler to install components without having to be concerned with how and where the conductor enters the industrial control panel. Product standards, UL 508 *Industrial Control Panels*, and NFPA 79 *Electrical Standard for Industrial Machinery* require the same wire bending space as does 430.10(B); therefore, this change establishes consistency between those standards and the *NEC*.

Code Language
409.104(B)
Wire Bending Space
Wire bending space within industrial control panels for field wiring terminals shall be in accordance with the requirements in 430.10(B).

Summary of Change

Text requiring compliance with Article 312 has been deleted.

Change at a Glance

Wire bending space for field wiring entering industrial control panels must now comply with Section 430.10(B). Requirements for wire bending and gutter space found in Article 312 no longer apply.

4

409.110(3)
Exception

Marking
NEC, p. 271

Proposal 11-14
Log 1954
ROP, p. 428

Comment
None

Change at a Glance

Industrial control panels which contain only control circuits and devices do not require a short-circuit current rating.

Analysis and Effect

Section 409.110(3) has been revised to clarify that industrial control panels which contain only control circuits and devices do not require a short-circuit current rating. Information from the submitter indicated that control-circuit devices normally do not have short-circuit current ratings. This needed change improves the application of the *Code* for manufacturers, installers, enforcers and users by specifying where short-current current ratings are required. A new definition has also been added to Section 409.2—a *control circuit* is "the circuit of a control apparatus or system that carries the electric signals directing the performance of the controller but does not carry the main power current."

Industrial control panels are rated 600 volts or less. Evaluations of industrial control panels are performed per the requirements provided in product standard ANSI/UL 508A, *General Information* included in the *Guide Information for Electrical Equipment* (UL White Book) product category (NITW), and other product categories, depending upon the installation location. Manufacturers of industrial control panels which contain only control circuits and devices will now have clear guidelines as to what information is required to be marked on these types of control equipment enclosures.

Code Language
409.110
Marking

An industrial control panel shall be marked with the following information that is plainly visible after installation:

3) Short-circuit current rating of the industrial control panel based on one of the following:
a. Short-circuit current rating of a listed and labeled assembly
b. Short-circuit current rating established utilizing an approved method

FPN: UL 508A, Supplement SB, is an example of an approved method.

Exception to (3): Short-circuit current rating markings are not required for industrial control panels containing only control circuit components.

Summary of Change

A new exception has been added to Section 409.110(3).

Article 410

Luminaires, Lampholders, and Lamps
NEC, p. 271

Proposal 18-40a, 18-42, 18-43, 18-4
Log 1804, 3167, 3179, 2929
ROP, p. 429-440

Comment 18-59
Log 2106
ROC, p. 267

Analysis and Effect

All sections within Article 410 except 410.1 have been renumbered within all 16 parts of the article. There is no change in the numbering sequence of the parts in the article. The renumbering provides room for future growth in Article 410 within each part of the article. This change should result in improved clarity and usability for users. Action by CMP-18 on Proposal 18-40a adds a general listing requirement that applies to luminaires and lampholders as addressed throughout Article 410. The internationally recognized term *luminaire* was introduced during the 2002 *NEC* development process to replace references to forms of the term *fixture,* because *luminaire* is broader in nature and applies to products beyond the scope of the *NEC*. The term *luminaire* is the more internationally recognized term for the equipment covered by Article 410. This action to remove references to forms of the term *fixture* in Article 410 and throughout the *NEC* completes this transition.

Change at a Glance

The requirements in Article 410 have been renumbered within the existing parts of the article, and references to the terms *lighting fixture, lighting fixtures,* or *fixtures* in the title and text of the article have been removed. A new listing requirement in 410.6 applies generally to all luminaires and lampholders.

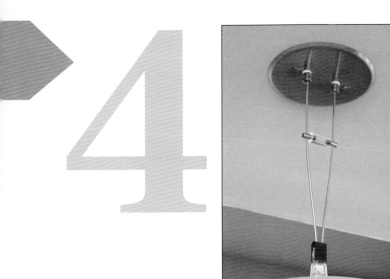

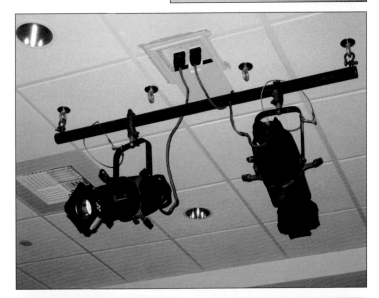

Code Language
Article 410
Luminaires, Lampholders, and Lamps

Part I General
    410.6 Listing Required (New)
        All luminaires and lampholders shall be listed.
Part II Luminaire Locations
Part III Provisions at Luminaire Outlet Boxes, Canopies, and Pans
Part IV Luminaire Supports
Part V Grounding
Part VI Wiring of Luminaires
Part VII Construction of Luminaires
Part VIII Installation of Lampholders
Part IX Construction of Lampholders
Part X Lamps and Auxiliary Equipment
Part XI Special Provisions for Flush and Recessed Luminaires
Part XII Construction of Flush and Recessed Luminaires
Part XIII Special Provisions for Electric-Discharge Lighting Systems of 1000 Volts or Less
Part XIV Special Provisions for Electric-Discharge Lighting Systems of More Than 1000 Volts
Part XV Lighting Track
Part XVI Decorative Lighting and Similar Accessories

Note: See the full text of Article 410 for locations of sections as renumbered within existing parts of the article.

Summary of Change
The sections within each part of Article 410 have been renumbered resulting from action on Proposals 18-40a, 18-42 and 18-43. A new 410.6 requiring listing has been added to Part I.

Analysis of Changes *NEC*-2008

Listing Required
NEC, p. 271

Proposal 18-40a
Log CP1804
ROP, p. 429

Comment 18-65
Log 2188
ROC, p. 268

Analysis and Effect

Action by CMP-18 on Proposal 18-40a results in a listing requirement that applies to all luminaries and lampholders. Substantiation in the proposal indicated that luminaire interior wiring, equipment suitability, construction features, clearances, location suitability and other safety measures are contained within the product safety standards. Inspection authorities rely heavily on product certifications as a basis for issuing approvals of installed equipment. Listed luminaires must meet the general requirements in 110.3(B) regarding conformance to applicable installation instructions included in the listing or labeling. This new requirement provides users with greater assurances that luminaires and equipment covered by Article 410 have been evaluated for the particular installation by qualified

Change at a Glance

All luminaires and lampholders are required to be listed.

electrical testing laboratories. Subsection .6 for this new listing requirement is consistent with other articles that include listing requirements.

Code Language
410.6
Listing Required
All luminaires and lampholders shall be listed.

Summary of Change

A new 410.6 covering listing requirements has been added to Part I of Article 410.

410.16(A), 410.16 (C)(5)

Luminaires in Clothes Closets
NEC, p. 272

Proposal 18-56, 18-60
Log 145, 1352
ROP, p. 443

Comment 18-66
Log 1407
ROC, p. 268

Change at a Glance

Surface-mounted or clothes-rod type fluorescent luminaires, or LED luminaires that are listed and identified for the use are now permitted to be installed within clothes closets, including storage spaces.

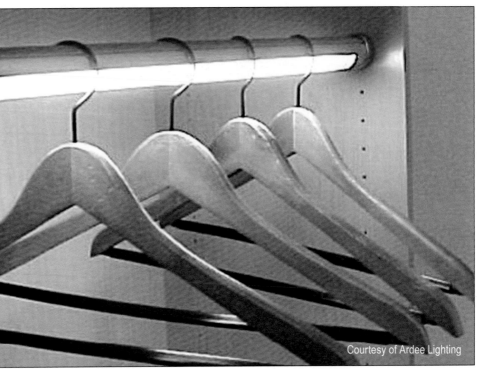

Courtesy of Ardee Lighting

Analysis and Effect

In addition to the reorganizing and renumbering of this section, LED luminaires and clothes-rod type luminaires now are permitted to be installed in clothes closets and storage spaces. These types of luminaires are intended to provide supplemental low-voltage or fluorescent lighting to areas of the closet that often may not be reached by conventional fixtures. The initial proposal raised concerns that no tests had been performed on the clothes closet rod-type luminaires, and the proposal was rejected. Subsequent testing and a witness test approval of the product by a well-respected electrical testing laboratory, which determined the suitability of the luminaire for use in a clothes closet, later resulted in acceptance by CMP-18. An example of the product tested utilized a 60-inch long Type T-5 fluorescent lamp, was hard-wired, and Type IC rated. The luminaire is rated to support 50 pounds of weight, and passed a test where 200 pounds of weight was applied to it. As with any electrical equipment, it is important to read the manufacturer's instructions and install the luminaire(s) per Section 110.3(B) and in accordance with the instructions included in the product listing and labeling provided by the electrical testing laboratory and manufacturer. These types of luminaires that are listed for the use are now permitted in the storage area of clothes closets.

Code Language
410.16

Luminaires in Clothes Closets
(A) Luminaire Types Permitted.
Listed luminaires of the following types shall be permitted to be installed in a closet:
(1) A surface-mounted or recessed incandescent luminaire with a completely enclosed lamp
(2) A surface-mounted or recessed fluorescent luminaire
(3) Surface-mounted fluorescent or LED luminaires identified as suitable for installation within the storage area.

(B) Luminaire Types Not Permitted

(C) Location
(5) Surface-mounted fluorescent or LED luminaires ... storage space where identified for this use.

Summary of Change

Two new subdivisions have been added to include provisions for LED luminaires. Section 410.8 was also reorganized and renumbered 410.16 as a result of the renumbering of Article 410.

Metal or Nonmetallic Poles Supporting Luminaires
NEC, p. 273

Proposal 18-69
Log 1942
ROP, p. 445

Comment
None

Analysis and Effect

The handhole covers integrated into luminaire pole manufacturing processes are typically not raintight, but are in configurations that afford suitable protection for the type of wet environment in which they are installed. This revision clarifies that raintight luminaire pole handhole covers are not necessary, but that the handhole covers for these poles are required to be suitable for the wet location. This revision is logical because luminaire poles are generally not required to be listed, and serve only as a support means for the listed luminaires installed at the top of the pole. A raintight requirement is over-restrictive, as indicated in the substantiation, and would also necessitate evaluation by electrical testing laboratories to ensure that the opening was raintight with the cover installed. These changes correlate with current industry practices in the manufacturing of luminaire support poles and provide more consistent requirements for wet locations where raintight features are unnecessary.

Change at a Glance

Handhole covers on light poles are not required to be raintight, but must be suitable for wet locations.

Code Language
410.30(B)

Metal or Nonmetallic Poles Supporting Luminaires

Metal or nonmetallic poles shall be permitted to be used to support luminaires and as a raceway to enclose supply conductors, provided the following conditions are met:

(1) A pole shall have a handhole not less than 50 mm × 100 mm (2 in. × 4 in.) with a cover suitable for use in wet locations to provide access to the supply terminations within the pole or pole base.

Summary of Change

The word "raintight" has been removed and the words "suitable for wet locations" have been incorporated into this section.

4

410.62(C)
(1)(2)c

**Cord-Connected
Installation**
NEC, p. 275

Proposal 18-40a, 18-78
Log CP1804, 3176
ROP, p. 429, 446

Comment: 18-65, 18-70,
18-77
Log: 268, 1977, 905
ROC, p. 268, 269, 270

Change at a Glance

Raceway sleeve assemblies are required for flexible cord penetrations at ceiling grid framing in suspended ceilings for cord connections to boxes above the ceiling.

Analysis and Effect

This section has been revised to clarify requirements for cords passing through suspended ceilings to terminate in junction boxes located above the suspended ceiling. Section 400.8 generally restricts cords from being installed where they penetrate floors or ceilings. Luminaires are often installed in office spaces using aircraft cable as the support means from ceiling grid framing members. The cord assembly is designed for installations centered over the ceiling grid frame. This revision recognizes luminaire cord and canopy assemblies that are manufactured for this purpose, and provides the necessary raceway sleeve for terminating the cord to the supply branch-circuit outlet box installed above the suspended ceiling. The revision clarifies the acceptable method of routing cords for these listed luminaire assemblies through ceilings, under the restrictions provided in this section.

Code Language
410.62(C)(1)

Cord-Connected Installation
A luminaire or a listed assembly...following conditions apply:
(1) The luminaire is located directly below the outlet or busway.
(2) The flexible cord meets all of the following:
a. [unchanged]
b. [unchanged]
c. Is terminated in a grounding-type attachment plug cap or busway plug, or is a part of a listed assembly incorporating a manufactured wiring system connector in accordance with 604.6(C), or has a luminaire assembly with a strain relief and canopy having a maximum 152 mm (6 in.) long section of raceway for attachment to an outlet box above a suspended ceiling.

Summary of Change

Additional text has been added to this section to address cords of listed luminaire and canopy assemblies that require ceiling grid penetration.

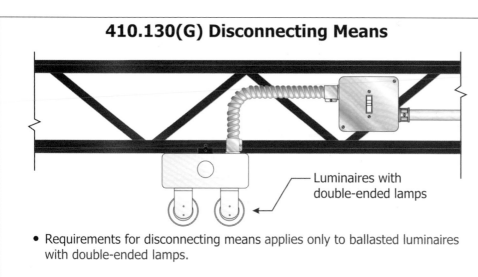

410.130(G) Disconnecting Means

Luminaires with double-ended lamps

- Requirements for disconnecting means applies only to ballasted luminaires with double-ended lamps.

- Disconnect must open all conductors, including the grounded conductor, when conneced to a multiwire branch circuit.

- The disconnect shall be a single device and where installed externally to the luminaire, it is required to located within sight from the luminaire.

410.130 (G)

Disconnecting Means
NEC, p. 279

Proposal 18-90b
Log CP1803
ROP, p. 449

Comment 18-79
Log 2091
ROC, p. 270

Analysis and Effect

Former Section 410.73(G) has been restructured into a list format to provide a more logical layout of the requirements and associated exceptions and renumbered as 410.130(G). These revisions are the result of CMP-18 actions on Proposals 18-91 through 18-96 and Comment 18-79 (Log No. 2091). This section provides requirements for luminaire disconnecting means and associated exceptions. The changes in 410.130(G)(1) apply only to fluorescent luminaires that receive double-ended lamps. As revised in 410.130(G)(2), all conductors supplying the ballast(s), including the grounded conductor, must be opened with this luminaire disconnecting means only where supplied by a multiwire branch circuit. The disconnecting means location has been clarified where it is not installed internal to the luminaire. As revised in 410.130(G)(3), the disconnecting means is required to be a single device and where it is installed external to the luminaire, it must be in sight from the luminaire.

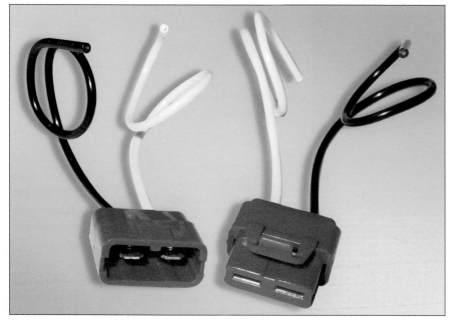

Courtesy of Thomas and Betts

Change at a Glance

The disconnect must open all conductors of the branch circuit when connected to a multiwire branch circuit; and those disconnecting means installed external to the luminaire shall be located in sight from the luminaire.

Code Language
410.130(G)
Disconnecting Means

(1) General. In indoor locations other than dwellings and associated accessory structures, fluorescent luminaires that utilize double-ended lamps and contain ballast(s) that can be serviced in place shall have a disconnecting means either internal or external to each luminaire. The line side terminals of the disconnecting means shall be guarded.

Exception No. 1: A disconnecting means shall not be required for luminaires installed in hazardous (classified) location(s).

Exception No. 2: A disconnecting means shall not be required for emergency illumination required in 700. 16.

Exception No. 3: For cord-and-plug-connected luminaires, an accessible separable connector or an accessible plug and receptacle shall be permitted to serve as the disconnecting means.

Exception No. 4: A disconnecting means shall not be required in industrial establishments with restricted public access where conditions of maintenance and supervision ensure that only qualified persons service the installation by written procedures.

Exception No. 5: Where more than one luminaire is installed and supplied by other than a multiwire branch circuit, a disconnecting means shall not be required for every luminaire when the design of the installation includes disconnecting means, such that the illuminated space cannot be left in total darkness.

(2) Multiwire Branch Circuits. When connected to multiwire branch circuits, the disconnecting means shall simultaneously break all the supply conductors to the ballast, including the grounded conductor.

(3) Location. The disconnecting means shall be located so as to be accessible to qualified persons before servicing or maintaining the ballast. Where the disconnecting means is external to the luminaire, it shall be a single device, and shall be attached to the luminaire or the luminaire shall be located within sight of the disconnecting means.

Summary of Change
This section has been revised and restructured into a list format to conform to *NEC Style Manual* requirements.

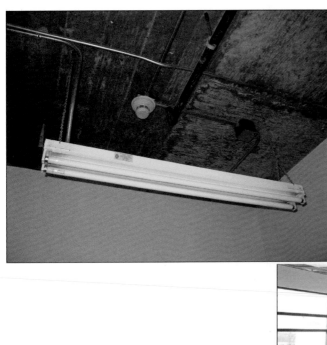

Analysis of Changes *NEC*-2008

Within Sight or Locked Type
NEC, p. 280

Proposal 18-100
Log 486
ROP, p. 451

Comment
None

Analysis and Effect

This change affects disconnecting means for lighting systems that operate at over 1000 volts. The first additional sentence provides consistency between similar rules that call for disconnecting means to be capable of being locked in the open position and the goal of worker safety. The phrase "capable of being locked in the open position" is used over 25 times in the *NEC*. The purpose is the same in every instance — that electrical workers are able to install a lock on the disconnecting means when it is located out of sight to prevent the circuit or system from being energized while they're working on it, and that the locking provision remains at the disconnect. Electrical requirements for worker safety should be consistent, and the wording for those requirements should be consistent where this phrase is used. The last sentence was added because of concerns that some of the portable units available for snapping on to circuit breakers do not remain with the switch or circuit breaker when the lock is not installed, but are portable and may be moved and no longer available or not found when needed to protect workers. Actions by CMP 11 in the 2002 cycle in 430.102(B) Exception made it clear that the provisions for adding a lock should be more substantial and not permit portable units. The *NEC* is primarily an installation code; NFPA 70E provides more information and specific requirements for worker safety, which includes lockout tag-out procedures and other essential rules relating to safe work practices. This *NEC* change clarifies for electrical workers and AHJs that the locking means for the disconnect must remain as part of the installed equipment.

Code Language
410.141(B)
Within Sight or Locked Type

The switch or circuit breaker shall be located within sight from the luminaires or lamps, or it shall be permitted elsewhere if it is provided with a means for locking in the open position. The provisions for locking or adding a lock to the disconnecting means must remain in place at the switch or circuit breaker whether the lock is installed or not. Portable means for adding a lock to the switch or circuit breaker shall not be permitted.

Summary of Change

Two additional sentences have been incorporated into this section to clarify the requirements for provisions to lock a disconnecting means in the open position.

Change at a Glance

The locking provisions must remain with the installed equipment whether the lock is installed or not; and portable types of locking means are not permitted to meet these *NEC* requirements for locking provisions.

4

410.151
(B) FPN

Connected Loads
NEC, p. 281

Proposal 18-65
Log 1670
ROP, p. 444

Comment 18-89
Log 1944
ROC, p. 272

Analysis and Effect

Substantiation provided with Proposal 18-65 (Log No. 1670) indicated there continues to be confusion about the connected load on lighting track, and about the relationship between 220.43(B) and the length of track and number of luminaires that can be installed on a length of track. Action by CMP-18 resulted in a new fine print note that clearly differentiates between the requirements in 220.43(B) and those in 410.151(B). The new fine print note clarifies that the length of track is not limited by 220.43(B), nor does this section limit the number of luminaires that can be installed to a length of track. Section 220.43(B) provides requirements for feeder and service load calculations, and 410.151(B) provides requirements for connected load.

Code Language
410.151(B)
Connected Load

FPN: The load calculation in 220.43(B) does not limit the length of track on a single branch circuit, and it does not limit the number of luminaires on a single track.

Summary of Change

A new fine print note has been added to clarify the application of 220.43(B) as it correlates with 410.151(B).

Change at a Glance

Section 220.43(B) is for load calculation purposes and does not limit the length of track on a branch circuit or the number of luminaires installed on the track.

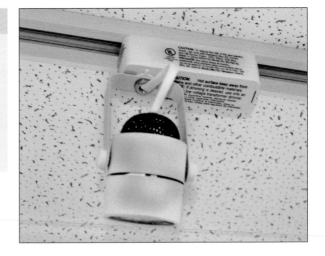

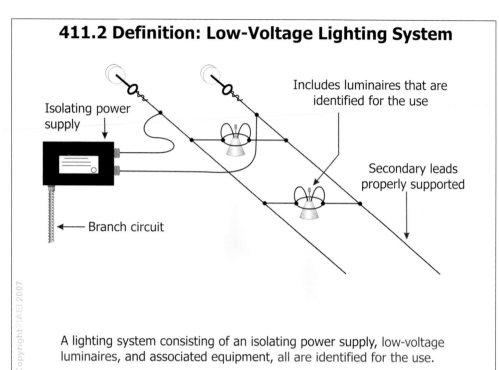

411.2 Definition: Low-Voltage Lighting System

Isolating power supply

Includes luminaires that are identified for the use

Secondary leads properly supported

Branch circuit

A lighting system consisting of an isolating power supply, low-voltage luminaires, and associated equipment, all are identified for the use.

Copyright IAEI 2007

411.2

Lighting Systems Operating at 30 Volts or Less
NEC, p. 281

Proposal 18-105
Log 2711
ROP, p. 452

Comment 18-91
Log 974
ROC, p. 273

Analysis and Effect

The definition of a *low voltage lighting system* has been revised. Language was added to clarify that a low voltage lighting system includes the luminaires, not just the power supply and associated equipment. Luminaires were not specifically included in the definition previously. Also, the output circuits are now "rated at not over 25 amperes," rather than "limited to 25 amperes," to align with ANSI/UL 1838, *Low Voltage Landscape Lighting Systems*, and UL 2108, *Low Voltage Lighting Systems*, which require that the low-voltage output circuit of the luminaire power supply is to be rated up to and including 25 amperes or 750 volt-amperes. The standards specify "rated" rather than "limited to." UL 1838 and UL 2108 also address possible risks of fire resulting from excess output current, and require the power supply to de-energize the output circuit within one hour when the circuit is loaded at 135 percent of 25 amperes. These test parameters mirror requirements of one of the tests required for a 25-ampere circuit breaker in UL 489, *Standard for Molded Case Circuit Breakers*. These changes will assist manufacturers, inspectors, and installers to understand better what is included in these types of installations and the appropriate standards for circuit protection.

Change at a Glance

A *low voltage lighting system* includes the luminaires, not just the power supply and associated equipment that are all identified for the use.

Code Language
411.2

Lighting Systems Operating at 30 Volts or Less

A lighting system consisting of an isolating power supply, the low-voltage luminaires, and associated equipment that are all identified for the use. The output circuits of the power supply are rated for not more than 25 amperes and operate at 30 volts (42.4 volts peak) or less under all load conditions.

Summary of Change

The definition of a *low voltage lighting system* has been revised.

4

411.3

Listing Required
NEC, p. 281

Proposal 18-106
Log 2712
ROP, p. 452

Comment 18-92
Log 219
ROC, p. 273

Change at a Glance

The use of field-assembled listed parts identified in 411.3(B) is permitted for low-voltage lighting systems.

Analysis and Effect

Section 411.3 has been revised by adding a new subdivision (B) which clarifies that low-voltage lighting systems—landscape types, for example—may be installed as a complete listed system, or as an assembly of listed parts. Previous *Code* language was viewed as not specifically permitting the use of a field assembly of listed parts from different manufacturers. It is now clear that this type of installation is permissible, which benefits installers and inspectors. Other types of low-voltage lighting are those which may be installed as under-cabinet lighting in custom homes or in commercial occupancies that include cords as part of the listed system, or those which include the use of exposed bare conductors and tend to be associated with luminaires that are artistic in nature. Concerns had been raised that the exposed bare conductors of these types of systems must meet all safety requirements of ANSI/UL 2108, and that only conductors and parts of systems that have been identified for use together are installed. This revision clarifies that exposed bare-conductor lighting systems must be listed for use as part of the same identified lighting system. Installers must be careful to follow all manufacturers' instructions, including minimum spacing requirements from luminaires to nearby objects or surfaces because of possible heating.

Code Language
411.3
Listing Required
Lighting systems operating at 30 volts or less shall comply with 411.3(A) or 411.3(B).
(A) Listed System. Lighting systems operating at 30 volts or less shall be listed as a complete system. The luminaires, power supply and luminaire fittings (including the exposed bare conductors) of an exposed bare conductor lighting system shall be listed for the use as part of the same identified lighting system.
(B) Assembly of Listed Parts. A lighting system assembled from the following listed parts shall be permitted:
(1) Low-voltage luminaires
(2) Low-voltage luminaire power supply
(3) Class 2 power supply
(4) Low-voltage luminaire fittings
(5) Cord (secondary circuit) for which the luminaires and power supply are listed for use
(6) Cable, conductors in conduit, or other fixed wiring method for the secondary circuit

The luminaires, power supply, and luminaire fittings (including the exposed bare conductors) of an exposed bare conductor lighting system shall be listed for use as part of the same identified lighting system.

Summary of Change

A new subdivision (B) has been added to Section 411.3.

411.4 Specific Location Requirements

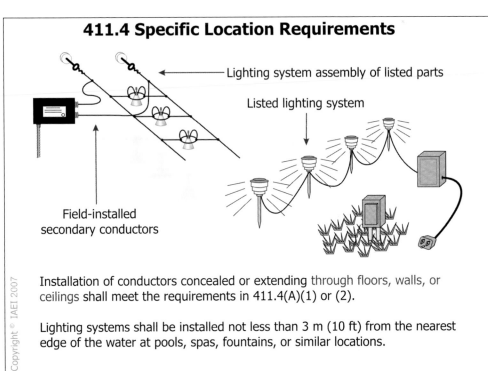

Lighting system assembly of listed parts

Listed lighting system

Field-installed secondary conductors

Installation of conductors concealed or extending through floors, walls, or ceilings shall meet the requirements in 411.4(A)(1) or (2).

Lighting systems shall be installed not less than 3 m (10 ft) from the nearest edge of the water at pools, spas, fountains, or similar locations.

Copyright © IAEI 2007

411.4

Specific Location Requirements
NEC, p. 282

Proposal 18-107
Log 2713
ROP, p. 453

Comment 18-94
Log 304
ROC, p. 274

Analysis and Effect

Section 411.4 has been revised to improve usability. The language clarifies that the location requirements apply to conductors installed in floors, ceilings, and walls. Previously, floors and ceilings were not mentioned in the requirements. It is now clear that low-voltage lighting conductors are permitted to be installed in these locations using any of the wiring methods specified in chapter 3, or using wiring supplied by a listed Class 2 power source and installed in accordance with 725.130. The installer must obviously check the uses permitted and not permitted for a chapter 3 wiring method before performing an installation. For example, new installations which utilize wiring methods found in Article 394 would not be permitted, unless by special permission. Low-voltage lighting systems near pools, spas, fountains, and similar locations must generally be located no closer than a minimum of 3 m (10 ft) horizontally from the nearest edge of the water, unless permitted by Sections 680.22, 23, 680.43(B), 680.51, or 680.72. Further information regarding low voltage lighting systems may be found in the ANSI/UL *Guide Information for Electrical Equipment*, in product category (IFDR).

Change at a Glance

Where low-voltage systems are installed in the locations identified in this section, they must meet the specific installation requirements in 411.4(A)(1) or (2) or 411.4(B).

Code Language

411.4

Specific Location Requirements

(A) Walls, Floors, and Ceilings. Conductors concealed or extended through a wall, floor, or ceiling shall be in accordance with (1) or (2):

(1) Installed using any of the wiring methods specified in Chapter 3.

(2) Installed using wiring supplied by a listed Class 2 power source and installed in accordance with 725.130.

(B) Pools, Spas, Fountains, and Similar Locations. Lighting systems shall be installed not less than 3 m (10 ft) horizontally from the nearest edge of the water, unless permitted by Article 680.

Summary of Change

The title of this section has been changed from "Locations Not Permitted" to "Specific Location Requirements."
Section 411.4 provides specific location requirements for low-voltage systems. Subdivision (A) has been revised to include locations in walls, ceilings, and floors.

4

422.51

Cord-and-Plug-Connected Vending Machines
NEC, p. 287

Proposal 17-27
Log 1739
ROP, p. 463

Comment
None

Change at a Glance

This section was revised to describe more clearly what qualifies as a vending machine.

Analysis and Effect

Section 422.51 covering cord-and-plug-connected vending machines was incorporated into Article 422 in the 2005 *NEC* cycle, with the principle requirement calling for ground-fault circuit-interrupter protection for vending machines. With the introduction of this new requirement, there came questions about what qualifies as a vending machine for appropriate application of this rule. This current revision describes the vending machines that are covered by this new rule. For example, the coin-operated children's amusement rides often located at the front of retail stores do not qualify for this ground-fault protection requirement. The new description removes the question about what constitutes a vending machine, and should result in more uniform and consistent application of this GFCI-protection requirement for all vending machines. With this requirement being effective January 1, 2005, vending manufacturers implemented changes in production to incorporate ground-fault circuit-interrupter protection as an integral part of the attachment plug or to incorporate it within the cord assembly not more than 300 mm (12 in.) from the attachment plug. This revision also addresses older vending machines and requires that they be connected to a GFCI-protected outlet. The new fine print note references industry and product standards that apply to vending machines.

Code Language
422.51

Cord-and-Plug-Connected Vending Machines

Cord-and-plug-connected vending machines manufactured or re-manufactured on or after January 1, 2005, shall include a ground-fault circuit interrupter as an integral part of the attachment plug or be located within 300 mm (12 in) of the attachment plug. Older vending machines manufactured or remanufactured prior to January 1, 2005, shall be connected to a GFCI-protected outlet. For the purpose of this section, the term *vending machine* means any self-service device that dispenses products or merchandise without the necessity of replenishing the device between each vending operation and is designed to require insertion of a coin, paper currency, token, card, key, or receipt of payment by other means.

FPN: For further information, see ANSI/UL 541-2005, *Standard for Refrigerated Vending Machines*, or ANSI/UL 751-2005, *Standard for Vending Machines*.

Summary of Change
A new last sentence and fine print note have been added to Section 422.51.

Electric Drinking Fountains
NEC, p. 287

Proposal 17-28
Log 506
ROP, p. 463

Comment 17-15
Log 463
ROC, p. 280

Analysis and Effect

This new section in Article 422 expands the protection provided by ground-fault circuit interrupters to outlets supplying electric drinking fountains. CMP-17 responded favorably to the information provided in Comment 17-15 to Proposal 17-28 by including this new section requiring GFCI protection for electric drinking fountains. Information provided indicated that fatalities have been attributed to these types of installations and appliances. Action by CMP-17 clearly indicates that this GFCI-protection requirement does not apply to bottled water coolers, but only to those electrical drinking fountains that provide a refrigeration feature as part of the appliance. The effect of this change is that all electric drinking fountains must be GFCI-protected, either as part of the drinking fountain assembly, or by GFCI protection of the circuit, or at the outlet to which the drinking fountain is connected.

Change at a Glance

Electric drinking water fountains must now be protected by ground-fault circuit interrupters. Bottled water coolers not affected by this new requirement.

Code Language
422.52
Electric Drinking Fountains
Electric drinking fountains shall be protected with ground-fault circuit-interrupter protection.

Summary of Change

A new section 422.52 has been added to Article 422 addressing ground-fault circuit-interrupter protection requirements for electric drinking fountains.

4

424.19

Disconnecting Means
NEC, p. 288

Proposal 17-31, 17-33
Log 388, 2036
ROP, p. 464

Comment 17-50
Log 464
ROC, p. 284

Analysis and Effect

Two additional sentences clarify the requirements related to the disconnecting means for fixed electric space-heating equipment. Substantiation with Proposal 17-31 identified the need to assist users with methods of determining the minimum rating of a disconnecting means supplying fixed electric space-heating equipment, which may include motor loads in addition to the heater load. The revision to this section makes it clear that the disconnecting means shall have an ampere rating not less than 125 percent of the total load of the motors and the heaters. The new last sentence relates to worker safety. The revision clarifies that the provisions for adding a lock to a switch or circuit breaker is required to remain in place whether or not the lock is installed. The change to this requirement does not exclude portable locking means that workers might carry to comply with other workplace safety rules, such as those in NFPA 70E; however, the new requirement is that if the switch or circuit breaker installed according to 424.19(A)(2)(2) is not within sight from the equipment it serves, it shall include lockable provisions that remain with and are either part of the equipment or an identified accessory feature intended for such applications.

Code Language
424.19
Disconnecting Means

Means shall be provided to simultaneously disconnect the heater, motor controller(s), and supplementary overcurrent protective device(s) of all fixed electric space-heating equipment from all ungrounded conductors. Where heating equipment is supplied by more than one source, the disconnecting means shall be grouped and marked. The disconnecting means specified in 424.19(A) and (B) shall have an ampere rating not less than 125 percent of the total load of the motors and the heaters. The provision for locking or adding a lock to the disconnecting means shall be installed on or at the switch or circuit breaker used as the disconnecting means and shall remain in place with or without the lock installed.

Summary of Change

Two additional sentences have been added to 424.19. The first sentence addresses minimum required ampere ratings for disconnects, and the second sentence addresses locking means characteristics for disconnecting means.

Change at a Glance

The disconnecting means covered by this section must have an ampere rating not less than 125% of the total of the motor and heater loads. The provisions for locking or adding a lock to the disconnect must remain in place whether or not the lock is installed.

Analysis of Changes *NEC*-2008

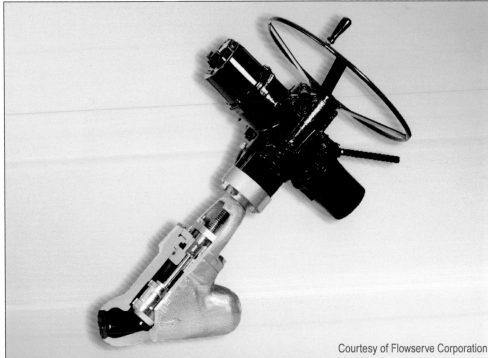

Courtesy of Flowserve Corporation

Valve Actuator Motor (VAM) Assemblies
NEC, p. 302

Proposal 11-17
Log 1691
ROP, p. 470

Comment 11-4
Log 814
ROC, p. 286

Analysis and Effect

This definition is now used in 430.102(A) Exception No. 3, which is new to *NEC*-2008. Valve actuator motors (VAMs) are typically utilized in industrial facilities for remotely opening or closing valves that control the flow of chemicals, petroleum products, water, wastewater or other types of liquids. These motors typically have short-time duty and high-torque characteristics. The conductors are sized based off the nameplate of the VAMs; the motors do not have a horsepower rating, due to their unique design. Each VAM is geared differently; therefore, these motors are rated by torque and not by horsepower. When the VAM is designed with more torque, the VAM will require more amperage based on that particular torque. VAMs are manufactured in 2-, 4-, 6-, and 8-pole motors. Each motor is rated by the full-load current and locked rotor current, depending upon motor size. VAMs are manufactured with internal automatic resetting thermal protection, and many are manufactured with reversing permanent split-capacitor type motors. They are available from 115 volts up to 480 volts ac, and with many different NEMA enclosures for different environments, including hazardous locations. VAMs typically, but not always, have the controller integral with the motor assembly and valve. The code-making panel's conclusion was that sizing conductors for VAMs could be accomplished through existing rules in 430.6(A)(1). Table 430.52 covers sizing ground-fault and short-circuit devices for VAMs under "single-phase motors," "ac polyphase motors other than wound rotor squirrel cage," or "ac polyphase motors other than Design B energy-efficient."

Code Language
430.2
Valve Actuator Motor (VAM) Assemblies

A manufactured assembly, used to operate a valve, consisting of an actuator motor and other components such as controllers, torque switches, limit switches, and overload protection.

FPN: VAMs typically have short-time duty and high-torque characteristics.

Summary of Change

This new definition of *valve actuated motor (VAM) assemblies* has been added to 430.2.

Change at a Glance

Valve actuated motors are now recognized in *Code* rules and the new term has been defined in 430.2.

4

430.11

Protection Against Liquids
NEC, p. 306

Proposal 11-22
Log 1502
ROP, p. 471

Comment
None

Change at a Glance

The revision clarifies requirements relating to protection for motors, motor terminals and motor lead insulation from liquids and damage from liquids, rather than from injury from liquids.

Analysis and Effect

The code panel voted to remove the word "injurious" from the previous text, because equipment cannot be injured but may be damaged by liquids. Motor enclosures and guards are intended to provide protection from spraying or dripping liquids. Motors must be installed as any other equipment, in a neat and workmanlike manner, with careful attention paid to mounting and cooling of the motor, and complying with all manufacturers' installation instructions and the listing instructions of other associated equipment. All of these requirements are found in chapter 1 of the *NEC*, along with types of enclosures for equipment, in Table 110.20. Often, more attention is given to the protection of motor controllers and control devices to assure that they are installed in a proper enclosure, than is given to the motor installation itself. This revision reminds installers, users, and inspectors of, and clarifies for them, the minimum requirements for protection against liquids in motor installations.

Code Language
430.11

Protection Against Liquids
Suitable guards or enclosures shall be provided to protect exposed current-carrying parts of motors and the insulation of motor leads where installed directly under equipment, or in other locations where dripping or spraying oil, water, or other liquid may occur, unless the motor is designed for the existing conditions.

Summary of Change

The word "injurious" has been removed from this section.

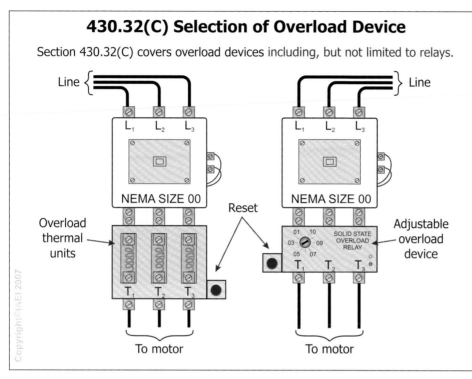

430.32(C) Selection of Overload Device

Section 430.32(C) covers overload devices including, but not limited to relays.

Line

Line

L_1 L_2 L_3

L_1 L_2 L_3

NEMA SIZE 00

NEMA SIZE 00

Reset

Overload thermal units

T_1 T_2 T_3

01 10
03 09
05 07

SOLID STATE OVERLOAD RELAY

T_1 T_2 T_3

Adjustable overload device

To motor

To motor

Copyright©IAEI 2007

Selection of Overload Device
NEC, p. 312

Proposal 11-37, 11-36
Log 157, 156
ROP, p. 475

Comment
None

Analysis and Effect

This revision covers all devices acceptable for use in providing overload protection by methods that comply with this section; coverage is not limited to just overload relays. Overload relays are devices, but not all overload protective devices are relays. Motor circuit protectors or fuses, for example, are types of devices which carry or control electric energy, but which do not utilize it for a purpose. (Properly selected fuses are permissible for motor overload protection). Also, after "incremental settings," the words "or sizing" have been added, because fuses (or overload heater relay elements) are sized as opposed to being adjusted, as a qualified person may adjust a device with adjustable settings with a screwdriver, for example. This revision aligns Section 430.32(C) with Sections 430.32(A)(1) and 430.32(B)(1) that refer to overload devices, not overload relays only, and clarifies *Code* language for installers, users, and inspectors.

Change at a Glance

Motor overload protection requirements in Section 430.32(C) have been revised to recognize devices in addition to overload relays that provide overload protection for motors.

Code Language
430.32(C)

Selection of Overload Device

Where the sensing element or setting or sizing of the overload device selected in accordance with 430.32(A)(1) and 430.32(B)(1) is not sufficient to start the motor or to carry the load, higher size sensing elements or incremental settings or sizing shall be permitted to be used, provided the trip current of the overload device does not exceed the following percentage of motor nameplate full-load current rating:

Motors with marked service factor	
1.15 or greater	140%
Motors with a marked temperature rise 40°C or less	140%
All other motors	130%

(See *Code* section for remainder of text).

Summary of Change

The word "relay" has been replaced with "device" in this section.

430.52(C)(1) Exception No. 2

Branch circuit

Disconnect

Where the rating specified in Table 430.52, or the rating modified by Exception No. 1, is not sufficient to carry the motor starting current...

Controller

Exception No. 2 is permitted when the next higher standard ampere rating allowed by Exception No. 1 is a standard size and is still not sufficient to start the motor.

Overload protection

Motor

Copyright© IAEI 2007

430.52 (C)(1) Exception No. 2

Rating or Setting In Accordance with Table 430.52
NEC, p. 314

Proposal 11-42
Log 2177
ROP, p. 476

Comment
None

REVISION!

Change at a Glance

Exception No. 2 is permitted when the next higher standard ampere rating allowed by Exception No. 1 is a standard size and still is not sufficient to start the motor.

Analysis and Effect

Section 430.52(C)(1) generally requires a motor branch-circuit short-circuit and ground-fault protective device to have a rating not to exceed the values in Table 430.52, with Exception No. 1 allowing an increase up to the next higher standard rating. Exception No. 2 addresses certain conditions where the branch-circuit short-circuit and ground-fault are insufficient to carry the starting current of the motor, and offers allowable increases in protective device ratings based on the type of device (fuse or breaker) applied in the circuit. The revision to Exception No. 2 clarifies that when the next higher standard size protective device permitted in Exception No. 1 is insufficient to carry the motor starting current, then Exception No. 2 can be applied in addition to conditions where the size selected is based on specific ratings specified in the table. Substantiation with the proposal provided a condition where the branch-circuit, short-circuit and ground-fault protective device rating ends up being a standard size and is still insufficient to carry the starting current of the motor. The revision allows Exception No. 2 to be applied where this situation occurs.

Code Language
430.52(C)(1)
Rating or Setting
In Accordance with Table 430.52
Exception No. 2: Where the rating specified in Table 430.52, or the rating modified by Exception No. 1, is not sufficient for the starting current of the motor: (Remainder of text unchanged)

Summary of Change

The words "or the rating modified by Exception No. 1" have been added to the exception.

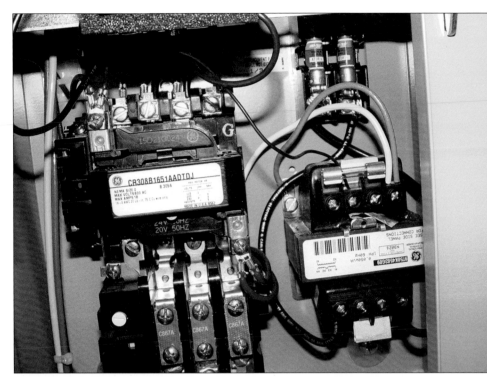

Electrical Arrangement of Control Circuits
NEC, p. 319

Proposal 11-52, 11-53
Log 838,1503
ROP, p. 479

Comment 11-19
Log 830
ROC, p. 291

Analysis and Effect

Action by CMP-11 removed the second paragraph of existing Section 430.73 that covers the electrical arrangement of motor control circuits and placed it in Section 430.74. Existing Section 430.74 has been relocated to a new Section 430.75. The first paragraph of existing Section 430.73 covering protection from physical damage for motor control circuits remains unchanged and alone in 430.73. Restructuring of these sections enhances usability, adds emphasis to the electrical arrangement of motor control circuits, places the electrical arrangement of motor control circuits in their own section, and emphasizes their importance for safety. Personnel safety is one of the two primary purposes of the *Code*. A ground fault in an improperly wired motor control circuit may cause it to malfunction and not shut off when it is required to, possibly causing serious injury to personnel or damage to property. This change emphasizes the importance of circuit arrangement for motor control circuits, and makes this important information regarding motor control circuit wiring easier to find. Further information regarding *Code* requirements for motor control circuits may be found in Part VI of Article 430. These changes are a good example of a code-making panel working positively to improve electrical safety and the usability of the *Code*.

Code Language
430.74

Electrical Arrangement of Control Circuits
Where one side of the motor control circuit is grounded, the motor control circuit shall be arranged so that an accidental ground in the control circuit remote from the motor controller will (1) not start the motor and (2) not bypass manually operated shutdown devices or automatic safety shutdown devices.

Summary of Change

Existing Section 430.74 has been re-numbered as 430.75. The second sentence of existing Section 430.73 has been moved to 430.74, and the first sentence of 430.73 remains in 430.73.

Change at a Glance

As reorganized, Section 430.73 covers protection requirements for control circuit conductors; 430.74 covers the electrical arrangement of control circuits; and the new 430.75 provides the requirements of control circuit disconnecting means.

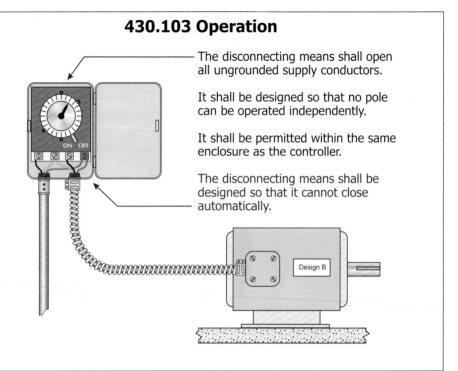

430.103 Operation

The disconnecting means shall open all ungrounded supply conductors.

It shall be designed so that no pole can be operated independently.

It shall be permitted within the same enclosure as the controller.

The disconnecting means shall be designed so that it cannot close automatically.

Copyright©IAEI 2007

Design B

430.103

Operation
NEC, p. 322

Proposal 11-71
Log 1115
ROP, p. 483

Comment
None

Change at a Glance

Disconnects covered by 430.103 are not permitted to close automatically.

Analysis and Effect

Information provided by the submitter indicated that automatically operated electrical disconnecting means, such as automatic time clock switches or other types of automatic switches, meet the criteria to qualify as a motor branch-circuit disconnecting means and controller as found in Sections 430.104, 430.110(A), 430.111(A) and (B)(1), 430.81(A) and 430.83(C) for many installations. Substantiation included with the proposal indicated that many of these types of switches have an external lever-operated switch mechanism, and raised concerns that if these types of switches are permitted as a disconnecting means for the motor, unsafe conditions may result. For example, if the time clock motor continues to run, the switch can automatically return to the *on* position, after manually being switched off, which could create a safety hazard for users or operators of the equipment or for those that perform maintenance or repairs on the system. The revision to the section clarifies for installers, users, and inspectors that these types of switches are not permitted to be used as the sole disconnecting means for a motor branch circuit, and that a manual disconnecting means meeting all appropriate requirements of the *Code* must be provided.

Code Language
430.103
Operation

The disconnecting means shall open all ungrounded supply conductors and shall be designed so that no pole can be operated independently. The disconnecting means shall be permitted in the same enclosure with the controller. The disconnecting means shall be designed so that it cannot be closed automatically.

Summary of Change

A new sentence has been added to the section that addresses automatically operated switches used as disconnecting means.

430.126 (A), (B), and (C)

Motor Overtemperature Protection
NEC, p. 325, 326

Proposal 11-78, 11-79, and 11-80
Log 3114, 1952, 1948
ROP, p. 485

Comment
None

Analysis and Effect

This *Analysis* text summarizes three NEMA proposals submitted to revise Section 430.126, all of which were accepted by Code-Making Panel 11. Information provided in the substantiation indicated that the requirements for overtemperature protection are dependent upon the application of the motor, and may not be required in all applications. The substantiation also emphasized that means to provide motor overtemperature protection are not limited to the controller or drive, but may be part of the motor system. Adjustable speed motors may be required to operate at reduced speeds or varying torque settings, which affect motor temperature. Some motors are externally cooled by air or liquids, and in these applications, using direct temperature sensing in the motor is preferred to better protect the motor from damage due to overtemperature. Other methods of protection may include some type of flow sensing meter or device that will shut down the motor if the cooling liquid system, for example, is not operating, for whatever reason. The addition of the text was made to better resemble industry practices, to clarify different options of acceptable motor overtemperature protection, which are more application specific, and to provide guidance for electrical inspectors as to what types of protection may be considered acceptable for protection of motors operated by adjustable speed drive controllers and equipment, which may be cooled by alternative means.

Code Language
430.126

Motor Overtemperature Protection

(A) General. Adjustable speed drive systems shall protect against motor overtemperature conditions where the motor is not rated to operate at the nameplate rated current over the speed range required by the application. This protection shall be provided… (See remainder of subdivision for *Code* text).

(B) Multiple Motor Applications. (See remainder of subdivision for *Code* text).

(C) Automatic Restarting and Orderly Shutdown. (See remainder of subdivision for *Code* text).

Summary of Change

Section 430.126 has been revised extensively for motor overtemperature protection. Former subdivision (B) has been deleted, and subdivisions (C) and (D) have become (B) and (C), respectively.

Change at a Glance

Adjustable speed drives are required to protect motors from overtemperature conditions where motors are not rated to operate at the nameplate rated current over the speed range required for the installed application of the motor.

430.243

Portable Motors
NEC, p. 327

Proposal 11-87
Log 106
ROP, p. 486

Comment 11-35
Log 791
ROC, p. 294

Change at a Glance

Grounding requirements for motors correlate effectively with the equipment grounding requirements in 250.114. Exemptions from the grounding requirements are provided in this section.

430.243 Portable Motors

Frames of portable motors operating at over 150 volts shall be guarded or grounded.

Listed motor-operated tools, appliances, and equipment are not required to be grounded where they are protected by a system of double insulation.

Double-insulated equipment must be distinctly marked.

Copyright © IAEI 2007

Listed motor-operated tools, appliances, and equipment connected by cord and plug are not required to be grounded unless specified in 250.114.

Analysis and Effect

This section has been revised to bring its requirements into line with those currently provided in Article 250 regarding the grounding of motors. The frames of portable motors supplied by a premises wiring systems that operate over 150 volts shall be grounded or guarded. Motor-operated appliances operating at not more than 150 V to ground and that do not involve water or use in wet locations, and that are currently listed may be connected by a two-conductor cord and attachment plug. The listing requirements for these appliances require leakage currents available at accessible metal parts to be monitored during various operating conditions including, in some cases, high humidity conditions, and to not exceed prescribed limits in the product standards. Section 250.114 covers grounding for residential and non-residential applications of motor-operated appliances, which include equipment that may be: double insulated, guarded, portable, connected by a cord and attachment plug, and operated either grounded or ungrounded, providing that all appropriate requirements are met per the application, use, and location of equipment. The actions by CMP-11 bring clarity and consistency to this section, and improve usability for the manufacturer, installer, user, and inspector as to what requirements must be met before the grounding requirement can be relaxed.

Code Language
430.243
Portable Motors
The frames of portable motors that operate over 150 volts to ground shall be guarded or grounded.

FPN No. 1 See 250.114(4) for grounding of portable appliances in other than residential occupancies.

Exception No. 1: Listed motor-operated tools, listed motor-operated appliances, and listed motor-operated equipment shall not be required to be grounded where protected by a system of double insulation or its equivalent. Double-insulated equipment shall be distinctively marked.

Exception No. 2: Listed motor-operated tools, listed motor-operated appliances, and listed motor-operated equipment connected by a cord and attachment plug other than those required to be grounded in accordance with 250.114.

Summary of Change

Section 430.243 has been revised to (1) add an exception for listed double insulated equipment similar to the current exception to 250.114; and (2) add an exception to refer to Section 250.114 for listed motor-operated appliances.

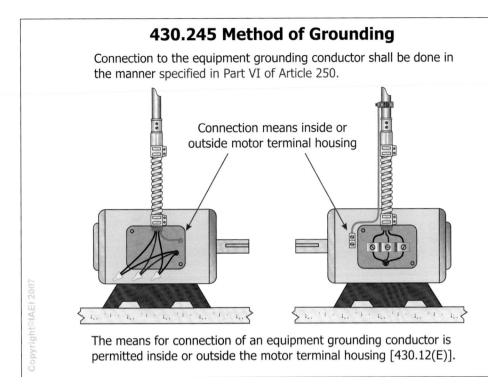

430.245 Method of Grounding

Connection to the equipment grounding conductor shall be done in the manner specified in Part VI of Article 250.

Connection means inside or outside motor terminal housing

The means for connection of an equipment grounding conductor is permitted inside or outside the motor terminal housing [430.12(E)].

Copyright©IAEI 2007

430.245

Method of Grounding
NEC, p. 327

Proposal 11-87a
Log 916
ROP, p. 487

Comment
None

Analysis and Effect

The words "where required" have been removed from Section 430.245. Grounding of all motor equipment is required unless (1) the motor or its associated equipment is permitted to be operated ungrounded; (2) the motor is double-insulated, guarded or inaccessible to contact with persons, or (3) it operates at 50 volts or less. General requirements for grounding equipment, whether required to be grounded or permitted to be grounded, including motors and motor-operated equipment, are found in Part VI of Article 250. The revision has been made in 430.245 to guide *Code* users to the general requirements for motor grounding, which are found in Article 250, and to provide specifics related to grounding of motor terminal housings, separate motor junction boxes, and controller-mounted devices in 430.245. Where grounding is not required but is done by choice, Article 250 should apply. Where grounding is done by choice, the requirements in Part VI of Article 250 and those of 430.245 apply. These changes correlate with the action on Proposal 11-1, which requires equipment to be grounded to be connected to an equipment grounding conductor.

Change at a Glance

Whether motors are grounded as a requirement or grounded by choice, the rules in Part VI of Article 250 apply.

Code Language
430.245

Method of Grounding
Connection to the equipment grounding conductor shall be done in the manner specified in Part VI of Article 250.

Summary of Change

This section has been revised to correlate better with grounding requirements found in Part VI of Article 250.

440.12 (A)(1) Exception and (B)(2), Exception

Rating and Interrupting Capacity
NEC, p. 333

Proposal 11-92
Log 1069
ROP, p. 487

Comment
None

Analysis and Effect

Listed unfused motor circuit switches, without fuseholders, having a horsepower rating not less than the equivalent horsepower determined in accordance with 440.12(A) or (B), are permitted to have an ampere rating less than 115 percent of the sum of all currents. The revision clarifies that unfused switches—commonly known as non-fused switches—are rated at 100 percent continuous current capacity, and if they also have the needed horsepower rating required for the disconnecting means, may be used to disconnect a hermetic refrigerant motor compressor or combination loads of compressor equipment. The revision also makes it clear that fused switches which have the fuse holders bypassed are not permitted for this purpose. The proposal was accepted by CMP-11 to be consistent with the product standards.

Summary of Change

The words "without fuseholders" have been added to the existing exception and the new exception.

Change at a Glance

Listed unfused motor circuit switches, *without fuseholders*, which have the required horsepower rating, are permitted to have an ampere rating less than 115 percent of the sum of all currents for the hermetic refrigerant motor compressor equipment.

Code Language
440.12(A)
Rating and Interrupting Capacity

(A) Hermetic Refrigerant Motor-Compressor. A disconnecting means serving a hermetic refrigerant motor-compressor shall be... (unchanged, see *Code* text).
(1) Ampere Rating. The ampere rating shall be at least 115 percent of the nameplate... (unchanged, see *Code* text).

Exception: A listed unfused motor circuit switch, without fuseholders, having a horsepower rating not less than the equivalent horsepower determined in accordance with 440.12(A)(2) shall be permitted to have an ampere rating less than 115 percent of the specified current.

(B) Combination Loads
(2) Full-Load Current Equivalent. The ampere rating of the disconnecting means shall be at least 115 percent... (unchanged, see *Code* text).

Exception: A listed unfused motor circuit switch, without fuseholders, having a horsepower rating not less than the equivalent horsepower determined by 440.12(B)(1) shall be permitted to have an ampere rating less than 115 percent of the sum of all currents.

440.14 Location

Disconnect is required to be installed within sight and readily accessible from air-conditioning and refrigerating equipment

Disconnect is permitted to be installed on or within the equipment

Disconnect shall not obscure the equipment data nameplate

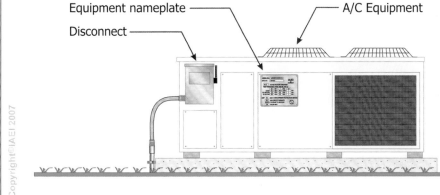

Equipment nameplate

Disconnect

A/C Equipment

440.14

Location
NEC, p. 334

Proposal 11-93
Log 124
ROP, p. 488

Comment
None

REVISION!

Analysis and Effect

Section 440.4(B) presently requires manufacturers to provide a visible data nameplate. Section 440.14 addresses the requirements for disconnecting means for air-conditioning and refrigerating equipment. The general requirement in this section is that disconnecting means be "located within sight from and readily accessible from" the equipment. The provisions of this section also permit the required disconnect to be "installed on or within" the equipment. This rule has been revised to clarify that the disconnecting means mounted on the air-conditioning and refrigerating equipment shall be installed so as not to create an obstruction for viewing the information on the equipment data nameplate. Substantiation provided with the proposal draws attention to installations where the nameplate was hidden by the field-installed disconnecting means required by this section. This revision should clarify that if the disconnect is installed on the equipment, it must not obscure the information on the equipment data nameplate; it must allow for ready and safe acquisition of pertinent information such as voltage, minimum circuit ampacity, maximum overcurrent protection, and other information such as refrigerant pressures and other necessary information for service personnel. This section also restricts disconnects from being installed on equipment covers or panels designed to permit access to the equipment.

Code Language
440.14
Location

Disconnecting means shall be located within sight from and readily accessible from the air-conditioning or refrigerating equipment. The disconnecting means shall be permitted to be installed on or within the air-conditioning or refrigerating equipment.

The disconnecting means shall not be located on panels that are designed to allow access to the air-conditioning or refrigeration equipment or to obscure the equipment nameplate(s).

Summary of Change

The words "or to obscure the equipment nameplate(s)" have been added to the last sentence of this section.

Change at a Glance

Disconnects mounted on air-conditioning equipment must not cover the equipment nameplate(s).

4

440.54(A)

Overload Protection
NEC, p. 336

Proposal 11-102
Log 411
ROP, p. 489

Comment
None

Change at a Glance

The revision clarifies that the equipment must identify the short-circuit and ground-fault protective device required.

Analysis and Effect

This change is an effort to promote consistency in how the term *approved* is being used throughout the *NEC*. Both *approved* and *identified* are defined in Article 100. *Approved*, "acceptable to the authority having jurisdiction." *Identified* (as applied to equipment), "recognizable as suitable for the specific purpose, function, use, environment, application, and so forth, where described in a particular *Code* requirement." The code-making panel recognizes that the more appropriate word to use here is *identified* because the manufacturer would provide these marks, and the equipment would be evaluated and identified for the use. For overload protection of motor-compressors and equipment that are on 15- or 20-ampere branch circuits which are not cord- and attachment plug-connected, the change will assist installers verify that the equipment is identified for the intended use, thus avoiding questions and potential misunderstandings by enforcement authorities; and it will assist inspectors by having ready for inspection, equipment that is marked as identified for the use, thus avoiding further investigation in order to see whether or not they can approve the equipment.

Code Language
440.54

Motor-Compressors and Equipment on 15- or 20- Ampere Branch Circuits – Not Cord-and-Attachment-Plug-Connected
Overload protection for...
(This portion of *Code* text remains unchanged).

(A) Overload Protection. The motor-compressor shall be provided with overload protection selected as specified in 440.52(A). Both the controller and motor overload protective device shall be identified for installation with the short-circuit and ground-fault protective device for the branch circuit to which the equipment is connected.

Summary of Change

The word "approved" has been replaced with the word "identified" in subdivision (A) of the section.

440.55(A) Overload Protection

Cord-and-plug-connected motor compressors and equipment on 15- and 20-ampere branch circuits

Motor compressor shall be provided with overload protection as specified in 440.52(A).

The controller and the overload protective device shall be identified for installation with the short-circuit and ground-fault protective device for the branch circuit to which the equipment is connected.

Identified

Motor compressor or equipment

Branch circuit

Copyright©IAEI 2007

Overload Protection
NEC, p. 337

Proposal 11-103
Log 408
ROP, p. 489

Comment
None

Analysis and Effect

The change is an effort to promote consistency in how the term *approved* is being used throughout the *NEC*. Both *approved* and *identified* are defined in Article 100. *Approved*, "acceptable to the authority having jurisdiction." *Identified* (as applied to equipment), "recognizable as suitable for the specific purpose, function, use, environment, application, and so forth, where described in a particular *Code* requirement." The code-making panel recognizes that the more appropriate word to use in this section is "identified" because the manufacturer would provide these marks, and the equipment would be evaluated and identified for the use.

For overload protection of motor-compressors and equipment that are cord- and attachment plug-connected and installed on 15- or 20-ampere branch circuits, the change will assist installers, as they verify that the equipment is identified for the intended use, thus avoiding questions and potential misunderstandings by enforcement authorities; and it will assist inspectors by having ready for inspection, equipment that is marked as identified for the use, thus avoiding further investigation in order to see whether or not they can approve the equipment.

Change at a Glance

The revision clarifies that the equipment must identify the short-circuit and ground-fault protective device required for the branch circuit connected.

Code Language
440.55

Cord-and-Attachment-Plug-Connected Motor-Compressors and Equipment on 15- or 20-Ampere Branch Circuits.
Overload protection for...
(This portion of *Code* text remains unchanged).

(A) Overload Protection. The motor-compressor shall be provided with overload protection selected as specified in 440.52(A). Both the controller and motor overload protective device shall be identified for installation with the short-circuit and ground-fault protective device for the branch circuit to which the equipment is connected.

Summary of Change

The word "approved" has been replaced with the word "identified" in subdivision (A) of the section.

460.10, 460.27

Grounding
NEC, p. 349

Proposal 11-109, 11-110
Log 1497, 1498
ROP, p. 497

Comment
None

Change at a Glance

Capacitor cases required to be grounded must be connected to the equipment grounding conductor.

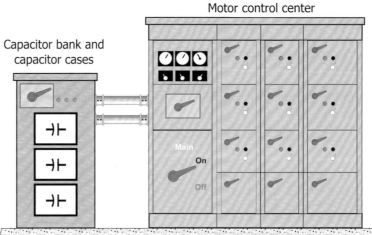

460.10 and 460.27 Capacitor Grounding

Motor control center

Capacitor bank and capacitor cases

Main
On
Off

Copyright©IAEI 2007

Capacitor cases are required to be connected to an equipment grounding conductor unless otherwise permitted in the exceptions.

Grounding requirements in 460.10 and 460.27 are more prescriptive.

Analysis and Effect

Two revisions clarify that capacitor cases are required to be connected to the equipment grounding conductor, rather than simply to be grounded per Article 250. Section 460.10 affects installations rated at 600 volts or less, and 460.27 gives grounding requirements for capacitors rated over 600 volts. These changes correlate with other global changes in the *Code* that clarify the use of appropriate grounding and bonding terms. The changes give more prescriptive language, and clarify that generally, for the purpose of grounding equipment, electrical equipment is required to be connected to the equipment grounding conductor. Types of equipment grounding conductors and methods of connecting equipment grounding conductors are found in Parts VI and VII of Article 250. The only exception is for capacitor installations operating at over 600 volts, where the capacitor units are supported on a structure designed to operate at other than ground potential, such as in some installations on industrial premises that incorporate ungrounded systems.

Code Language
460.10
Grounding

Capacitor cases shall be connected to the equipment grounding conductor.

Exception: Capacitor cases shall not be connected to the equipment grounding conductor where the capacitor units are supported on a structure designed to operate at other than ground potential.

460.27
Grounding

Capacitor cases shall be connected to the equipment grounding conductor. If the capacitor neutral point is connected to a grounding electrode conductor, the connection shall be made in accordance with Part III of Article 250.

Exception: Capacitor cases shall not be connected to the equipment grounding conductor where the capacitor units are supported on a structure designed to operate at other than ground potential.

Summary of Change

The words "shall be connected to an equipment grounding conductor" have been incorporated into these sections.

Analysis of Changes *NEC*-2008

480.5

Disconnecting Means
NEC, p. 351

Proposal 13-16
Log 1947
ROP, p. 498

Comment 13-21
Log 1421
ROC, p. 301

Analysis and Effect

Action by CMP-13 on Comment 13-21 (Log No. 1421) resulted in a new requirement for installing a disconnecting means for all ungrounded conductors derived from battery systems. The disconnecting means is required to be located within sight from and readily accessible from the battery system. Substantiation in the proposal and comment clearly identified a safety concern for those involved in maintenance operations of battery systems. The requirement for providing a disconnecting means addresses concerns about personnel safety expressed in the negative comments to the proposals. The disconnecting means is now a requirement for all battery systems over 30 volts. This new requirement also correlates with a requirement for battery conductor overcurrent protection as provided in 240.21(H) which was accepted by Panel 10 as a result of actions on Comment 10-13 (Log No. 1846) to Proposal 10-33 (Log. No. 1672).

Change at a Glance

A disconnecting means is required for all ungrounded conductors derived from a battery system, and it must be readily accessible from and located within sight from the battery system.

Code Language
480.5

Disconnecting Means

A disconnecting means shall be provided for all ungrounded conductors derived from a stationary battery system over 30 volts. A disconnecting means shall be readily accessible and located within sight of the battery system.

Summary of Change

A new section 480.5 covering battery disconnecting means requirements has been added to Article 480.

Analysis of Changes *NEC*-2008

Chapter

5

Selected •••••••• Changes

500.1,
500.5(A)
500.5(B)
500.5(B)(1)
500.5(B)(2)
500.5(D)
500.5(D)(1)
500.5(D)(2)
500.8(A)(1)
500.8(A)(6)
503.1, 503.5
503.128
503.130(A)
503.140
503.145
504.10(B)

Article 506
506.2
506.5
506.5(B)(1)
506.5(B)(2)
506.5(B)(3)
506.6(C)
506.6(D)
506.9(B)
506.16, 506.17(5)
506.20(E)(2)

Scope
NEC, 358

Proposal 14-1a
Log CP1400
ROP, p. 503

Comment
None

Change at a Glance

Words were changed in the *Code* to make it clear that locations with vapors produced from both flammable and combustible liquids are principle factors that prompt requirements for area classification and special consideration for electrical equipment and installations.

Analysis of Changes *NEC*-2008

Analysis and Effect

Action by CMP-14 adds the terms *flammable liquid-produced vapors* and *combustible liquid-produced vapors* to the list of materials that require an analysis to determine if special electrical equipment and wiring is needed to minimize the risk of fire or explosion hazards. This revision clarifies that locations with vapors produced from both flammable and combustible liquids are a principle contributing factor that prompts requirements for area classification and special consideration for electrical equipment and installations. The literal text of previous editions of the *Code* applied only to flammable liquids and did not include combustible liquids or the vapors produced by either of these materials. While many *NEC* users recognized the need to address combustible liquids when higher temperatures were encountered, the revision makes it clear the concerns for electrical installations are the same. These revisions were made globally in affected sections of Articles 500 through 506 to provide uniform use and application of the terms and phrases. Examples of combustible liquids are acetic acid, acrylic acid, butyl acetate, and ethyl butanol. Refer to NFPA 30A for additional information about combustible liquids and flammable liquids.

Code Language
500.1
Scope — Articles 500 Through 504

Articles 500 through 504 cover the requirements for electrical and electronic equipment and wiring for all voltages…where fire or explosion hazards may exist due to flammable gases, flammable liquid-produced vapors, combustible liquid-produced vapors, combustible dusts, or ignitible fibers/flyings.

See other sections of the *NEC* that refer to flammable gases, flammable liquid-produced vapors, combustible liquid-produced vapors, combustible dusts, or ignitible fibers/flyings.

Summary of Change

This change revises the phrase "flammable gases or vapors, flammable liquids, combustible dusts, or ignitible fibers or flyings" to "flammable gases, flammable liquid-produced vapors, combustible liquid-produced vapors, combustible dusts, or ignitible fibers/flyings" in multiple sections within Articles 500, 501, 502, 503, 504, and 506. An editorial change revises the term *fibers or flyings* to *fibers/flyings*.

3.3.25.1 Combustible Liquid. Any liquid that has a closed-cup flash point at or above 100°F (37.8°C), as determined by the test procedures and apparatus set forth in 1.7.4. Combustible liquids are classified as Class II or Class III as follows: (1) Class II Liquid — any liquid that has a flash point at or above 100°F (37.8°C) and below 140°F (60°C); (2) Class IIIA — any liquid that has a flash point at or above 140°F (60°C), but below 200°F (93°C); (3) Class IIIB — any liquid that has a flash point at or above 200°F (93°C).

3.3.25.2 Flammable Liquid. Any liquid that has a closed-cup flash point below 100°F (37.8°C), as determined by the test procedures and apparatus set forth in 1.7.4. Flammable liquids are classified as Class I as follows: Class I Liquid — any liquid that has a closed-cup flash point below 100°F (37.8°C) and a Reid vapor pressure not exceeding 40 psia (2068.6 mm Hg) at 100°F (37.8°C), as determined by ASTM D 323, Standard Method of Test for Vapor Pressure of Petroleum Products (Reid Method). Class I liquids are further classified as follows: (1) Class IA liquids — those liquids that have flash points below 73°F (22.8°C) and boiling points below 100°F (37.8°C); (2) Class IB liquids — those liquids that have flash points below 73°F (22.8°C) and boiling points at or above 100°F (37.8°C); (3) Class IC liquids — those liquids that have flash points at or above 73°F (22.8°C), but below 100°F (37.8°C).

— Extracted from NFPA 30A, *Flammable and Combustible Liquids Code*. Used as permitted by NFPA.

5

501.5, 502.5, 503.5

Special Occupancies, Equipment or Conditions
None

Proposal 14-24, 14-55, 14-75
Log 3194, 3197, 3198
ROP, p. 511, 520, 525

Comment
None

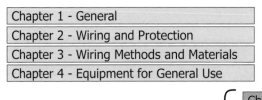

501.5, 502.5, and 503.5 Deleted Text

| Chapter 1 - General |
| Chapter 2 - Wiring and Protection |
| Chapter 3 - Wiring Methods and Materials |
| Chapter 4 - Equipment for General Use |

} Applies generally to all electrical installations

Supplements or modifies Chapters 1 through 4 {

| Chapter 5 - Special Occupancies |
| Chapter 6 - Special Equipment |
| Chapter 7 - Special Conditions |

Copyright©IAEI 2007

Section 90.3 already provides the requirements that Chapters 1 through 4 apply generally and those rules are often modified by Chapters 5, 6, and 7.

This revision removes first paragraph and exception in each article to eliminate the unnecessary redundancy.

Analysis and Effect

Section 90.3 provides guidance for the application of the *NEC* and clearly indicates that chapters 1 through 4 apply generally, and chapters 5, 6, and 7 revise or supplement the general rules for "special occupancies, equipment or conditions." The deleted text had been included in Articles 501, 502, and 503 as a precaution to users so that general requirements were not overlooked, while they focused more specific attention on the "special" requirements. Deleting this information clarifies that the application and relationship of special requirements and general requirements in Articles 501, 502, and 503 are not different from other requirements in chapter 5, 6 and 7.

Change at a Glance

Section 90.3 already provides the same requirements. This revision removes the redundancy.

Code Language

None because text and exceptions were deleted.

Summary of Change

The first paragraph and exception in Sections 501.5, 502.5, and 503.5 have been deleted.

Analysis of Changes *NEC*-2008

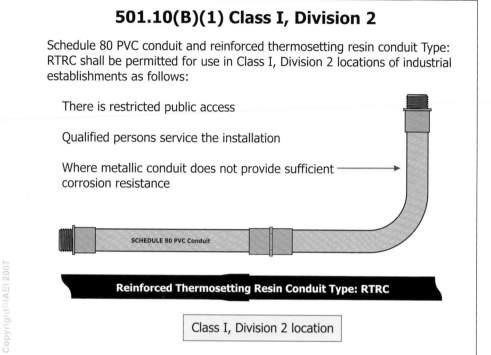

501.10(B)(1) Class I, Division 2

Schedule 80 PVC conduit and reinforced thermosetting resin conduit Type: RTRC shall be permitted for use in Class I, Division 2 locations of industrial establishments as follows:

There is restricted public access

Qualified persons service the installation

Where metallic conduit does not provide sufficient corrosion resistance

SCHEDULE 80 PVC Conduit

Reinforced Thermosetting Resin Conduit Type: RTRC

Class I, Division 2 location

501.10(B)(1)(7)

Wiring Methods
Class I, Division 2
NEC, p. 367

Proposal 14-33, 14-33a
Log 3629, CP 1402
ROP, p. 514, 515

Comment 14-8
Log 548
ROC, p. 305

Analysis and Effect

Wiring methods have been expanded and listed in 501.10(B)(1) to include reinforced thermosetting resin conduit (RTRC) and Schedule 80 PVC conduit. Although there were allowances in the *NEC* for nonmetallic wiring methods in Class I, Division 2 locations, substantiation indicated that many petroleum and/or chemical facilities include areas with a highly corrosive environment that can potentially damage metal raceways. This revision allows an option for using suitable nonmetallic conduits where exposed to physical damage. The result was the creation of proposal 14-33a that incorporates these two nonmetallic wiring methods. This type of wiring in Class I, Division 2 locations is limited for use only in industrial establishments with restricted public access, where the conditions of maintenance and supervision ensure that only qualified persons service the installation, and where metallic conduit does not provide sufficient corrosion resistance. Although this section has been expanded to include Type RTRC and PVC conduit as wiring methods in Division 2 locations, restrictions in item (7) have inherent limitations on the use of nonmetallic wiring methods in Class I, Division 2 hazardous locations. These revisions identify where seals are required for boundaries as defined in 501.15(A)(4). The Class I, Division 1 wiring method shall extend into the Division 2 area to the explosionproof seal, which is required to be located on the Division 2 side of the boundary between the Class I, Division 1 and Division 2 locations.

Code Language

501.10(B)

Class I, Division 2

(1) General

(7) In industrial establishments with restricted public access where the conditions of maintenance and supervision ensure that only qualified persons service the installation and where metallic conduit does not provide sufficient corrosion resistance, reinforced thermosetting resin conduit (RTRC), factory elbows, and associated fittings, all marked with the suffix –XW, and Schedule 80 PVC conduit, factory elbows, and associated fittings shall be permitted.

Where seals are required for boundary conditions as defined in 501.15(A)(4), the Division 1 wiring method shall extend into the Division 2 area to the seal, which shall be located on the Division 2 side of the Division 1–Division 2 boundary.

Summary of Change

A new item (7) has been added to Section 501.10(B)(1).

Change at a Glance

In industrial locations, where metallic conduit does not provide sufficient corrosion resistance, Schedule 80 PVC conduit and Type RTRC conduit, with their factory elbows and associated fittings may be installed if all conditions in the requirement are met.

501.30(B)

Types of Equipment Grounding Conductors
NEC, p. 372

Proposal 14-44
Log 1504
ROP, p. 517

Comment
None

Change at a Glance

Flexible conduit and liquid-tight flexible metal conduit generally are not permitted to be used as an equipment grounding conductor in Class I, Division 2 locations without an additional bonding jumper installed.

501.30(B) Types of Equipment Grounding Conductors

Flexible metal conduit and liquidtight flexible metal conduit shall not be used as the sole ground-fault current path.

Where equipment bonding jumpers (internal or external) are installed, they shall comply with 250.102.

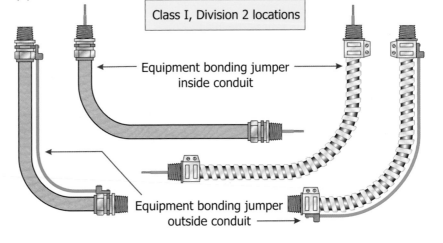

Class I, Division 2 locations

Equipment bonding jumper inside conduit

Equipment bonding jumper outside conduit

Copyright©IAEI 2007

Analysis and Effect

Section 501.30(B) provides specific requirements for flexible metal conduit and liquidtight flexible metal conduit used as wiring methods in Class I, Division 2 locations. Section 250.118 recognizes these two wiring methods as equipment grounding conductors generally, but there are specific restrictions such as length, rating of overcurrent devices protecting the conductors, types of fittings, and whether the flexible wiring is to be installed where flexibility (anticipated movement) is necessary after installation. Section 501.30(B) modifies the general requirements in 250.118(5) and (6) by being more restrictive and does not permit the flexible conduit to be used as an equipment grounding conductor without an additional bonding jumper being installed. As revised, this section will clearly still permit these flexible methods but they are not permitted to serve as the sole ground-fault current path, which requires the use of equipment bonding jumpers. These equipment bonding jumpers must be installed to meet the requirements of 250.102 which addresses the maximum length and sizing provisions for internally or externally installed equipment bonding jumpers. The revision provides clarification of requirements for equipment grounding and bonding in hazardous (classified) locations while improving correlation with the general equipment grounding requirements provided in Article 250.

Code Language
501.30(B)

Types of Equipment Grounding Conductors
Flexible metal conduit and liquidtight flexible metal conduit shall not be used as the sole ground-fault current path. Where equipment bonding jumpers are installed, they shall comply with 250.102.

The exception remains unchanged.

Summary of Change

This section has been revised to remove the text "flexible metal conduit and liquidtight flexible metal conduit is used as permitted by 501.10(B) and is to be relied on to complete a sole equipment grounding path." The remainder of the text in this section was revised to clarify the requirements.

Analysis of Changes *NEC*-2008

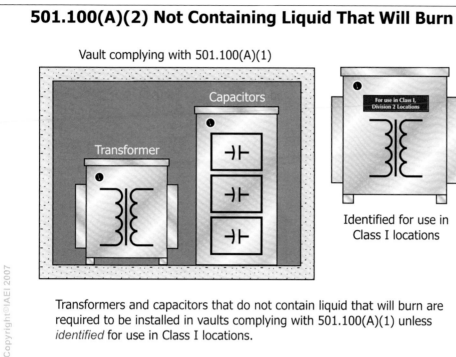

501.100(A)(2) Not Containing Liquid That Will Burn

Vault complying with 501.100(A)(1)

Capacitors

Transformer

For use in Class I,
Division 2 Locations

Identified for use in
Class I locations

Transformers and capacitors that do not contain liquid that will burn are required to be installed in vaults complying with 501.100(A)(1) unless *identified* for use in Class I locations.

Copyright©IAEI 2007

501.100 (A)(2)

Not Containing Liquid That Will Burn
NEC, p. 372

Proposal 14-47
Log 622
ROP, p. 518

Comment
None

REVISION

Analysis and Effect

This revision provides clarity and improves usability of this requirement. *Approved* is defined in Article 100 as "acceptable to the authority having jurisdiction." Equipment used in a hazardous (classified) location is required to be approved by the authority having jurisdiction as provided in 110.2. The factors that serve as a basis for inspector approvals of installations and systems in hazardous (classified) locations are the appropriate use of listed or labeled equipment, a manufacturer's self evaluation or owner's engineering judgment, and equipment that is identified for specific use as provided in 500.8(A)(1). The revision to this rule clarifies that transformers and capacitors that (1) do not contain liquid that will burn, and (2) are not installed in a vault are required to be identified for installation in those hazardous (classified) locations. Such identification is typically marked on the equipment to provide users with direction on equipment use and suitability, along with other necessary installation requirements. This revision is also consistent with recent changes within the hazardous (classified) locations articles in chapter 5 that were targeted at addressing the appropriate use of the terms *listed*, *identified*, and *approved*.

Code Language
501.100(A)(2)

Not Containing Liquid That Will Burn

Transformers and capacitors that do not contain a liquid that will burn shall be installed in vaults complying with 501.100(A)(1) or be identified for Class I locations.

Summary of Change

The word "approved" has been replaced by the word "identified" in this section.

Change at a Glance

Transformers and capacitors that do not contain a liquid that will burn must either be installed in vaults complying with 501.100(A)(1), or be *identified* for Class I locations.

5

503.30(B)

Types of Equipment Grounding Conductors
NEC, p. 383

Proposal 14-81a
Log CP 1405
ROP, p. 526

Comment
None

Change at a Glance

Liquidtight flexible metal conduit generally is not permitted to be used as an equipment grounding conductor in Class III, Division 1 and Division 2 locations without an additional bonding jumper installed.

503.30(B) Types of Equipment Grounding Conductors

Liquidtight flexible metal conduit shall not be used as the sole ground-fault current path.

Where equipment bonding jumpers (internal or external) are installed, they shall comply with 250.102.

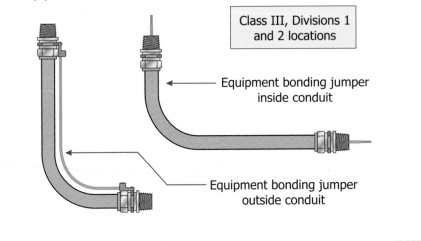

Class III, Divisions 1 and 2 locations

Equipment bonding jumper inside conduit

Equipment bonding jumper outside conduit

Copyright©IAEI 2007

Analysis and Effect

Section 503.10 provides the suitable wiring methods for use in Class III, Division 1 or 2 locations. Where flexibility is necessary, liquidtight flexible metal conduit is permitted where the requirements in 503.140 are met. Flexible metal conduit is not a wiring method recognized by 503.10(A) as being suitable for use in a Class III location. Section 503.30(B) provides specific requirements for liquidtight flexible metal conduit used as wiring method in Class III locations. Section 250.118 recognizes this wiring method as an equipment grounding conductor generally, but there are specific restrictions such as length, rating of overcurrent devices protecting the conductors, types of fittings, and whether the flexible wiring is installed where flexibility (anticipated movement) is necessary after installation. Section 503.30(B) modifies the general requirements in 250.118(6) by being more restrictive and does not permit the liquidtight flexible metal conduit to be used as an equipment grounding conductor without an additional bonding jumper installed. These equipment bonding jumpers must be installed to meet the requirements of 250.102 which addresses the maximum length and sizing provisions for internally or externally installed equipment bonding jumpers. The revision clarifies the requirements for equipment grounding and bonding in hazardous (classified) locations while improving correlation with the general equipment grounding requirements provided in Article 250.

Code Language
503.30(B)
Types of Equipment Grounding Conductors
Liquidtight flexible metal conduit shall not be used as the sole ground-fault current path. Where equipment bonding jumpers are installed, they shall comply with 250.102.

The exception remains unchanged.

Summary of Change

This section has been revised to restrict liquidtight flexible metal conduit from being used as the sole ground-fault current path.

504.2

Simple Apparatus
NEC, p. 385

Proposal 14-86
Log 2457
ROP, p. 527

Comment 14-39
Log 127
ROC, p. 313

Analysis and Effect

The revision to this fine print note expands the information to provide some specific examples of apparatus that qualify as *simple apparatus* and better aligns the *NEC* definition of the term with that used in the international arena. Item (b) now provides two examples of devices that store energy and may qualify as simple apparatus based on well-defined parameters. The substantiation identified capacitors and inductors as examples of such qualifying components. This revision will allow these additional components, without evaluation by a qualified electrical testing laboratory, to be included as part of an intrinsically safe system. This revision places additional responsibility on the installer and approving authority to understand and determine the impact of these simple components used in the overall intrinsically safe system.

Change at a Glance

Components that store energy, such as capacitors or inductors, now are permitted to be included as part of an intrinsically safe system without evaluation by a qualified electrical testing laboratory.

Code Language
504.2

Simple Apparatus
FPN: The following are examples of simple apparatus:

(a) ...text remains unchanged.

(b) Sources of stored energy consisting of single components in simple circuits with well-defined parameters, for example, capacitors or inductors, whose values are considered when determining the overall safety of the system

(c) Sources of generated energy, for example, thermocouples and photocells, which do not generate more than 1.5 V, 100 mA, and 25 mW

Summary of Change

Item (b) following the definition of the term *simple apparatus* in the FPN has been revised and former (b) has been re-identified as item (c).

5

504.70

Sealing
NEC, p. 387

Proposal 14-97
Log 2504
ROP, p. 529

Comment
None

504.70 Sealing

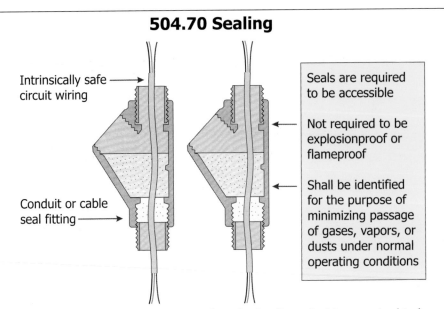

Intrinsically safe circuit wiring

Conduit or cable seal fitting

Seals are required to be accessible

Not required to be explosionproof or flameproof

Shall be identified for the purpose of minimizing passage of gases, vapors, or dusts under normal operating conditions

Copyright©AEI 2007

Conduit and cable seals for intrinsically safe circuits and wiring required to be sealed in accordance with 501.15, 502.15, 505.16, and 506.16, shall be sealed to mimize the passage of gases, vapors, or dusts.

Change at a Glance

Conduit and cable seals containing intrinsically safe circuit wiring are not required to be explosionproof or flameproof, but shall be accessible, and identified for the purpose of minimizing passage of gases, vapors, or dusts under normal operating conditions.

Analysis and Effect

Section 501.15(B)(2) of *NEC*-2005 was revised to recognize that boundary seals at Class I, Division 2 locations are not required to be explosionproof, but are required to be identified for the purpose of minimizing the passage of gases. Similar changes have been incorporated into 504.70 that deal with conduit and cable seals for intrinsically safe circuit and system wiring. While there is no need for explosionproof sealing techniques for intrinsically safe circuits or systems, these changes clearly require the sealing fitting, technique, and material used to accomplish the seal to be identified for the specific purpose of minimizing gas or vapor passage across the seal. These changes do not prohibit the use of explosionproof sealing fittings and their associated compounds, but provide for alternative methods that are manufactured to accomplish the desired results. While Section 504.70 in previous editions indicated the seals were not required to be explosionproof, it did not clearly specify what the seals were intended, or required, to accomplish. This revision provides specific guidance related to the purpose of the required seals within the rule. Product safety standards provide specific test requirements that verify seals will "minimize the passage of gases." The revised text provides a basis to evaluate the performance of the seal, whether the evaluation takes place in a qualified electrical testing laboratory or in the field.

Code Language 504.70

Sealing

Conduits and cables that are required to be sealed by 501.15, 502.15, 505.16, and 506.16 shall be sealed to minimize the passage of gases, vapors, or dusts. Such seals shall not be required to be explosionproof or flameproof but shall be identified for the purpose of minimizing passage of gases, vapors, or dusts under normal operating conditions and shall be accessible.

Summary of Change

This section has been revised to clarify the requirements for conduit and cable seals containing intrinsically safe circuit wiring. References were also included to Articles 502, 505, and 506 where seals are not required to be explosionproof or flameproof.

505.7(A) Implementation of Zone Classification System

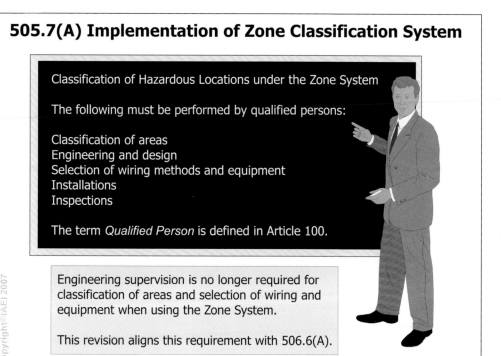

Classification of Hazardous Locations under the Zone System

The following must be performed by qualified persons:

Classification of areas
Engineering and design
Selection of wiring methods and equipment
Installations
Inspections

The term *Qualified Person* is defined in Article 100.

Engineering supervision is no longer required for classification of areas and selection of wiring and equipment when using the Zone System.

This revision aligns this requirement with 506.6(A).

Copyright©IAEI 2007

Implementation of Zone Classification System
NEC, p. 392

Proposal 14-109
Log 2714
ROP, p. 532

Comment 14-45
Log 1188
ROC, p. 314

Analysis and Effect

Action by Panel 14 resulted in two significant changes regarding implementation of electrical wiring and systems in hazardous (classified) locations that are classified using the Zone classification system. First, a registered professional engineer is no longer required. Second, all individuals involved with wiring systems in areas classified using the Zone System must be qualified. The substantiation in the proposal pointed to establishing consistency between the same requirements in 506.6(A) that were incorporated in *NEC*-2005. While use of the Zone System for area classification within the boundaries of North America is still minimal, it was determined that using the Zone System should not be limited to just those instances where they would be under the supervision of a registered professional engineer. Accordingly, CMP-14 responded to Proposal 14-148 (Log No. 363) by clarifying that the elements involved in installation, design, engineering, and inspection all require qualified persons, some of which may or may not be registered professional engineers. The effects of this change are that a registered professional engineer is no longer necessary to meet the requirements of this rule, and all individuals that are involved in Zone System area classification, installations, designs, equipment selection, and inspections must be qualified to do so. This section also parallels the same provisions in Section 506.6(A).

Code Language
505.7(A)
Implementation of Zone Classification System

Classification of areas, engineering and design, selection of equipment and wiring methods, installation, and inspection shall be performed by qualified persons.

Summary of Change

The title of subdivision (A) in this section has been changed from "Supervision of Work" to "Implementation of Zone Classification System." The requirement for supervision by a qualified registered professional engineer has been removed from this rule.

Change at a Glance

Zone systems now are no longer required to be classified by a registered professional engineer, but the persons designing, installing and inspecting the installation must be qualified.

5

511.2 and 511.3

Commercial Garages, Repair and Storage
NEC, p. 409

Proposal 14-156
Log 3412
ROP, p. 543

Comment 14-77
Log 1946
ROC, p. 321

Change at a Glance

New definitions differentiate between a major repair garage and a minor repair garage to improve clarity and usability of reorganized Section 511.3.

Analysis and Effect

Action by CMP-14 on Comment 14-77 (Log No. 1946), resulted in two definitions in a new Section 511.2 that clearly describe what constitutes a major repair garage and what qualifies as a minor repair garage. The definitions are extracted material from NFPA 30A and add consistent and practical correlation between the *NEC* and the standard from which many of the requirements in 511.3 have been derived. Usability is enhanced by providing a ready reference to information that differentiates between requirements where minor repairs and major repair operations and services for self-propelled vehicles are performed. The reformatted layout of 511.3 retains all current requirements of this section, but it is presented in a far more user-friendly fashion. As revised, the section provides clear rules regarding the relationship between areas that are classified without ventilation and those that are either reduced in classification or unclassified as a result of providing appropriate amounts of ventilation. New subdivision (E) provides a more positive declaration of area classification regarding adjacent areas or rooms that are adequately cut off or provided with appropriate quantities of air movement to warrant the area as unclassified.

Summary of Change

Two new definitions of the terms m*ajor repair garage* and m*inor repair garage* have been added to a new 511.2. Existing 511.3(A) and (B) have been rearranged in a more logical layout under a single heading of Area Classification.

Code Language

511.2
Definitions

Major Repair Garage. A building or portions of a building where major repairs, such as engine overhauls, painting, body and fender work, and repairs that require draining of the motor vehicle fuel tank are performed on motor vehicles, including associated floor space used for offices, parking, or showrooms [30A, 2008]

Minor Repair Garage. A building or portions of a building used for lubrication, inspection, and minor automotive maintenance work, such as engine tune-ups, replacement of parts, fluid changes (e.g., oil, antifreeze, transmission fluid, brake fluid, air conditioning refrigerants), brake system repairs, tire rotation, and similar routine maintenance work, including associated floor space used for offices, parking, or showrooms. [30A, 2008]

511.3 (in part)
Area Classification (See *NEC*-2008 for complete text as reorganized)
(A) Parking Garages
(B) Repair Garages, With Dispensing
(C) Major Repair Garages
(D) Minor Repair Garages
(E) Modifications to Classification

Courtesy of The Austin Company

513.2 & 513.3 (C)(2)

Aircraft Painting Hangars
NEC, p. 412

**Proposal 14-165a,
14-165b**
Log 1413, 1412
ROP, p. 545

Comment
None

Analysis and Effect

Section 513.3(C) has been revised and restructured into a list format to meet the *NEC Style Manual* requirements. A new (C)(2) provides area classification for *aircraft painting hangars*. Previous editions of the *NEC* did not include hazardous area classification for aircraft hangars used for painting. NFPA Standard 409-2005 has been revised specifically to separate the hazardous locations near aircraft for aircraft paint hangars from those of general maintenance. Aircraft paint hangars while constructed like huge paint booths do not have the same dimensional clearances found in traditional paint booths. The shape of the aircraft creates clearances far greater than that found in any other painting system. This creates a level of safety not found in traditional paint booths and supports hazardous location classification that is less than the entire hangar. The new definition *aircraft painting hangar* clearly describes what constitutes an aircraft painting hangar to facilitate appropriate application of the area classification boundaries provided in the new provisions in Section 513.3(C)(2). These revisions provide designers, installers, and enforcement with necessary information that establishes the extent of the Class I locations where aircraft is painted in hangars.

Change at a Glance

Aircraft painting hangars now are defined in the *Code*, and classification area boundaries are given.

Code Language

513.2
Aircraft Painting Hangar
An aircraft hangar constructed for the express purpose of spray/coating/dipping applications and provided with dedicated ventilation supply and exhaust.

513.3(C)
Vicinity of Aircraft
(1) Aircraft Maintenance and Storage Hangars. [current text of *NEC*-2005 513.3(C) is not changed]

(2) Aircraft Painting Hangars. The area within 3 m (10 ft) horizontally from aircraft surfaces from the floor to 3 m (10 ft) above the aircraft shall be classified as Class I, Division 1 or Class I, Zone 1. The area horizontally from aircraft surfaces between 3.0 m (10 ft) and 9.0 m (30 ft) from the floor to 9.0 m (30 ft) above the aircraft surface shall be classified as Class I, Division 2 or Class I, Zone 2.

FPN: See NFPA 33-2007, *Standard for Spray Application Using Flammable or Combustible Materials,* for information on ventilation and grounding for static protection in spray painting areas.

Summary of Change

A new definition of the term *aircraft painting hangar* has been added to Section 513.2; and Section 513.3(C) has been expanded to include area classification requirements for aircraft painting hangars.

5

517.2, 517.11 FPN

Patient Care Vicinity
NEC, p. 431, 432

Proposal 15-23, 15-25a
Log 1793, CP1500
ROP, p. 554

Comment
None

Change at a Glance

This change distinguishes between areas where patients receive care within a health care facility and where the patient may be present but not under care; this difference significantly affects which wiring methods are required for the location.

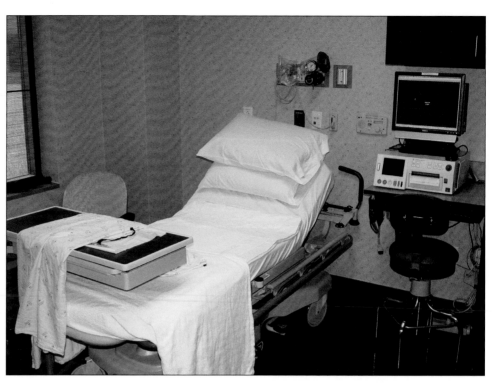

Analysis and Effect

The term *patient vicinity* has been changed to read *patient care vicinity*. This revision now accurately correlates with the same definition in NFPA 99 *Standard for Health Care Facilities,* which is the document from which this term is extracted. To that end, the definition includes bracketed information in accordance with 90.5(C) that provides users with a direct reference to NFPA 99 and the section in which the definition originates. *Patient care vicinity* is more specific to areas where patients are expected to receive care, rather than where they are located within a health care facility. This revision will be helpful for *Code* users when determining the extent of patient care locations and specifically the vicinity where certain types of care are administered. This revision distinguishes between areas where patients receive care within a facility and where they might be present but not under care. No changes have been made to the current text that includes distance measurements from a patient bed in its nominal location. Action by CMP-15 also resulted in companion proposal 15-25a (Log No. CP1500), which revises the term *patient vicinity* to *patient care vicinity* where it is used within the various sections in Article 517.

Code Language
517.2
Patient Care Vicinity

In an area in which patients are normally cared for, the *patient care vicinity* is the space with surfaces likely to be contacted by the patient or an attendant who can touch the patient. Typically in a patient room, this encloses a space within the room not less than 1.8 m (6 ft) beyond the perimeter of the bed in its nominal location, and extending vertically not less than 2.3 m (7 1/ 2 ft) above the floor. [99:3.3.140]

Summary of Change

The word "care" has been inserted in the title of this definition and between the words "patient" and "vicinity" within the text of the definition. Bracketed information has been inserted as follows: [NFPA 99:3.3.140]. The term *patient vicinity* has been changed to *patient care vicinity* in the following sections:

517.11 FPN
517.13(B) Exception No. 2
517.14 (two locations)
517.19(C) (two locations)
517.19(C) FPN
517.82(B)

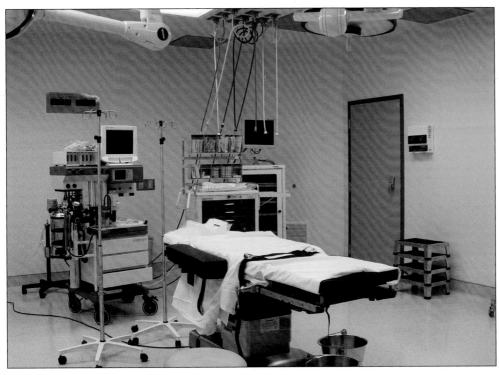

517.2,
517.20,
517.20(A),
517.60

Wet Procedure Locations
NEC, p. 431, 434, 442

Proposal 15-4
Log 2113
ROP, p. 552

Comment 15-17, 15-17a
Log 2329, CP1500
ROC, p. 324

Analysis and Effect

Action by CMP-15 on Comments 15-17 (Log No. 2329) and 15-17a (Log No. CC1500) resulted in adding the word "procedure" to the definition of *wet location* in 517.2. The definition of wet location is provided in 517.2 under the general defined terms related to patient care areas. The definition of wet location in NFPA 99 Standard for Health Care Facilities 2005 Edition includes the word "procedure" which provides a clear differentiation between a general wet location defined in Article 100. The word "procedure" is now incorporated into the title of this definition. Sections 517.20(A) and the FPN to 517.60 both refer to locations that are wet because of the health care procedures performed on patients such as those related to many surgical procedures. The revisions to this defined term clarify and improve usability within the rules in Article 517 that apply where electrical systems and circuits are installed in *wet procedure locations*.

Summary of Change

The word "procedure" has been incorporated into the definition of *wet location* in 517.2 and in Sections 517.20(A) and 517.60 FPN. The defined term of *wet procedure location* is provided under the general definition of *patient care area*.

Code Language

517.2

Patient Care Areas. Any portion of a health care facility... and with the following definitions of the area classification.

Wet Procedure Locations. Those spaces within patient care areas where a procedure is performed and that are normally subject to wet conditions while patients are present. These include standing fluids on the floor or drenching of the work area, either of which condition is intimate to the patient or staff. Routine housekeeping procedures and incidental spillage of liquids do not define a wet location.

517.20(A)

Receptacles and Fixed Equipment. All receptacles and fixed equipment within the area of the wet procedure location shall have ground-fault circuit-interrupter protection for personnel if interruption of power under fault conditions can be tolerated, or be served by an isolated power system if such interruption cannot be tolerated.

517.60

Anesthetizing Location Classification

FPN: If either of the anesthetizing locations in 517.60(A) or 517.60(B) is designated a wet procedure location, refer to 517.20.

Change at a Glance

Wet procedure locations as defined in 517.2 are much different than general wet locations defined in Article 100, and this change describes how.

517.19(D)

Proposal 15-38, 15-39
Log 1645, 1711
ROP, p. 557

Comment
None

Change at a Glance

Type MC and MI cables
used as feeder conductors
for critical areas of health
care facilities are required
to be suitable as equipment
grounding conductors as
defined in Section 250.118.

517.19(D) Panelboard Grounding and Bonding

Section 517.19(D) covers grounding and bonding requirements for feeders supplying critical branch switchboards or panelboards. Bonding shall be ensured by any of the means specified in 517.19(D)(1), (2), or (3).

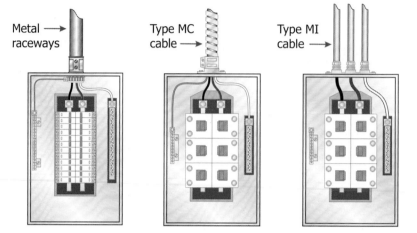

Metal raceways   Type MC cable   Type MI cable

Type MC cable and Type MI cable are required to be suitable as equipment grounding conductors in accordance with 250.118.

Copyright©IAEI 2007

Analysis and Effect

The title of this section has been revised to clarify that both equipment grounding and bonding are covered in the requirement. Grounding of the panelboard or switchboard can be assured by an equipment grounding conductor of the wire type included with the feeder where properly sized. The copper sheath of Type MI cable is suitable for grounding where used with suitable fittings, whereas the steel alloy sheath MI cable is not. MC cables in the larger sizes (for feeders) typically include an equipment grounding conductor of the wire type in accordance with the product standard. Adding the proposed text helps clarify what is required relative to the equipment grounding.

Where an equipment grounding conductor included in the feeder as required by 215.6 is a conductor (wire type), grounding should be assured by proper connection of the equipment grounding conductors at termination points all the way back to the point of origin of the feeder. The redundant equipment grounding conductor paths required by 517.13(A) and (B) are not currently applicable in this section for feeders. Adding the words "and bonding" is appropriate because the section covers both grounding and bonding provisions.

Code Language
517.19(D)
Panelboard Grounding and Bonding
Where a grounded electrical distribution system is used and metal feeder raceway or Type MC or MI cable that qualifies as an equipment grounding conductor in accordance with 250.118 is installed, grounding of a panelboard or switchboard shall be ensured by one of the following bonding means at each termination or junction point of the metal raceway or Type MC or MI cable:

(1) A grounding bushing and a continuous copper bonding jumper, sized in accordance with 250.122, with the bonding jumper connected to the junction enclosure or the ground bus of the panel

(2) Connection of feeder raceways or Type MC or MI cable to threaded hubs or bosses on terminating enclosures

(3) Other approved devices such as bonding-type locknuts or bushings.

Summary of Change
The words "and bonding" were added to the title of Section 517.19(D). The words "that qualifies as an equipment grounding conductor in accordance with 250.118 is installed" have been added to the requirements of this section.

Alarm and Alerting Systems
NEC, p. 437

Proposal 15-63
Log 2510
ROP, p. 560

Comment
None

Analysis and Effect

Section 517.32 includes a list of loads that are required to be connected to the life safety branch of the essential electrical system in a hospital. Section 517.32(C) addresses alarm and alerting systems and has been expanded to include a new item (3) that includes mechanical, control, and other accessories that are essential to the proper functioning of life safety systems in hospitals. The life safety branch of the emergency system is required to supply power for lighting, receptacles, and equipment which are all vital elements of the life safety system. Substantiation with the proposal brought awareness to the fact that certain HVAC controls, dampers, and some motors are related to the safety of life. This revision refers specifically to mechanical, controls or other accessories that required for effective life safety operations, such as smoke control systems, smoke evacuation systems, and stair pressurization. Even though many engineering designs often specified these systems to be connected to the life safety branch of the emergency system, previous editions of the *Code* contained no such provisions to permit this practice. This revision clarifies that specific circuits required for life safety system operation shall be permitted to be connected to the life safety branch. It is recognized that many mechanical loads such as environmental fans, air-conditioning equipment and so forth are usually connected to the equipment system branch of a hospital. The words "shall be permitted" in new item (3) result in a permissive provision within a list of loads that are required to be connected without option. This clarifies that design and engineering teams are afforded the option to connect such loads where determined essential to the system design, but it is not mandatory as compared to most other loads identified in this section.

Change at a Glance

Mechanical, control, and other accessories such as dampers, and some motors required for effective life safety systems can be connected to the life safety branch.

5

Code Language
517.32(C)
Alarm and Alerting Systems

Alarm and alerting systems including the following:

(1) Unchanged

(2) Unchanged

(3) Mechanical, control, and other accessories required for effective life safety systems operation shall be permitted to be connected to the life safety branch.

Summary of Change

Section 517.32(C) has been revised by including a new item (3).

517.32(E) Generator Set and Transfer Switch Location

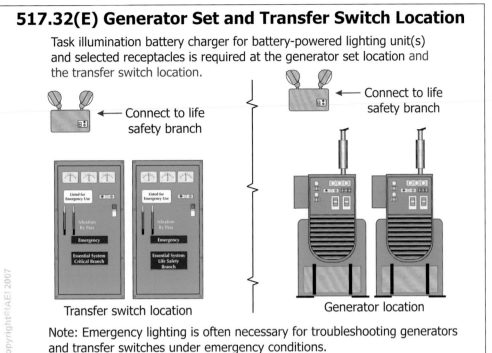

Task illumination battery charger for battery-powered lighting unit(s) and selected receptacles is required at the generator set location and the transfer switch location.

← Connect to life safety branch

← Connect to life safety branch

Transfer switch location

Generator location

Note: Emergency lighting is often necessary for troubleshooting generators and transfer switches under emergency conditions.

Copyright© IAEI 2007

517.32(E)

Generator Set and Transfer Switch Locations
NEC, p. 437

Proposal 15-61
Log 2509
ROP, p. 560

Comment
None

REVISION

Analysis and Effect

Section 517.32 provides a list of loads that are required to be connected to the life safety branch of the essential electrical system of hospitals. The revision to item (E) clarifies that illumination of essential system transfer switch locations is equally as important as the generator set location to provide minimum levels of illumination for troubleshooting and repair procedures during normal power source interruptions. Transfer switches in the life safety branch of an essential electrical system in a hospital are essential pieces of equipment that must operate when normal power to the hospital is interrupted for any reason. These transfer switches are required to be electrically operated and mechanically held in the alternate source mode. For operation of bypass features and other testing and diagnostics during power loss conditions, minimum levels of illumination are necessary. This revision clarifies that battery-operated lighting units for transfer switch locations are to be connected to the life safety branch. The changes to this section also correlate with the same language used in NFPA 99, which resulted in the bracketed information being inserted following the text in this section.

Code Language
517.32(E)

Generator Set and Transfer Switch Locations

Task illumination battery charger for battery-powered lighting unit(s) and selected receptacles at the generator set and essential transfer switch locations. [NFPA 99: 4.4.2.2.2.2(5)]

Summary of Change

Section 517.32(E) has been revised to reference transfer switch locations in addition to generator set locations. Bracketed information has been inserted following the requirements of this section as follows: [NFPA 99: 4.4.2.2.2.2(5)]

Change at a Glance

Generator set and transfer switch locations both require task illumination and power for selected receptacles.

517.32(F)

Life Safety Branch
NEC, p. 437

Proposal 15-64
Log 2511
ROP, p. 560

Comment
None

Analysis and Effect

Generator sets installed as an essential electrical system alternate power source for a hospital usually include accessories that are essential for normal generator operation. These alternate generator power sources supply the life safety branch, the critical branch, and the equipment system when the normal power service to the hospital is interrupted. Since the life safety branch is supplied by the generator, it is logical that any generator accessory loads be connected to the life safety branch. This revision clarifies that accessories necessary for proper operation and performance of the generator are required to be connected to the life safety branch. Substantiation in the proposal indicated that accessories such as day tanks, crankcase heaters, lights and receptacles in outdoor generator enclosures, and so forth are necessary for generator set operation since it is a life safety system. The proposal addressed concerns for outdoor generator enclosures and associated generator accessories contained within such enclosures, however, action by CMP-15 resulted in a new requirement that is not limited to just outdoor generators in enclosures since the same concerns apply to generators installed in indoor applications. Previous editions of the *Code* include a requirement for connecting such loads in the equipment system connected to the alternate power source as provided in 517.34(C). The changes to this section recognize that the alternate power source in the form of a generator usually supplies the entire essential electrical system of a health care facility which validates connecting generator set accessories to the life safety branch.

Change at a Glance

Generator set accessories such as crankcase heaters, lights and receptacles may now be connected to the life safety branch.

Code Language
517.32

Life Safety Branch
(Text remains unchanged)

(F) Generator Set Accessories. Generator set accessories as required for generator performance.

Renumber existing items (F) to (G) and (G) to (H)

Summary of Change

A new item (F) covering generator set accessories has been added to this section. The remainder of the section has been renumbered accordingly.

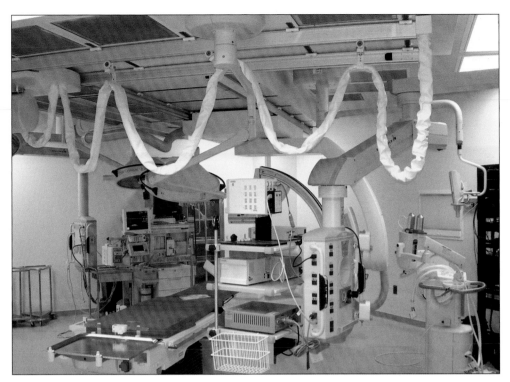

517.34
(A)(7)

**Equipment for Delayed
Automatic Connection**
NEC, p. 438

Proposal 15-66
Log 2520
ROP, p. 561

Comment
None

Analysis and Effect

Section 517.34(A) provides a list of necessary equipment loads that are required to be automatically restored to operation at appropriate time-lag intervals following the transfer and restoration of the emergency system loads. The equipment addressed in this section is related to essential facility operations, which includes operating rooms and delivery rooms. This section has been revised to incorporate ventilation systems for operating rooms and delivery rooms. Substantiation with the proposal clearly identified that ventilation systems should be connected to the equipment system for the same reasons that the loads described in 517.34(A)(6) are connected to the equipment system. This equipment ensures that air circulation, filtration, and air pressure relationships are maintained for infection control purposes. The requirement for space heating in 517.34(B)(1) is not specific to air movement and permits manual transfer, which is not acceptable for infection control purposes. Section 517.34(A) does not recognize operating room and delivery room air handing units for connection to the life safety branch. The automatic time-lag delay for transfer of this essential equipment is acceptable and recognized by the *NEC* under the equipment branch provisions of Section 517.34(A).

Code Language
517.34(A)(7)

Equipment for Delayed Automatic Connection
Supply, return, and exhaust ventilating systems for operating and delivery rooms.

Summary of Change

A new item (7) covering ventilation systems for operating and delivery rooms has been added to Section 517.34(A).

Change at a Glance

All ventilation systems for operating and delivery rooms are permitted to be connected by delayed automatic connection to the equipment branch.

517.160
(A)(5)

Installations
Conductor Identification
NEC, p. 447

Proposal 15-106
Log 3656
ROP, p. 566

Comment
None

Change at a Glance

Conductors for isolated power systems installed in health care facilities must now have a distinctive colored stripe other than white, green, or gray.

517.160(A)(5) Conductor Identification

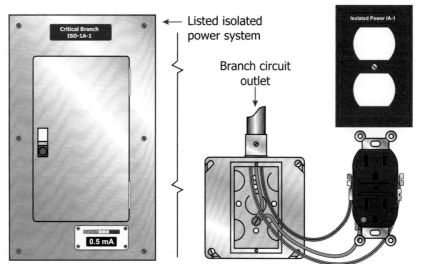

Isolated power system circuit conductors are required to be identified by the colors specified in 517.160(A)(5) and include a distinctive colored stripe other than white, green, or gray.

Copyright©IAEI 2007

Analysis and Effect

Section 517.160 provides all of the installation and equipment requirements for isolated power systems installed in health care facilities. Section 517.160(A)(5) includes a specific color code requirement for branch-circuit conductors connected to these systems. Action by CMP-15 resulted in a new color code scheme that will be required for isolated power system secondary circuit conductors. Substantiation with the proposal identified a need to establish a distinct identification means for the conductors supplied by these systems for safety concerns. The color orange is already designated where identification is required for conductors used on high-leg systems as provided in 110.15. The substantiation also indicated that the colors brown, orange, and yellow are often used for 480Y/277-volt branch-circuit and feeder wiring, even though 210.5(C) does not require these specific colors. In effect, the change provides a new requirement for identification striping in addition to the specific conductor insulation colors brown, orange, and yellow. This revision does not specify if the stripe is required along the entire length of the conductor, or if it can be field applied at accessible points on the wiring system. The revision results in a requirement for identification with only one stripe, which must be a color other than white, gray, or green. This new identification requirement enhances worker safety by identifying these conductors in a manner that leaves no question as to their intended service.

Code Language
517.160(A)(5)
Installations
(5) Conductor Identification
The isolated circuit conductors shall be identified as follows:
 (1) Isolated Conductor No. 1 — Orange with a distinctive colored stripe other than white, green, or gray
(2) Isolated Conductor No. 2 — Brown with a distinctive colored stripe other than white, green, or gray

For 3-phase systems, the third conductor shall be identified as yellow with a distinctive colored stripe other than white, green, or gray. Where isolated circuit conductors supply 125-volt, single-phase, 15- and 20-ampere receptacles, the striped orange conductor(s) shall be connected to the terminal(s) on the receptacles that are identified in accordance with 200.10(B) for connection to the grounded circuit conductor.

Summary of Change

This section has been revised to add the words "with a distinctive colored strip other than white, green, or gray" after the color designations of brown, orange, and yellow provided within this section.

518.5

Supply
NEC, p. 449

Proposal 15-116, 15-115
Log 3316, 1601
ROP, p. 569

Comment
None

Courtesy of Leviton Mfg., Inc.

Analysis and Effect

A new class of listed solid-state sine wave dimmers has been introduced to the professional performance lighting market. This type of dimming system varies the amplitude of the applied voltage waveform without any nonlinear switching effects found in traditional phase-control solid-state dimmers. Section 518.5 has been revised to recognize the operating characteristics of both solid-state sine wave, 3-phase, 4-wire dimming systems and solid-state phase control 3-phase, 4-wire dimming control systems, and clearly differentiates between the operation characteristics of the two systems. The substantiation indicated that this new type of solid-state sine wave dimmer is a linear load; therefore, the feeder neutral conductor supplying these systems does not have to be considered a current-carrying conductor. The feeder neutral supplying traditional solid-state phase-control 3-phase, 4-wire dimming control systems does have to be counted a current-carrying conductor. The new mandatory exception has been added to assist users in determining when the feeder neutral supplying a dimming system that uses both types of dimmers must be counted as a current-carrying conductor for the purpose of applying ampacity correction factors in accordance with 310.15. The new FPN provides users with a useful reference to 520.2 where two new informative definitions of solid-state dimmer types have been added.

Code Language
518.5
Supply

Portable switchboards and portable power distribution equipment shall be supplied only from listed power outlets of sufficient voltage and ampere rating. Such power outlets shall be protected by overcurrent devices. Such overcurrent devices and power outlets shall not be accessible to the general public. Provisions for connection of an equipment grounding conductor shall be provided. The neutral conductor of feeders supplying solid-state phase control, 3-phase, 4-wire dimmer systems shall be considered a current-carrying conductor for purposes of derating. The neutral conductor of feeders supplying solid-state sine wave, 3-phase, 4-wire dimming systems shall not be considered a current-carrying conductor for purposes of derating.

Exception: The neutral conductor of feeders supplying systems that use or may use both phase-control and sine-wave dimmers shall be considered as current-carrying for the purposes of derating.

FPN: For definitions of solid-state dimmer types, see 520.2.

Summary of Change

A new sentence recognizing solid-state sine wave 3-phase, 4-wire dimming systems has been added to this section along with a new exception. A new fine print note references 520.2.

Change at a Glance

Solid-state sine wave dimmers are considered a linear load. Feeder neutral conductor supplying these systems does not have to be considered a current-carrying conductor.

5

520.2

Theaters, Audience Areas of Motion Picture and Television Studios, Performance Areas, and Similar Locations
NEC, p. 449, 450

Proposal 15-125
Log 3317
ROP, p. 576

Comment
None

Courtesy of Leviton Mfg., Inc.

Analysis and Effect

Two new definitions have been added to 520.2. The operational characteristics of two types of solid-state dimmers are clearly differentiated in these definitions. The introduction of the new type of *solid-state sine wave dimmers* presented a need to address the type of steady-state current controlled by each type, because this current affects sizing current-carrying conductors of feeders supplying equipment that incorporates these dimmers (dimming control panels and equipment assemblies). These definitions establish a clear and distinct difference between the two types. Essentially, the traditional *solid-state phase-control dimmers* control current in a manner where the wave shape does not follow the wave shape of the applied voltage; it is nonlinear. Whereas, the solid-state sine wave dimmers control current where the wave shape does follow the waveform of the applied voltage; it is linear. Substantiation indicated that Article 520 includes multiple references to solid-state dimmers and nonlinear loads with specific requirements. These definitions will assist users in establishing where current requirements in Article 520 apply only to solid-state phase-control dimmers as compared to the new solid-state sine wave types. These definitions also correlate with changes made in 518.5 and help clarify the type of current wave shapes that impact whether neutral conductors of 3-phase, 4-wire feeders are required to be counted as current-carrying conductors for ampacity correction factor purposes.

Code Language
520.2
Definitions

Solid-State Phase-Control Dimmer. A solid-state dimmer where the wave shape of the steady-state current does not follow the wave shape of the applied voltage, such that the wave shape is nonlinear.

Solid-State Sine Wave Dimmer. A solid-state dimmer where the wave shape of the steady-state current follows the wave shape of the applied voltage, such that the wave shape is linear.

Summary of Change

Two new definitions of the terms *solid-state phase-control dimmer* and *solid-state sine wave dimmer* have been added to 520.2.

Courtesy of Leviton Mfg., Inc.

520.27(B)

Neutral Conductor
NEC, p. 451

Proposal 15-129
Log 3318
ROP, p. 577

Comment
None

REVISION

Analysis and Effect

The introduction and use of solid-state, sine wave 3-phase, 4-wire dimming systems presented a need to address neutral conductor current-carrying capacities. Section 520.27 provides requirements for feeders supplying stage switchboards. These revisions have incorporated new requirements for feeder neutral conductors supplying 3-phase, 4-wire stage switchboards that include solid-state sine wave dimming systems. As revised, this section differentiates between the requirements for these two types of dimming systems. The neutral conductor of solid-state, sine wave 3-phase, 4-wire dimming systems does *not* have to be considered a current-carrying conductor for the purposes of applying ampacity correction factors. The neutral conductor of solid-state, phase-control 3-phase, 4-wire dimming systems *is* required to be considered a current-carrying conductor. These revisions increase usability and clarify when the neutral of feeders supplying stage switchboards must be considered a current-carrying conductor. New rules also address designs and installations where the feeder supplies a stage switchboard that includes both types of dimming systems. In these cases, the neutral of the feeder is required to be considered a current-carrying conductor. The qualifying condition that determines whether the neutral conductor of solid-state, sine wave dimming systems is not current-carrying is that it is installed and used in 3-phase, 4-wire systems. This change correlates with similar changes incorporated in 520.53(O)(2) covering neutral conductor sizing for feeders supplying portable switchboards on stages.

Code Language
520.27(B)
Neutral Conductor

For the purpose of derating, the following shall apply:

(1) The neutral conductor of feeders supplying solid-state, phase-control 3-phase, 4-wire dimming systems shall be considered as a current-carrying conductor.

(2) The neutral conductor of feeders supplying solid-state, sine wave 3-phase, 4-wire dimming systems shall not be considered a current-carrying conductor.

(3) The neutral conductor of feeders supplying systems that use or may use both phase-control and sine wave dimmers shall be considered as current-carrying.

Change at a Glance

The feeder neutral conductor(s) of a solid-state, sine wave 3-phase, 4-wire dimming systems does *not* have to be considered as a current-carrying conductor for the purposes of derating.

Summary of Change

Section 520.27(B) has been restructured into a list format in accordance with the *NEC Style Manual* and revised to include requirements for the neutral conductors supplying phase-control dimming systems and sine-wave dimming systems.

5

Article 522

Control Systems for Permanent Amusement Attractions
NEC, 458, 459

Proposal 15-121
Log 2111
ROP, p. 573

Comment 15-64
Log 150
ROC, p. 335

Change at a Glance

This new article covers requirements for control circuit power sources, conductors, and associated control wiring in or on all structures that are part of a permanent amusement attraction.

Analysis and Effect

The amusement ride industry and amusement theme parks with permanently installed attractions have undergone tremendous growth over the past 50 years and become a mainstay for the population, because of the enjoyment it brings to the populace. In 1950, there were about 50 of these types of parks in the United States; now there are about 450. Though the traveling amusement industry has rides that are ever more sophisticated and professional in their own right, they differ from permanent installations through continual setting up and tearing down of equipment, and more rugged use from wear-and-tear is the norm. Concerns were raised among industry professionals that these types of installations had special needs and considerations that warranted their own article in the *Code*, specific to their installation and use. Because there was no specific *Code* standard for them, many AHJs were compelled to use Article 725, for instance, which to some was too restrictive. There are thousands of micro devices and smaller conductors (30 AWG) used in this industry. Sophisticated monitoring systems are utilized for these rides. Many have choreographed movements, musical accompaniment, and are highly complex. Some mimic humans and animals in their speech, action, and activities. Engineers, designers, electricians, and inspectors have been challenged for years to classify these locations and to agree on the appropriate wiring standard for these specialized installations. The new standard is a starting place for improved understanding and clearer requirements, and will benefit all concerned, while maintaining high standards for safety.

Code Language

I
General.

522.1

Scope. This article covers the installation of control circuit power sources and control circuit conductors for electrical equipment, including associated control wiring in or on all structures, that are an integral part of a permanent amusement attraction.

522.2

Control Circuit. For the purposes of this article, the circuit of a control system that carries the electrical signals directing the performance of the controller but does not carry the main power current.

(For remainder of article, see text in the *Code...*)

Summary of Change

New article and new text.

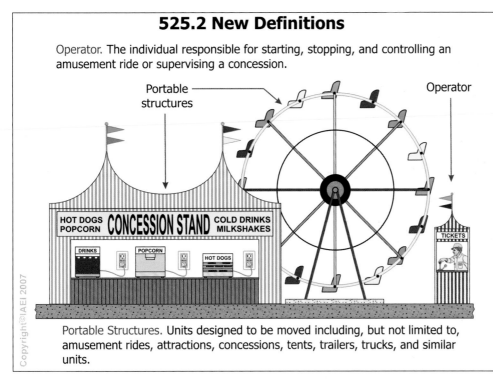

525.2 New Definitions

Operator. The individual responsible for starting, stopping, and controlling an amusement ride or supervising a concession.

Portable structures

Operator

HOT DOGS POPCORN **CONCESSION STAND** COLD DRINKS MILKSHAKES

DRINKS   POPCORN   HOT DOGS

TICKETS

Copyright©IAEI 2007

Portable Structures. Units designed to be moved including, but not limited to, amusement rides, attractions, concessions, tents, trailers, trucks, and similar units.

525.2

Carnivals, Circuses, Fairs, and Similar Events
NEC, p. 460

Proposal 15-144a
Log CP1501
ROP, p. 581

Comment 15-70
Log 1539
ROC, p. 336

Analysis and Effect

Section 2.2.2.2 of the *NEC Style Manual* requires that defined terms be located in the .2 section of that article. *Operator* and *portable structures* are used multiple times within Article 525, which necessitates common definitions for consistent application where these terms are used. *Code* rules should mean what they imply by the use of defined words and terms. Action by CMP-15 on Proposal 15-144a and Comment 15-70 resulted in the development of definitions for these terms. Defining these terms in 525.2 will assist users from the standpoint of promoting more consistent application of the rules in which they are used. The definition of *operator* clarifies that an operator is one who actually is controlling (including starting and stopping the equipment) and not just an owner of the property or manager of the event. The definition of *portable structures*

Change at a Glance

The terms *operator* and *portable structures* have been defined to clarify the requirements and application within the rules in which they are used.

clarifies the types of entities covered by the rules in Article 525 where this term is used. Examples of the types of structures that constitute *portable structures* are provided within this new definition. It should be noted that these definitions are specific to these terms as used in the rules in Article 525, even though these terms are also used elsewhere in the *NEC*.

Code Language
525.2
Definitions
Operator. The individual responsible for starting, stopping, and controlling an amusement ride or supervising a concession.

Portable Structures. Units designed to be moved including, but not limited to, amusement rides, attractions, concessions, tents, trailers, trucks, and similar units.

Summary of Change
Two new definitions have been added to Article 525 in new Section 525.2.

525.11

**Multiple Sources
of Supply**
NEC, p. 460

**Proposal 15-150
Log 2895**
ROP, p. 582

**Comment 15-71
Log 1360**
ROC, p. 336

Change at a Glance

Bonding jumpers installed
in accordance with 525.11
must be sized using Table
250.122 for the rating
of the largest overcur-
rent device supplying the
structures—in no case can
bonding jumper be sized
smaller than 6 AWG.

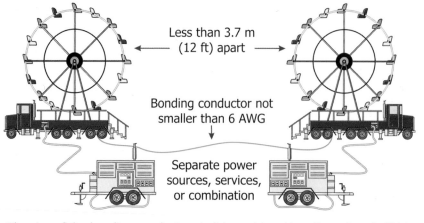

525.11 Multiple Sources of Supply

Where separate power sources supply portable structures located less than 3.7 m (12 ft) apart, the equipment grounding conductors of all sources of supply shall be bonded together at the portable structures.

Less than 3.7 m (12 ft) apart

Bonding conductor not smaller than 6 AWG

Separate power sources, services, or combination

Copyright©IAEI 2007

The size of the bonding conductor shall be not less than the values in Table 250.122 based on the rating of the largest overcurrent device supplying the structures, but <u>not smaller than 6 AWG</u>.

Analysis and Effect

Article 525 covers mobile or portable amusement rides, attractions, structures, and other features associated with carnivals, circuses, fairs, and similar events. Section 525.11 provides a bonding requirement to minimize differences of potential that can exist between structures when supplied from different power sources. Differences of potential can exist between the metal parts of such attractions or structures when multiple separate power sources are used for these events. The requirement for bonding that was introduced in *NEC*-2005 lacked direction about sizing bonding conductors where installed. This revision provides clear direction about the minimum sizes for such bonding conductors. Table 250.122 must be used for sizing the bonding conductor, and the rating of the largest overcurrent device supplying multiple structures determines the minimum size for the bonding conductor. For example, if two amusement rides were within 1.8 m (6 ft) of each other and supplied from two separate generators, the bonding requirement in 525.11 applies. If one was supplied by a 100-ampere circuit and the other supplied by a 200-ampere circuit, the minimum size for the required bonding conductor would be not less than 6 AWG copper. This revision establishes the minimum size of 6 AWG for such bonding conductors. Action by CMP-15 responded to concerns about possible physical damage to smaller bonding conductors by providing a minimum size of 6 AWG in this requirement.

Code Language
525.11

Multiple Sources of Supply

Where multiple services or separately derived systems, or both, supply portable structures, the equipment grounding conductors of all the sources of supply that serve such structures separated by less than 3.7 m (12 ft) shall be bonded together at the portable structures. The bonding conductor shall be sized in accordance with Table 250.122 based on the largest overcurrent device supplying the portable structures, but not smaller than 6 AWG.

Summary of Change

A new last sentence has been added that provides requirements for sizing bonding conductors between structures that are supplied power from different power systems, but placed less than 3.7 m (12 feet) apart.

547.5(G)

NEC, p. 469

Proposal 19-21
Log 1130
ROP, p. 590

Comment
None

Analysis and Effect

A new sentence has been added to 547.5(G) to require a GFCI-protected general-purpose receptacle at each location in agricultural areas where an accessible non-GFCI-protected receptacle is located. It was indicated during panel discussion of this proposal that the change will allow specific non-GFCI-compatible utilization equipment to operate, while improving safety by providing an alternate GFCI-protected receptacle in these locations for personnel protection. This change permits non-GFCI-protected equipment that meets other requirements in the *Code* for grounding, and so forth to be utilized, but also provides protection for personnel where 125-volt, 15- or 20-ampere rated equipment is used.

Change at a Glance

In agricultural buildings or areas, an accessible receptacle supplying a dedicated load does not require GFCI protection when a GFCI-protected receptacle is located within three feet of it for portable or temporary use.

Code Language
547.5(G)

Receptacles

All 125-volt, single-phase, 15- and 20-ampere general-purpose receptacles installed in the locations listed in (1) through (4) shall have ground-fault circuit-interrupter protection:
(1) Areas having an equipotential plane
(2) Outdoors
(3) Damp or wet locations
(4) Dirt confinement areas for livestock

GFCI protection shall not be required for an accessible receptacle supplying a dedicated load where a GFCI protected receptacle is located within 900 mm (3 ft) of the non-GFCI-protected receptacle.

Summary of Change

A new sentence has been added to subdivision (4).

Analysis of Changes *NEC*-2008

547.8(B) and (C)

Luminaires
NEC, p. 469

Proposal 19-23, 19-24
Log 1013, 1129
ROP, p. 591

Comment
None

Change at a Glance

Luminaires in agricultural buildings exposed to physical damage shall have a suitable guard, and if placed in a wet location shall be watertight.

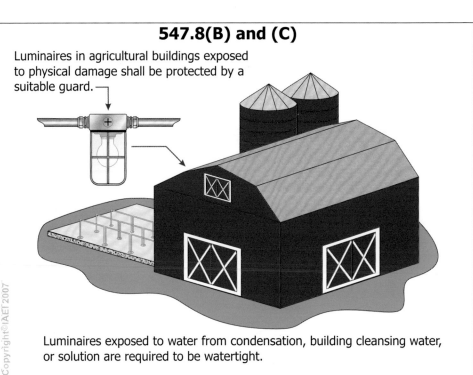

547.8(B) and (C)

Luminaires in agricultural buildings exposed to physical damage shall be protected by a suitable guard.

Luminaires exposed to water from condensation, building cleansing water, or solution are required to be watertight.

Copyright©IAET 2007

Analysis and Effect

It is now clear for owners, maintenance persons, installers and inspectors that luminaires in agricultural buildings that are exposed to physical damage require a suitable guard, and if placed in a wet location, shall be watertight.

Information provided by the submitter of the proposal indicated that the words "that may be" in the previous *Code* language were ambiguous and uncertain, and not easily enforceable as a clear *Code* requirement. Installation requirements should coincide with the prevailing conditions, including location.

The revised wording is more editorial in nature, but clearly expresses the objective of the code-making panel. Also, the language will now better correlate with 410.10, Luminaires in Specific Locations, which helps consistency within the *Code*.

Code Language
547.8(B)

Exposed to Physical Damage
Luminaires exposed to physical damage shall be protected by a suitable guard.

(C)

Exposed to Water
Luminaires exposed to water from condensation, building cleansing water, or solution shall be watertight.

Summary of Change

The words "that may be" have been deleted from the requirement.

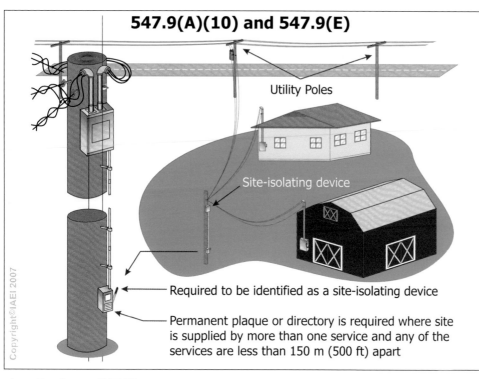

547.9(A)(10) and 547.9(E)

Utility Poles

Site-isolating device

— Required to be identified as a site-isolating device

— Permanent plaque or directory is required where site is supplied by more than one service and any of the services are less than 150 m (500 ft) apart

Copyright©IAEI 2007

547.9 (A)(10), 547.9(E)

Electrical Supply to Building(s) or Structure(s) from a Distribution Point
NEC, p. 470

Proposal 19-27, 19-29a
Log 2922, CP1903
ROP, p. 592

Comment
None

Analysis and Effect

Site-isolating devices are required for electrical systems that serve agricultural buildings, or portions of buildings or areas of like nature where excessive dust and water accumulate, and/or where corrosive environments may exist because of animal excrement, and where corrosive vapors exist per Section 547.9.

An electric utility or the property owner may provide this type of electrical equipment. In some installations, two switches may be required or provided — one by the *Code*, and one by the utility in accordance with their engineering standards or practices. Where an existing service with a utility-owned site-isolating device is supplemented with an additional service as permitted in 230.2, additional site-isolating devices must be installed. All devices must be identified as isolating switches.

Two changes occurred to this section of the *Code*. First, site-isolating devices are required to have marking to identify them as a site-isolating switch and be located on the switch-operating handle or immediately adjacent to it. Second, where a site is supplied by more than one service, with any two or more services located a distance of 150 m (500 ft) or less apart, as measured in a straight line, a permanent plaque or directory must be installed at each service site-isolation switch. The permanent plaque at each switch must give the location of each of the other services or site-isolation devices, and the buildings or structures that are served by each switch. Some site-isolation devices may be installed in series (utility on the line side, then the customer device).

The objective is to improve safety when more than one of these devices is installed at an agricultural site of this type, particularly because sites are now being supplied with multiple services due to load capacity and the need for different voltages. The distance of 500 ft. or less between distribution points is derived from the distribution policies of many utilities that for safety reasons prohibit more than one service where located less than 500 ft. apart.

It is now clear that site-isolation devices are required to be permanently identified with plaques; and where there is more than one service to the property the number of devices fed by a common service, and the loads attached to the devices must be identified on the equipment.

Change at a Glance

Where site-isolating devices exist on an agricultural property as addressed by 547.1 and .2, they must be permanently identified with a plaque which is located at the switch handle, defines the load(s) served, specifies the number of services to the site, and the number of disconnects fed from the same service.

5

Code Language
547.9(A)(10)
Site-Isolating Device Marking

A site-isolating device shall be permanently marked to identify it as a site-isolating device. This marking shall be located on the operating handle or immediately adjacent thereto.

547.9(E)
Identification

Where a site is supplied by more than one service with any two services located a distance of 150 m (500 ft) or less apart, as measured in a straight line, a permanent plaque or directory shall be installed at each of these distribution points denoting the location of each of the other distribution points and the buildings or structures served by each.

Summary of Change
New text was added to this section requiring specific identification for site-isolating devices.

Equipotential Planes and Bonding of Equipotential Planes
NEC, p. 470

Proposal 19-35, 19-36, 19-37
Log 2595, 2597, 3415
ROP, p. 594

Comment 19-18, 19-19
Log 2218, 2191
ROC, p. 341, 342

Analysis and Effect

Fine Print Note No. 2 in *NEC*-2005 has been moved to FPN No. 3, and a new FPN No. 2 has been added to the section. The use of electrically heated livestock waterers brings with it concerns of electrical safety of shock and electrocution prevention for personnel and livestock. It also brings concerns about equipotential planes for the purpose of stabilizing voltage between earth, concrete surfaces, and metal parts that are likely to become energized. All of these components must be kept at zero volts potential between them for electrical safety.

A new reference from the American Society of Agricultural and Biological Engineers describes the safe installation of electrically heated livestock waterers, including the requirement for bonding of all metallic parts and the installation of equipotential planes. The term *equipotential plane* as defined in 547.2 includes a concrete floor or deck of some kind. The new reference in FPN 2 will increase the awareness and use of this engineering practice, and provides guidance for connecting livestock waterers to the equipment grounding conductor and the equipotential plane.

Another change clarifies that it is not the objective of the *Code* to require equipotential planes (typically accomplished by bonding steel mesh and reinforcing bars which are placed in concrete slabs, and walls, and so forth), in all areas of livestock confinement. The *Code* proposal(s) that were accepted remove the apparent mandatory requirement in *NEC*-2005 for outdoor concrete decks to be installed in all outdoor locations where livestock is confined. This revision clarifies that equipotential planes must be installed in concrete floors or slabs of animal confinement areas indoors and outdoors where metallic equipment that is accessible to livestock may become energized. The equipotential plane includes the area where livestock stands and is in contact with metallic equipment that may become energized.

Change at a Glance

Equipotential planes are required to be installed in concrete slabs only in livestock confinement areas that contain metal parts that may become energized and are accessible to livestock.

Code Language
547.10

Equipotential Planes and Bonding of Equipotential Planes

(A) Where Required. Equipotential planes shall be installed where required in (A)(1) and (A)(2).

(1) Indoors. Equipotential planes shall be installed in confinement areas with concrete floors where metallic equipment is located that may become energized and is accessible to livestock.

(2) Outdoors. Equipotential planes shall be installed in concrete slabs where metallic equipment is located that may become energized and is accessible to livestock.

The equipotential plane shall encompass the area where the livestock stands while accessing metallic equipment that may become energized.

(B) Bonding

FPN No. 2: Methods for safe installation of livestock waterers are described in American Society of Agricultural and Biological Engineers (ASABE) EP342.2-1995, *Safety for Electrically Heated Livestock Waterers.*

Summary of Change

A new fine print note and new text have been added to clarify the required locations of equipotential planes.

Analysis of Changes *NEC*-2008

551.4

General Requirements
NEC, p. 481, 482

Proposal 19-74
Log 2598
ROP, p. 601

Comment
None

Analysis and Effect

Many recreational vehicle parks require a service with a larger size than is available from a single-phase service from most utility companies, and/or require a 3-phase service for 3-phase loads such as water pumps, etc. Due to 120/240-volt 3-phase service not being available from some utility companies, the park will be served with a 208Y/120-volt 3-phase service. The *Code* change proposal stated that experience from serving parks with 208Y/120-volt 3-phase services has resulted in no problems; neither has the service voltage been a problem to the park and recreational vehicle owners. In order to comply with *Code* language in *NEC*-2005, some recreational park owners were required to install a transformer to convert from 208Y/120-volt to 120/240-volt for line-to-line connected equipment, which was considered by some as an unnecessary cost burden for the park owner. New *Code* language reflects how some RV parks have been served by 208Y/120-volt power sources, as allowed per special permission granted by AHJs for those specific installations, due to the circumstances mentioned. It is now clear to RV Park owners, electrical installers and inspectors that 208Y/120-volt power sources are permitted for RV Parks. Manufacturers of recreational vehicles (RVs) also will be affected by this change, and more equipment supplied by this voltage will be available in the marketplace in the future.

Code Language
551.4
General Requirements

(A) Not Covered. A recreational vehicle not used for the purposes as defined in 551.2 shall not be required ... (see *Code* text). It shall, however, meet all other applicable requirements of this article if the recreational vehicle is provided with an electrical installation intended to be energized from a 120-volt, 208Y/120-volt or 120/240-volt, nominal, ac power-supply system.

(B) Systems. This article covers combination electrical systems, generator installations, and 120-volt, 208Y/120-volt, or 120/240-volt, nominal, systems.

Summary of Change

208Y/120-volt power sources have been added as permitted power sources.

Change at a Glance

Recreational vehicles and RV park services, feeders, and branch circuits are permitted to be served by 208Y/120-volt power sources.

5

551.47 (R)(4)

Prewiring for Generator Installation
NEC, p. 488

Proposal 19-88a
Log CP1902
ROP, p. 605

Comment
None

551.47(R)(4) Pre-wiring for Generator Installation

Generators listed specifically for RV use are required when not installed in the RV at the time of manufacture.

A label conforming to 551.46(D) is required on the cover of each junction box containing incomplete wiring.

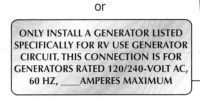

ONLY INSTALL A GENERATOR LISTED SPECIFICALLY FOR RV USE GENERATOR CIRCUIT. THIS CONNECTION IS FOR GENERATORS RATED 110-125-VOLT AC, 60 HZ, _____ AMPERES MAXIMUM

or

ONLY INSTALL A GENERATOR LISTED SPECIFICALLY FOR RV USE GENERATOR CIRCUIT. THIS CONNECTION IS FOR GENERATORS RATED 120/240-VOLT AC, 60 HZ, _____ AMPERES MAXIMUM

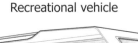
Recreational vehicle

Analysis and Effect

The new language in this section provides added guidance to the installer of the generator in RVs where the RV manufacturer has pre-wired the RV for the future installation of a generator set.

Change at a Glance

Generators which are specifically listed for RV use are now required when not installed at the time of RV manufacture and the RV is pre-wired for generator installation at a later date.

Code Language
551.47(R)(4)

Prewiring for Generator Installation
(4) A label conforming to 551.46(D) shall be placed on the cover of each junction box containing incomplete circuitry and shall read, as appropriate, either

ONLY INSTALL A GENERATOR LISTED SPECIFICALLY FOR RV USE GENERATOR CIRCUIT. THIS CONNECTION IS FOR GENERATORS RATED 110–125-VOLT AC, 60 HZ, _____ AMPERES MAXIMUM.

or

ONLY INSTALL A GENERATOR LISTED SPECIFICALLY FOR RV USE GENERATOR CIRCUIT. THIS CONNECTION IS FOR GENERATORS RATED 120/240-VOLT AC, 60 HZ, _____ AMPERES MAXIMUM.

Summary of Change
New text added

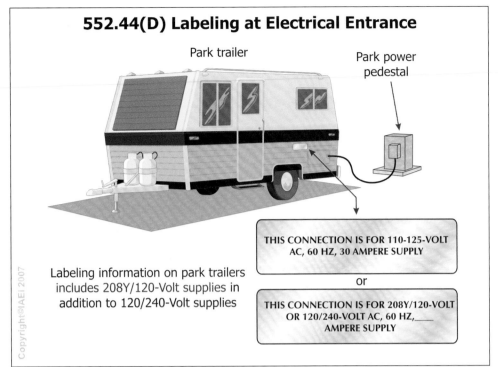

552.44(D) Labeling at Electrical Entrance

Park trailer

Park power pedestal

Labeling information on park trailers includes 208Y/120-Volt supplies in addition to 120/240-Volt supplies

THIS CONNECTION IS FOR 110-125-VOLT AC, 60 HZ, 30 AMPERE SUPPLY

or

THIS CONNECTION IS FOR 208Y/120-VOLT OR 120/240-VOLT AC, 60 HZ,_____ AMPERE SUPPLY

Copyright©IAEI 2007

552.44(D)

Labeling at Electrical Entrance
NEC, p. 497

Proposal 19-105a
Log CP1900
ROP, p. 608

Comment
None

Analysis and Effect

Many recreational vehicle or park trailer type of parks require a service with a larger size than is available from a single-phase service from most utility companies, and/or require a 3-phase service for 3-phase loads such as water pumps, etc. Due to a 120/240-volt 3-phase service not being available from some utility companies, the park often will be served with a 208Y/120-volt 3-phase service. The *Code* change proposal stated that experience with serving parks with 208Y/120-volt 3-phase services has resulted in no problems; neither has the service voltage been a problem to the park trailer owners. Similar changes occurred in Article 551 for recreational vehicles, and recreational vehicle parks. *Code* language in *NEC*-2005 required the recreational park owner to install a transformer to convert from 208Y/120-volt to 120/240-volt for line-to-line connected equipment in order to meet *Code* requirements, which was considered by some as an unnecessary cost burden for the park owner. New *Code* language reflects how some park trailer installations or RV parks have been served by 208Y/120-volt power sources, as allowed per special permission granted by AHJs for those specific installations, due to the circumstances mentioned. It is now clear to park trailer owners, electrical installers and inspectors that 208Y/120-volt power sources are permitted for park trailer installations.

Code Language
552.44(D)

Labeling at Electrical Entrance
Each park trailer shall have permanently affixed to the exterior skin, at or near the point of entrance of the power-supply assembly, a label ...(See *Code* text for remainder of paragraph)

THIS CONNECTION IS FOR 208Y/120-VOLT OR 120/240-VOLT AC, 3-POLE, 4-WIRE, 60 HZ,_____ AMPERE SUPPLY.

The correct ampere rating shall be marked in the blank space.

Summary of Change

208Y/120-volt power sources have been added as permitted power sources.

Change at a Glance

Park trailers and services, feeders, and branch circuits for park trailers are now permitted to be served by 208Y/120-volt power sources.

5

555.9

Electrical Connections
NEC, p. 504

Proposal 19-117
Log 134
ROP, p. 612

Comment 19-46
Log 385
ROC, p. 346

Change at a Glance

Requirements have been revised for splices of conductors on or under docks and piers, including the types of connectors required – (listed and identified for use in marine environments), locations of enclosures and locations of splices.

Analysis and Effect

Concerns were raised about placing splices in enclosures mounted in or on fixed or floating docks or piers. Information provided by the submitter of the *Code* change proposal indicated that:

1. The use of sealed, waterproof wire-to-wire splices in wet locations is common practice and has been permitted in Section 110.14(B) of the *Code*.

2. Corrosion and insulation degradation is not an issue if the splice is designed and installed for marine environments. Engineered concrete floating docks and piers are designed to respond to wave action that limits or eliminates water splashing on the deck and junction boxes located in the dock sections, even in storm conditions.

3. The splices are typically not located in areas that would have high surf, as that would damage the connection system and dock/pier. Additional provided information argued that the exclusion of utilizing wire-to-wire splices for engineered concrete floating docks is impractical, and in many instances and locations places undue hardship on the dock owner and installing contractor with no additional safety benefit.

In the comment stage of the proposal, the code panel deleted the words "Type 6P" which were originally required because a Type 6P enclosure rated for prolonged or temporary submersion may not be needed in every case. In lieu of the 6P box, the panel added the requirement for sealed wire connector systems to be listed and identified for submersion. It is now clear that splices are permitted in enclosures mounted to floating docks and piers, that sealed wire connector systems listed and identified for submersion (rated for this type of use in a marine environment) are required, and that the splices must be made in an enclosure which is approved for the use by the AHJ. In addition, electrical connections must be located at least 12 inches above the deck of a floating pier, and/or at least 12 inches above the deck of a fixed pier, but not below the electrical datum plane.

Electrical connections shall be located at least 305 mm (12 in.) above the deck of a floating pier. Conductor splices, within approved junction boxes, utilizing sealed wire connector systems listed and identified for submersion shall be permitted where located above the waterline but below the electrical datum field for floating piers.

All electrical connections shall be located at least 305 mm (12 in.) above the deck of a fixed pier but not below the electrical datum plane.

Summary of Change

New text regarding electrical connections was added to Section 555.9.

5

555.21

Motor Fuel Dispensing Stations — Hazardous (Classified) Locations
NEC, p. 506, 507

Proposal 19-126, 19-127
Log 223, 2950
ROP, p. 614

Comment 19-48
Log 1402
ROC, p. 347

Analysis and Effect

This change has been well received and brings needed clarification to electrical installation requirements where motor fuels are dispensed in marinas and boatyards. As a result of the proposal, a task group was formed to coordinate the requirements in Article 555 for Motor Fuel Dispensing with those found in Article 514. The task group has added no new requirements to the proposal, but altered terms to better align with NFPA 30A-2003, Motor Fuel Dispensing Facilities and Repair Garages, and NFPA 303-2000, Fire Protection Standard for Marinas and Boatyards, which includes docks, piers and wharfs.

The submitter explained that floating docks are commonly manufactured with expanded foam cores that are encapsulated in concrete. Flush-mounted deck boxes are

Change at a Glance

Motor fuel dispensing facilities at marinas and boatyards—requirements revised and clarified.

cast in place. One or more 4-inch PVC chases are installed between deck boxes, and from the deck boxes to the end of the dock sections. This is done to accommodate installation of gasoline pipes, diesel fuel lines, water and waste disposal piping as well as for installation of power, communications, television and other wiring. This construction provides boxes at deck level that can easily collect gasoline liquid and vapors that are heavier-than-air. Gasoline spills can occur at marinas for all the same reasons they do at land-based fuel dispensing facilities.

The PVC chases allow gasoline liquid and vapor to travel throughout the length of the dock sections. As a result, the surface of the deck on the dock is equivalent to the surface above the earth within Class I, Division 2 space located around motor fuel dispensers found in Table 514.3(B). The area below the surface of the deck is considered as a Class I, Division 1 location where gasoline liquid or vapors can accumulate in enclosures or travel through the PVC chases, as found within the enclosed area below gasoline dispensers specified in Table 514.3(B). The gasoline dispensers are typically installed over a large deck box designed to allow conduits to enter the bottom of dispensers from the PVC chases.

The phrase, "tubs, voids, pits, vaults, boxes, depressions, piping chases, or similar spaces where flammable liquids or vapors can accumulate" was added from NFPA 30A for consistency. User-friendly language has been added to help the user correctly apply the requirements of Tables 514.3(B)(1) and 514.3(B)(2). An exception was added to clarify declassification methods for dock sections that abut and for those that do not, so that the requirements of the section parallel those in 514.3. Two other exceptions are added to provide a reasonable boundary of Class I Division 1 and 2 areas.

Code Language
555.21
Motor Fuel Dispensing Stations — Hazardous (Classified) Locations.

(A) General. Electrical wiring and equipment located at or serving motor fuel dispensing locations shall comply with Article 514 in addition to the requirements of this article. All electrical wiring for power and lighting shall be installed on the side of the wharf, pier, or dock opposite from the liquid piping system.

FPN: For additional information, see NFPA 303-2006, *Fire Protection Standard for Marinas and Boatyards*, and NFPA 30A-2007, *Motor Fuel Dispensing Facilities and Repair Garages*.

(B)
Classification of Class I. Division 1 and 2 Areas
The following criteria shall be used for the purposes of applying Table 514.3(B)(1) and Table 514.3(B)(2) to motor fuel dispensing equipment on floating or fixed piers, wharfs or docks.

(1) Closed Construction. Where the construction of floating docks, piers, or wharfs is closed so that there is no space between the bottom of the dock, pier, or wharf and the water, such as concrete enclosed expanded foam or similar construction, and having integral service boxes with supply chases:

(a) The space above the surface of the floating dock, pier, or wharf shall be a Class I, Division 2 location with distances as identified in Table 514.3(B)(1) Dispenser and Outdoor.

(b) The space below the surface of the floating dock, pier, or wharf, having areas or enclosures such as tubs, voids, pits, vaults, boxes, depressions, fuel piping chases, or similar spaces where flammable liquid or vapor can accumulate shall be a Class I, Division 1 location.

Exception No. 1: Dock, pier, or wharf sections that do not support fuel dispensers and abut but are 6.0 m (20 ft) or more from dock sections that support fuel dispenser(s) shall be permitted to be Class I, Division 2 where documented air space is provided between dock sections to permit flammable liquids or vapors to dissipate and not travel to these dock sections. Such documentation shall comply with 500.4(A).

Exception No. 2: Dock, pier, or wharf sections that do not support fuel dispensers and do not directly abut sections that support fuel dispensers shall be permitted to be unclassified where documented air space is provided and where flammable liquids or vapors cannot travel to these dock sections. Such documentation shall comply with 500.4(A).

Summary of Change
New text has been added for clarification of fueling facilities in marinas and boatyards.

5

590.4(D)

Receptacles
NEC, p. 508

Proposal 3-115a
Log CP302
ROP, p. 630

Comment 3-87
Log 1203
ROC, p. 354

Change at a Glance

Circuits for temporary power installations are required to have an equipment grounding conductor that is connected to the grounding terminal of the receptacle and meets all requirements of 250.118, no exceptions.

Analysis and Effect

The word "continuous," and the phrase "that qualifies as an equipment grounding conductor in accordance with 250.118" were added as definite requirements for both metal raceways and cables which supply power to receptacles used for temporary wiring. These changes clarify that the metal cables or raceways for temporary wiring installations must be continuous and must qualify as an equipment grounding conductor, per 250.118. If the metal raceway or metal cable is not continuous or does not qualify as an equipment grounding conductor, then a separate equipment grounding conductor must be included in the branch-circuit wiring method. It was also clarified, and is equally important, that the qualifying equipment grounding conductor is required to be connected to the equipment grounding conductor termination point at the receptacle outlet. These changes increase the safety of temporary wiring installations, correlate with code-wide changes which brought clarity and more prescriptive language to grounding requirements and provide clear guidelines for installers, maintenance people, and inspectors as to the equipment grounding requirements of the *NEC*, and methods for accomplishing grounding.

Code Language
590.4(D)
Receptacles

All receptacles shall be of the grounding type. Unless installed in a continuous metal raceway that qualifies as an equipment grounding conductor in accordance with 250.118 or a continuous metal-covered cable that qualifies as an equipment grounding conductor in accordance with 250.118, all branch circuits shall include a separate equipment grounding conductor, and all receptacles shall be electrically connected to the equipment grounding conductor(s). (See *Code* for remainder of text).

Summary of Change

The word "continuous" and the phrase "that qualifies as an equipment grounding conductor in accordance with 250.118" have been added twice to the second sentence of the section.

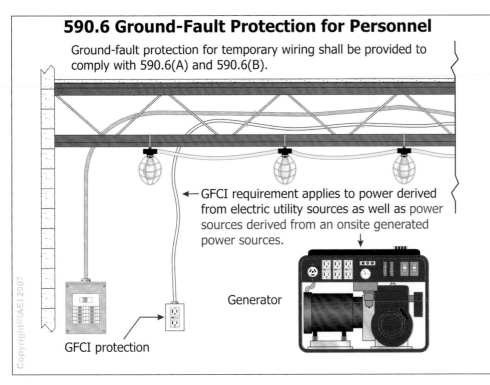

590.6 Ground-Fault Protection for Personnel

Ground-fault protection for temporary wiring shall be provided to comply with 590.6(A) and 590.6(B).

← GFCI requirement applies to power derived from electric utility sources as well as power sources derived from an onsite generated power sources.

Generator

GFCI protection

Copyright©IAEI 2007

590.6

Ground-Fault Protection for Personnel
NEC, p. 508

Proposal 3-125
Log 1717
ROP, p. 631

Comment 3-88
Log 1633
ROC, p. 355

REVISION

Analysis and Effect

This new text clarifies that GFCI protection is required for all temporary power sources that supply power for 15-, 20-, and 30-ampere 125-volt receptacles, whether utility or generator powered. There are many shock or electrocution hazards associated with temporary installations when construction, remodeling, maintenance, repair, or demolition, and so forth, are underway. Cords may be cut or damaged; tools and equipment are used in harsh environments and/or wet locations; and steel, concrete, earth, and other grounded surfaces are abundant. Substantiation provided with the proposal indicated that when Section 305.6(A) Exception 1 was deleted in the 2002 *NEC* cycle, and the section was re-numbered as 527.6(A), some generator manufacturers incorrectly assumed that GFCI protection was no longer required for generators supplying temporary power. Concerns were raised regarding how this new requirement for GFCI protection would affect portable generators used for home standby power use. Home standby power use was reported to be 70 percent of portable generator use, as indicated in Proposal #3-129. Information submitted stated that load imbalance and capacitive leakage were problems for generator operation in these applications due to GFCI tripping concerns. It should be noted that generators for optional standby use are covered by Article 702, not 590, and that the function of GFCI protection is to protect personnel from electric shock or electrocution. Most often when a GFCI operates, it indicates a problem with electrical wiring or equipment that must be investigated and repaired by a qualified person and should not be assumed to be nuisance tripping. This revision eliminates a possible misunderstanding of the *NEC*, and clarifies for generator manufacturers, users of temporary power, and enforcement authorities that receptacles installed for temporary installations are required to be protected by a ground-fault circuit interrupter, regardless of the source of the power. This change correlates with revisions to Section 445.20, regarding the new requirements for GFCI protection of portable generator receptacle outlets.

> ### Change at a Glance
>
> GFCI protection is required for all 125-volt 15-, 20-, and 30-amp receptacles used for all temporary wiring installations regardless of whether the power is supplied from an electrical utility service or from an on-site generator.

Code Language
590.6
Ground-Fault Protection for Personnel

Ground-fault protection for personnel for all temporary wiring installations shall be provided to comply with 590.6(A) and (B). This section shall apply only to temporary wiring installations used to supply temporary power to equipment used by personnel during construction, remodeling, maintenance, repair, or demolition of buildings, structures, equipment, or similar activities. This section shall apply to power derived from an electric utility company or from an on-site-generated power source.

Summary of Change

A new last sentence has been added to Section 590.6.

Analysis of Changes *NEC*-2008

Chapter

6

Selected Changes

6

600.2

Definitions
Section Sign
NEC, p. 510

Proposal 18-111
Log 526
ROP, p. 633

Comment
None

Change at a Glance

The change clarifies that subassemblies may be physically joined to form a single sign unit, or installed as separate remote parts (subassemblies) of an overall sign.

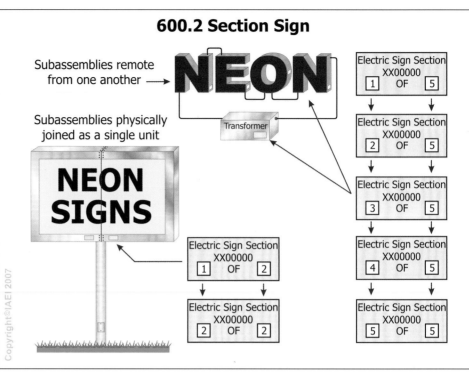

Analysis and Effect

New requirements that reference *section signs* were introduced in Section 600.12, which resulted in the development of a new definition of the term in 600.2 in *NEC*-2005. This revision to the definition clarifies what constitutes a listed section sign. There are two types of manufactured section signs that are installed in the field, and both types should be included in the description. Listed section signs can be manufactured and delivered to jobsites in multiple subassemblies and assembled and installed as a single unit, or installed and wired as an overall listed sign made up of subassemblies remote from one another and connected with field-installed wiring between the subassemblies.

The previous definition did not differentiate between the two types of listed section signs. This revision clarifies that subassemblies may be physically joined to form a single sign unit, or they may be installed as separate remote parts (subassemblies) of an overall sign. This change also clarifies that the multiple parts of a section sign are referred to as subassemblies; the only field wiring involved are the interconnections and wiring between subassemblies or field-installed wiring between the subassemblies that are remote from one another, and the field-installed wiring between the subassemblies and the power source, which could be a transformer or electronic power supply.

Code Language
600.2

Definitions

Section Sign. A sign or outline lighting system, shipped as subassemblies, that requires field-installed wiring between the subassemblies to complete the overall sign. The subassemblies are either physically joined to form a single sign unit or are installed as separate remote parts of an overall sign.

Summary of Change

A new last sentence has been added to the definition of *section sign* in Section 600.2 as follows: "The subassemblies are either physically joined to form a single sign unit or are installed as separate remote parts of an overall sign."

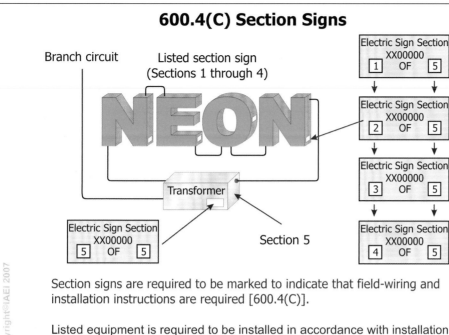

600.4(C) Section Signs

Branch circuit   Listed section sign
(Sections 1 through 4)

NEON

Transformer

Electric Sign Section
XX00000
[5] OF [5]

Section 5

Electric Sign Section
XX00000
[1] OF [5]

Electric Sign Section
XX00000
[2] OF [5]

Electric Sign Section
XX00000
[3] OF [5]

Electric Sign Section
XX00000
[4] OF [5]

Section signs are required to be marked to indicate that field-wiring and installation instructions are required [600.4(C)].

Listed equipment is required to be installed in accordance with installation instructions included in the listing [110.3(B)].

600.4(C)

Section Signs
NEC, p. 510

Proposal 18-113
Log 2861
ROP, p. 633

Comment
None

Analysis and Effect

This section covering marking requirements for signs and outline lighting systems has been revised to include an additional marking indicating that field-wiring and installation instructions are required. Section 110.3(B) requires listed or labeled equipment to be installed and used in accordance with instructions included in the listing or labeling. Listing and labeling of equipment serves as the primary basis for approvals by the authority having jurisdiction. This revision establishes continuity between requirements in Section 600.3 and UL 48, the product standard for electric signs. Section 41.1.1 of UL 48 requires installation instructions for listed signs, including listed section signs. Section signs that are shipped as subassemblies are required to include all subassemblies and interconnected field-installed wiring that is specifically indicated on the required installation instructions. The UL Guide Information for Electrical Equipment (White Book) under category (UXYT) for signs clearly indicates, "the acceptability of the assembled sections in the field rests with the authority having jurisdiction." To carry out the approval process, AHJs should verify the installed listed section sign is in accordance with its associated installation instructions. This revision does not change UL 48, because this is an existing requirement of that standard. Manufacturers of listed section signs are required to provide installation instructions for the field installer. This revision should provide sign installers with reasonable assurances of attaining approvals from the AHJ for listed section signs where installation instructions are provided, and the installation is consistent with those instructions.

Code Language
600.4(C)
Section Signs
Section signs shall be marked to indicate that field-wiring and installation instructions are required.

Summary of Change
A new subdivision (C) has been added to Section 600.4 and reads as follows: "(C) Section Signs. Section signs shall be marked to indicate that field-wiring and installation instructions are required."

Change at a Glance

Section signs are now required to be marked to indicate that field installation instructions are required (for the installer to follow during installation, and made available for the AHJ to perform the sign inspection).

6

600.7

Grounding and Bonding
NEC, p. 511, 512

Proposal 18-123
Log 338
ROP, p. 635

Comment 18-95a, 18-96,
18-97, 18-98, 18-99
Log CC1800, 386, 1195,
1197, 1268
ROC, p. 355, 356, 357, 358

Change at a Glance

The change clarifies what bonding is intended to accomplish, where bonding conductors or jumpers are required to be connected, and how to connect them per 250.8.

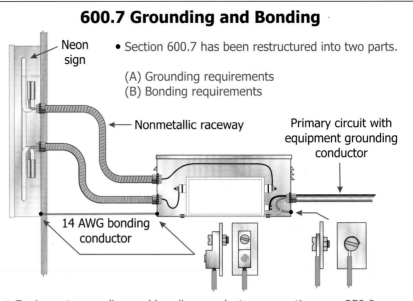

600.7 Grounding and Bonding

- Neon sign
- Section 600.7 has been restructured into two parts.

  (A) Grounding requirements
  (B) Bonding requirements

- Nonmetallic raceway
- Primary circuit with equipment grounding conductor
- 14 AWG bonding conductor

Copyright©IAEI 2007

- Equipment grounding and bonding conductor connections per 250.8
- Bonding conductor shall connect parts together and be connected to the associated transformer/power supply equipment grounding conductor

Analysis and Effect

These revisions resulted in restructuring the section into subdivision (A) covering grounding requirements, and subdivision (B) covering bonding requirements. The title of the section has been changed to include the words "and bonding" to reflect what is covered by these rules. Substantiation provided with the proposal indicated a need for clarifying the requirements of this section and differentiating between the requirements for grounding and bonding of electric signs and outline lighting systems. The revisions direct users and enforcement as to what bonding is intended to accomplish and where the bonding conductors or jumpers are required to be connected. Previous editions of the *Code* did not provide clear direction about where the bonding conductor path is required to originate or to be connected. By referencing 250.8, this section now directs users how bonding and grounding conductor connections should be accomplished.

Summary of Change

The title of Section 600.7 has been revised by adding the words "and bonding."
Section 600.7 has been reorganized to provide a more logical layout and to promote increased usability. The proposed revision divides this section into two parts "Grounding" and "Bonding" and involves restructuring the section into a list format in accordance with the *NEC Style Manual*.

Code Language
600.7
Grounding and Bonding

(A) Grounding
   (1) Equipment Grounding
   (2) Size of Equipment Grounding Conductor
   (3) Connections
   (4) Auxiliary Grounding Electrode
   (5) Metal Building Parts

(B) Bonding
   (1) Bonding of Metal Parts
   (2) Bonding Connections
   (3) Metal Building Parts
   (4) Flexible Metal Conduit Length
   (5) Small Metal Parts
   (6) Nonmetallic Conduit
   (7) Bonding Conductors
   (8) Signs in Fountains

See Sections 600.7(A) and (B) for actual *Code* text as revised.

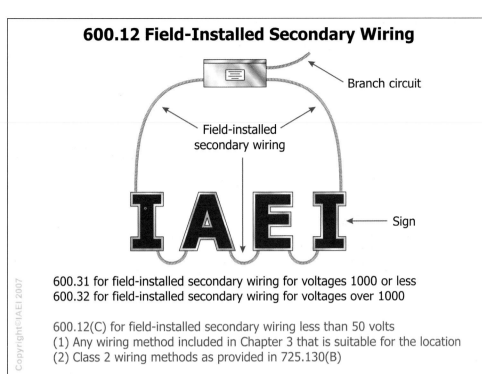

600.12 Field-Installed Secondary Wiring

Branch circuit

Field-installed secondary wiring

Sign

600.31 for field-installed secondary wiring for voltages 1000 or less
600.32 for field-installed secondary wiring for voltages over 1000

600.12(C) for field-installed secondary wiring less than 50 volts
(1) Any wiring method included in Chapter 3 that is suitable for the location
(2) Class 2 wiring methods as provided in 725.130(B)

Copyright©IAEI 2007

Field-Installed Secondary Wiring
NEC, p. 512, 513

Proposal 18-133
Log 856
ROP, p. 638

Comment 18-103
Log 292
ROC, p. 358

Analysis and Effect

Section 600.12 was new in *NEC*-2005 and provided users with requirements for field-installed secondary circuit wiring, but it applied only to section signs. This section has been revised to cover the field-installed secondary wiring for all electric signs and outline lighting systems. Field-installed secondary wiring can be 1000 volts or less, over 1000 volts, or less than 50 volts, such as the wiring associated with LED illuminated signs and outline lighting systems. Prior to these revisions, there were no clear requirements for the secondary circuit wiring associated with these Class 2 low-voltage circuits. Field-installed wiring rated at less than 50 volts is required to be installed either in one of the wiring methods provided in chapter 3 of the *Code,* or Class 2

> ### Change at a Glance
> Guidance for the wiring methods for low-voltage secondary circuits of electric signs and outline lighting systems is now provided in the *Code* rule.

wiring is permitted to be installed in accordance with the requirements in 725.130(A) or (B). These changes should improve clarity by providing installers and inspectors with clear rules within Article 600 that can be applied to these installations and systems.

Code Language
600.12
Field-Installed Secondary Wiring
Field-installed secondary circuit wiring for electric signs and outline lighting systems shall be in accordance with 600.12(A), (B), or (C).

 (A) 1000 Volts or Less. Secondary circuit wiring of 1000 volts or less shall comply with 600.31.

 (B) Over 1000 Volts. Secondary circuit wiring of over 1000 volts shall comply with 600.32.

 (C) Less Than 50 Volts. Secondary circuit wiring less than 50 volts shall be installed in accordance with either of the following:

 (1) Any wiring method included in Chapter 3 suitable for the conditions.

 (2) Where the power source complies with the requirements in 725.121, wiring methods shall be permitted to be installed in accordance with 725.130(A) or (B)

Summary of Change
This section has been restructured into a list format to meet the requirements in the *NEC Style Manual.*

600.32(K)

Splices
NEC, p. 515

Proposal 18-154
Log 407
ROP, p. 642

Comment
None

Change at a Glance

Splices in high-voltage secondary circuit conductors must be made in listed enclosures rated over 1000 volts, and splice enclosures must be accessible after installation and listed for the location.

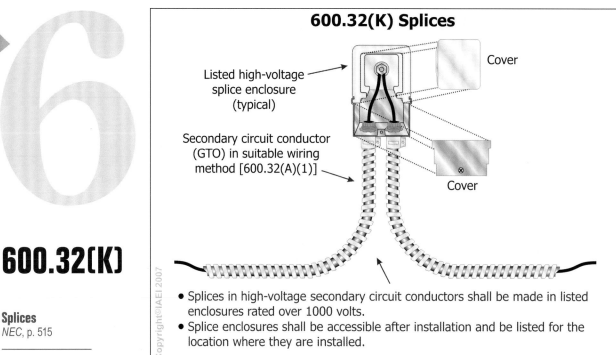

600.32(K) Splices

Listed high-voltage splice enclosure (typical)

Cover

Secondary circuit conductor (GTO) in suitable wiring method [600.32(A)(1)]

Cover

Copyright©IAEI 2007

- Splices in high-voltage secondary circuit conductors shall be made in listed enclosures rated over 1000 volts.
- Splice enclosures shall be accessible after installation and be listed for the location where they are installed.

Analysis and Effect

Part II of Article 600 addresses field-installed skeleton tubing installations that often include splices in high-voltage secondary circuit conductors. Previous editions of the *Code* did not include specific requirements for high-voltage splice enclosures within Article 600 and specifically in Part II. Only electrode connections are covered in 600.42, which address the connections between the high-voltage secondary conductors and the neon tubing. This revision to 600.32 should provide needed guidance and rules for such equipment and for the locations of such devices. Various manufacturers currently produce listed devices designed for this purpose. Requirements to locate the splice device at an accessible location are consistent with low-voltage splice requirements contained in chapter 3, and including information about the location where the device is installed should provide guidance as to when high-voltage splice enclosures are installed in dry, damp, or wet locations. Splice enclosures are required to be listed for dry, damp, or wet locations. Listed signs covered by Part I should already include this as part of the manufacturing process to meet the minimum requirements of the product standard.

Code Language
600.32(K)
Splices

Splices in high-voltage secondary circuit conductors shall be made in listed enclosures rated over 1000 volts. Splice enclosures shall be accessible after installation and listed for the location where they are installed.

Summary of Change

A new subdivision (K) requires splices to be made in listed enclosures that are accessible after installation.

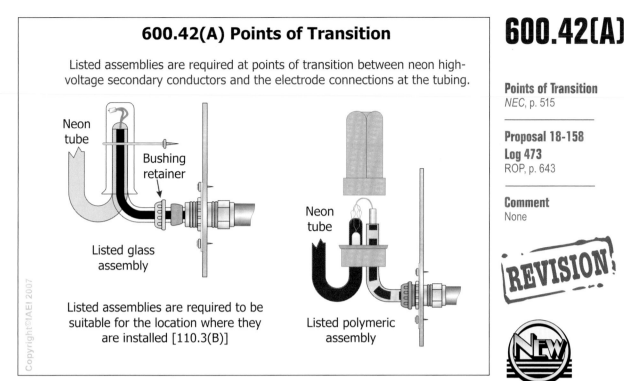

600.42(A) Points of Transition

Listed assemblies are required at points of transition between neon high-voltage secondary conductors and the electrode connections at the tubing.

Neon tube

Bushing retainer

Listed glass assembly

Neon tube

Listed polymeric assembly

Listed assemblies are required to be suitable for the location where they are installed [110.3(B)]

Copyright©IAEI 2007

600.42(A)

Points of Transition
NEC, p. 515

Proposal 18-158
Log 473
ROP, p. 643

Comment
None

REVISION!

NEW

Analysis and Effect

This part of field-installed skeleton tubing installations was not adequately covered by 600.32 of previous editions of the *NEC*. This revision adds a requirement that is clear and easy to follow. Secondary wiring methods are covered in 600.32(A), and the electrode connection enclosures are covered in 600.42. Where high-voltage secondary wiring is installed for field-installed skeleton tubing, the *point of transition* from the high-voltage secondary wiring method to the electrode connection at the neon tubing seems to be the most challenging part of the installation. It also is the point where the most failures are occurring. There are listed glass and nonmetallic products available to readily accomplish these transitions. One of the most critical points in any electrical installation is the connection. Generally, if something is going to fail in an electrical circuit, it usually starts at the connection point. These revisions provide a specific set of requirements for making transitions at connections between the GTO cable and the tubing. Requiring that these points of transition assemblies be listed provides reasonable assurances that the installations will meet the approval criteria of the AHJ. As with any listed product, installing these assemblies in accordance with the installation instructions is essential, and applying these products in locations for which they are suitable should result in installations that are essentially safe.

Code Language
600.42(A)
Points of Transition
Where the high-voltage secondary circuit conductors emerge from the wiring methods specified in 600.32(A), they shall be enclosed in a listed assembly.

Summary of Change
A new subdivision (A) has been inserted in Section 600.42 and is titled "Points of Transition." The remainder of this section has been renumbered accordingly.

Change at a Glance

In high-voltage secondary wiring for field-installed skeleton tubing, the connection points are required to be a listed *point of transition* from the high-voltage secondary wiring method to the electrode connection at the neon tubing.

620.2

Elevators, Dumbwaiters, Escalators, Moving Walks, Platform Lifts, and Stairway Chairlifts
NEC, p. 524

Proposal 12-16a
Log CP1201
ROP, p. 649

Comment
None

Change at a Glance

Remote machine rooms and spaces and control room spaces are now defined locations in 620.2.

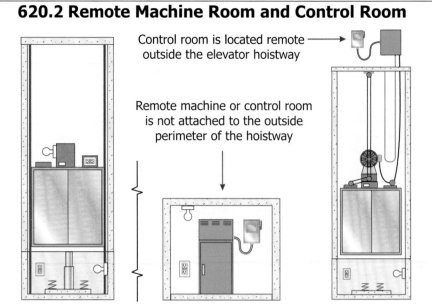

620.2 Remote Machine Room and Control Room

Control room is located remote outside the elevator hoistway

Remote machine or control room is not attached to the outside perimeter of the hoistway

Copyright©IAEI 2007

Section 620.2 defines remote machine rooms or spaces and remote control rooms or spaces for elevators and dumbwaiters.

Analysis and Effect

This change correlates the *NEC* with the Safety Code for Elevators and Escalators, A17.1-2004. Remote machine rooms and spaces are being installed and will now be in compliance with the *NEC*. In recent years the elevator industry and technology have introduced many advanced designs. These designs include equipment and systems that are without a dedicated room. These new configurations also require flexibility for the location of the machine and control rooms or spaces. The *NEC* must remain current with the new technologies and systems introduced. The traditional machine room attached to the hoistway configuration (as was typical installation practice in the past), may or may not be installed. Machine and control rooms and spaces are now recognized for installation remote from the hoistway.

This revision in Article 620 and the new definitions will allow engineers and designers to have more flexibility and versatility when assigning floor spaces and locations to accommodate new elevator and dumbwaiter technologies and to install associated machines and control equipment in locations remote from the hoistway.

Code Language
620.2
Definitions

Remote Machine Room and Control Room (for Elevator, Dumbwaiter). A machine room or control room that is not attached to the outside perimeter or surface of the walls, ceiling or floor of the hoistways.

Remote Machinery Space and Control Space (for Elevator, Dumbwaiter). A machinery space or control space that is not within the hoistway, machine room, or control room, and that is not attached to the outside perimeter or surface of the walls, ceiling, or floor of the hoistway.

Summary of Change

Two new definitions have been added to 620.2.

620.21(A)(1)(e) Wiring Methods in Hoistways

Elevator pit sump pump is permitted to be cord-connected.

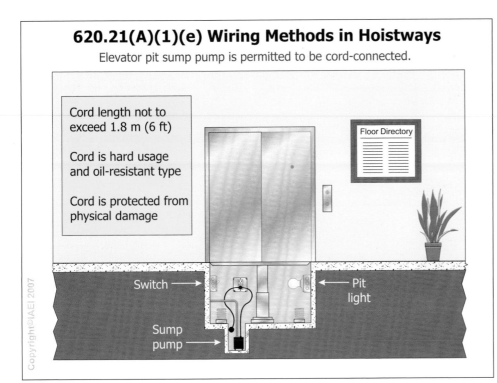

Cord length not to exceed 1.8 m (6 ft)

Cord is hard usage and oil-resistant type

Cord is protected from physical damage

Floor Directory

Switch

Pit light

Sump pump

Copyright©IAEI 2007

620.21(A) (1)(e)

Elevators
Hoistways
NEC, p. 527

Proposal 12-25
Log 3096
ROP, p. 650

Comment 12-9
Log 75
ROC, p. 365

Analysis and Effect

The previous editions of the *NEC* provided no allowance for the use of cord-connected equipment in elevator pits. The revisions to this section allow for use of cord-connected sump pumps in elevator pits in a more practical application. This change is consistent with commonly accepted practices of installing cord-connected sump pumps and oil recovery pump motors. This new section will permit the use of cords for a sump or oil recovery pump motor but limits the length and type of cord permitted. Where cord is installed for these applications, it is required to be an oil-resistant hard usage type, and it is limited to lengths not exceeding 1.8 m (6 ft). The cord also is required to be protected from physical damage. These new provisions for cord connection do not affect the current requirements for a GFCI-protected receptacle outlet.

Change at a Glance

Sump pumps in elevator pits are now permitted to be cord- and plug-connected when the cord is listed as oil-resistant and hard-usage type, no longer than 1.8 m (6 ft) in length, and located where it is protected from physical damage.

Code Language
620.21(A)(1)(e)
Elevators
(1) Hoistways

A sump pump or oil recovery pump located in the pit shall be permitted to be cord connected. The cord shall be a hard usage oil-resistant type, of a length not to exceed 1.8 m (6 ft), and shall be located to be protected from physical damage.

Summary of Change

A new item (e) has been added to Section 620.21(A)(1) that addresses cord-connected sump pumps installed in elevator pits.

6

620.21(A)
(3)(e)

Elevators
Flexible Cords and Cables
NEC, p. 528

Proposal 12-31
Log 1214
ROP, p. 652

Comment 12-11
Log 76
ROC, p. 365

Change at a Glance

Flexible cords and cables are permitted in machine rooms or spaces and control rooms or spaces without raceways when they are not longer than 1.8 m (6 ft), and they are flame-retardant and protected from physical damage; they must also be part of the elevator equipment, or driving machine.

Analysis and Effect

The revision to this section expands the allowance for flexible cords and cables installed with elevator power equipment and control wiring. Flexible cords and cables of the flame-retardant type will now be permitted as wiring methods in elevator machine rooms, control rooms, machinery spaces and control spaces. There are specific requirements for any cords or cables installed to meet the provisions of this section. These cords and cables must be part of a piece of listed equipment, part of a driving machine or a driving machine brake, and must be protected from physical damage. This new provision allows elevator equipment manufacturers to build equipment with factory-installed cord assemblies if listed. This change could eliminate, in some cases, the required disconnect cable from being locked in the open position for those pieces of equipment, if cord- and plug-connected.

Code Language
620.21(A)(3)(e)
Elevators

(e) Flexible cords and cables in lengths not to exceed 1.8 m (6 ft) that are of a flame-retardant type and located to be protected from physical damage shall be permitted in these rooms and spaces without being installed in a raceway. They shall be part of the following:

(1) Listed equipment,
(2) A driving machine, or
(3) A driving machine brake

Summary of Change

A new item (e) has been added to 620.21(A)(3) that addresses flexible cords and cables installed and used in elevator machine rooms or spaces and elevator control rooms or spaces.

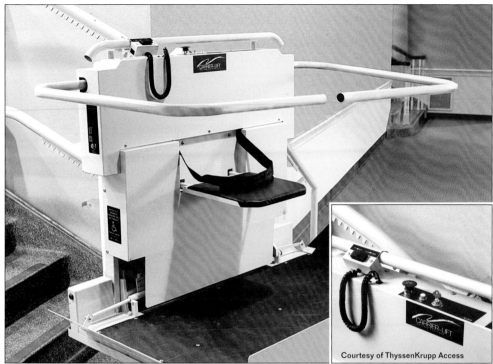

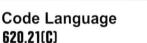

Courtesy of ThyssenKrupp Access

620.21
(C)(3)

Platform Lifts and Stairway Chairlift Raceways
NEC, p. 528

Proposal 12-35
Log 3533
ROP, p. 652

Comment
None

Analysis and Effect

This change recognizes that manufacturers of this special lift equipment often incorporate cord and cable connections. The revision to this section will permit the use of cords and cables on low-voltage circuits for platform lifts and stairway chairlifts, with some specific limitations. Cord connections are currently permitted for elevator installations; this change will now permit cord connections for platform lifts and stairway chairlifts. Installers are allowed to use flexible cords and cables for the low-voltage applications used on platform lifts and stairway chairlifts where the cords/cables are components of listed equipment. The cords must be of the jacketed and flame-retardant type, be not over 1.8 m (6 ft) in length, and be protected from physical damage.

Change at a Glance

Cords and cables are now permitted to be installed for low-voltage circuits of wheelchair lifts and stairway chairlifts, if they are of the jacketed and flame-retardant type, and are not over 1.8 m (6 ft) in length, and are protected from physical damage.

Code Language
620.21(C)

Platform Lifts and Stairway Chairlift Raceways

(1) No change

(2) No change

(3) **Flexible Cords and Cables.** Flexible cords and cables that are components of listed equipment and used in circuits operating at 30 volts rms or less or 42 volts dc or less shall be permitted in lengths not to exceed 1.8 m (6 ft.), provided the cords and cables are supported and protected from physical damage and are of a jacketed and flame-retardant type.

Summary of Change

A new item (3) has been added to 620.21(C) that includes provisions for cord-connected platform lift and stairway chairlift wiring.

6

620.51(A)
Exception
No. 2

Disconnecting Means
Type
NEC, p. 530

Proposal 12-57
Log 3537
ROP, p. 656

Comment 12-19
Log 2093
ROC, p. 367

Change at a Glance

An individual branch circuit that supplies a stairway chairlift is permitted to be cord- and plug-connected, provided it complies with 422.16(A) and the cord does not exceed 1. 8 m (6 ft) in length.

Analysis and Effect

This revision incorporates a new exception to permit a stairway chairlift to be cord-and-plug-connected when the stairway chairlift is designed to be cord- and plug-connected. Action by CMP-12 resulted in a new exception recognizing cord connection for stairway chairlift equipment. CMP-12 responded favorably to additional information provided in the substantiation with Comment 12-19 and clarified the need to include provisions for cord- and plug-connecting this type of equipment, which is often connected to branch-circuit wiring using a hard connection without a flexible cord and plug. Substantiation in the proposal indicated that some stairway chairlift equipment is often supplied with a flexible cord for connection to a receptacle. This change will permit cord-and-plug-connection for this type of equipment where specifically designed to be cord-and-plug-connected and where it may need to be removed for service, similar to many appliances. A cord-and-plug-connected stairway chairlift allows the unit to be easily disconnected for service or maintenance operations.

Code Language
620.51(A)
Disconnecting Means
(A) Type

Exception No. 1: (Existing exception re-identified as Exception No. 1)

Exception No. 2: Where an individual branch circuit supplies a stairway chairlift, the stairway chairlift shall be permitted to be cord-and-plug-connected, provided it complies with 422.16(A) and the cord does not exceed 1.8 m (6 ft) in length.

Summary of Change

A new Exception No. 2 has been added to 620.51(A), and the existing exception has been re-identified as Exception No. 1.

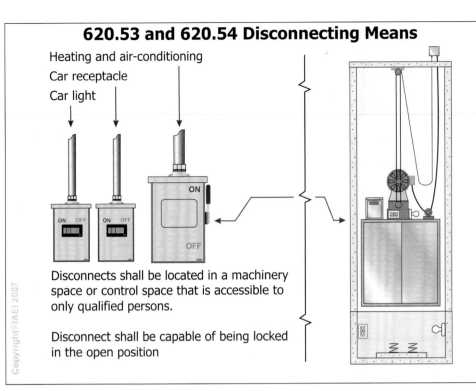

620.53 and 620.54 Disconnecting Means

Heating and air-conditioning
Car receptacle
Car light

ON
OFF

ON OFF
ON OFF

Disconnects shall be located in a machinery space or control space that is accessible to only qualified persons.

Disconnect shall be capable of being locked in the open position

Copyright©IAEI 2007

Disconnecting Means
NEC, p. 532

Proposal 12-61, 12-64
Log 1224, 1225
ROP, p. 657

Comment
None

Analysis and Effect

The change to 620.53 gives some additional flexibility for the required disconnecting means locations for car lights, receptacle(s), and ventilation equipment. The change to 620.54 gives the same flexibility for the disconnecting means location for heating and air-conditioning. An important element of this revision is that the remote location outside the hoistway is permitted solely where the disconnecting means is accessible only to qualified persons. The term *qualified persons* is defined in Article 100 and includes specific criteria. Industry trends are often eliminating elevator machine rooms where possible. Machine rooms are rated rooms that take up additional square footage in buildings. Although the room can be eliminated and reduced to spaces dedicated to elevator machines and control equipment, the requirements for safety disconnects are still included in the *NEC*. This revision provides needed flexibility for locating equipment disconnects remote, but solely where they are accessible only to qualified persons.

Change at a Glance

The required disconnecting means for car lights, receptacle(s), ventilation, heating, or air-conditioning equipment may be located in a machinery or control space outside the hoistway that is readily accessible to only qualified persons.

Code Language

620.53

Car Light, Receptacle(s), and Ventilation Disconnecting Means

(The last sentence now reads:)
Where there is no machine room or control room, the disconnecting means shall be located in a machinery space or control space outside the hoistway that is readily accessible to only qualified persons.

620.54

Heating and Air-Conditioning Disconnecting Means

(The last sentence now reads:)
Where there is no machine room or control room, the disconnecting means shall be located in a machinery space or control space outside the hoistway that is readily accessible to only qualified persons.

Summary of Change

The last sentences of 620.53 and 620.54 have been revised to include the new text as follows: "a machinery space or control space outside the hoistway that is readily accessible to only qualified persons."

625.2 Electric Vehicle

Neighborhood electric vehicles are not intended for use on highways.

Equipped with the following:

- Automotive grade headlights
- Seatbelts
- Windshield
- Brakes
- Other safety equipment

Smaller than traditional cars

- Top speed of 25 mph
- Can only be used on streets posted 35 mph speed limits
- Suitable for on-road use, not on highways

Copyright©IAEI 2007

625.2

Electric Vehicle
Charging System
NEC, p. 534

Proposal 12-76
Log 404
ROP, p. 660

Comment
None

REVISION!

Change at a Glance

Electric vehicles include those intended for all roads, not just highways.

Analysis and Effect

In *NEC*-2005, the term *neighborhood electric vehicle* was added to the definition of electric vehicle. The term *highway use* does not apply to n*eighborhood electric vehicles* (NEVs). The National Traffic Safety Administration defines neighborhood electric vehicles as low-speed vehicles with a top speed of 25 MPH. These vehicles are intended and suitable for use on local roads only, not on highways. Accordingly, the appropriate term for all the listed vehicles is *on-road use*. This change could affect the type of vehicles some retirement communities will allow within the community. As defined now, the neighborhood electric vehicles have a top speed of 25 MPH and would not be allowed on any marked highways. The revision also broadens the definition to apply to all electric vehicles, rather than those just for highway use.

Code Language
625.2
Definitions
Electric Vehicle. An automotive-type vehicle for on-road use,...(remainder unchanged).

Summary of Change

The word "highway" was changed to "on-road" in the first sentence of the definition of the term *electric vehicle*.

Electrified Truck Parking Space
NEC, 538–543

Proposal 12-81
Log 1650
ROP, p. 661

Comment 12-44
Log 2025
ROC, p. 373

Analysis and Effect

This article was developed by the Truck Stop Electrification (TSE) Committee of the National Electric Transportation Infrastructure Working Council (IWC), sponsored by the Electric Power Research Institute (EPRI). The TSE Committee is a multi-industry group of professional volunteers, involving truck manufacturers, TSE designers, component manufacturers, utilities, and members of the National Association of Truck Stop Operators, Society of Automotive Engineers (SAE), Environmental Protection Agency, Department of Energy, Department of Defense, IEEE, EPRI, and others working together to develop the TSE infrastructure. Over the past several years, the attention of regulatory agencies and environmental groups has focused on means to reducing truck idling, thereby reducing emissions and fuel consumption. More than twenty states and cities have already adopted legislation to reduce the number of hours a truck idles. Developing a standardized, safe and efficient means of reducing fuel consumption and emissions is the primary objective. This article provides rules that can be applied to electrical installations and systems designed for supplying electrical power and services to trucks while they are parked. This article includes provisions similar to those that already exist in Articles 550 and 551 that also include requirements for permanent power facilities. The development of *Code* rules for truck stop electrification targets reducing idle time for over-the-road heavy-duty trucking fleets. Truck idle time can account for more than 50 percent of total trip time. With approximately 1.4 million heavy-duty long haul trucks on American roads, a mechanism to connect these trucks to an electrified parking space can help reduce the 1.2 billion gallons of diesel fuel consumed annually by idling. Not only fuel savings but emissions reductions would occur. This article ensures that applicable minimum electrical safety requirements are in place for this specialized equipment. Requirements for standardized wiring methods, materials and configurations will result in uniform electrified truck parking spaces that will be installed and used throughout the country. This will ensure that all truck fleets will have the ability to connect to "shore power" to run cab amenities (hotel loads) and the heating, ventilation and air-conditioning systems necessary for heating and cooling. The environmental benefits of this change will result in significantly better air quality near the sites and will reduce fuel consumption.

Change at a Glance

Article 626 provides installation requirements for truck stops that will supply electrical and communications services so that truck engines will be shut off for a time to lessen carbon emissions and to reduce fuel consumption.

Code Language
Article 626
Electrified Truck Parking Space

Part I. General

Part II. Electrified Truck Parking Space Electrical Wiring Systems

Part III. Electrified Truck Parking Space Supply Equipment

Part IV. Transport Refrigerated Units (TRUs)

See *NEC*-2008 Article 626 for full text of the new article.

Summary of Change
A new Article 626 entitled "Electrified Truck Parking Space" was added to chapter 6 of the *NEC*. The new article is divided into four parts.

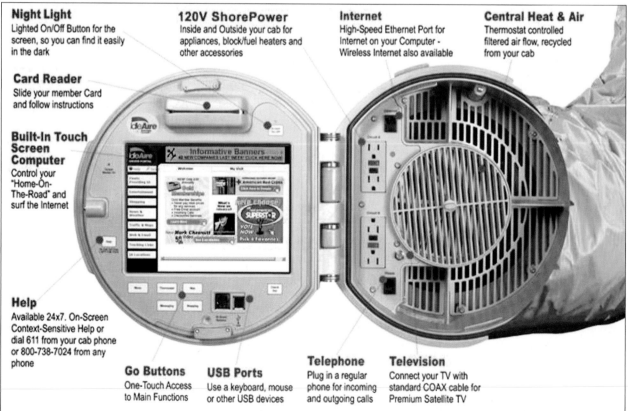

Night Light
Lighted On/Off Button for the screen, so you can find it easily in the dark

Card Reader
Slide your member Card and follow instructions

Built-In Touch Screen Computer
Control your "Home-On-The-Road" and surf the Internet

Help
Available 24x7. On-Screen Context-Sensitive Help or dial 611 from your cab phone or 800-738-7024 from any phone

120V ShorePower
Inside and Outside your cab for appliances, block/fuel heaters and other accessories

Internet
High-Speed Ethernet Port for Internet on your Computer - Wireless Internet also available

Central Heat & Air
Thermostat controlled filtered air flow, recycled from your cab

Go Buttons
One-Touch Access to Main Functions

USB Ports
Use a keyboard, mouse or other USB devices

Telephone
Plug in a regular phone for incoming and outgoing calls

Television
Connect your TV with standard COAX cable for Premium Satellite TV

Courtesy of Idleaire Technologies Corp.

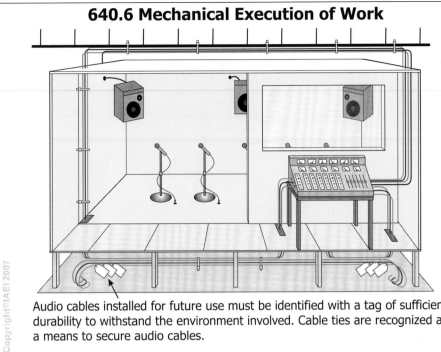

640.6 Mechanical Execution of Work

Audio cables installed for future use must be identified with a tag of sufficient durability to withstand the environment involved. Cable ties are recognized as a means to secure audio cables.

Copyright©IAEI 2007

640.6

Mechanical Execution of Work
NEC, p. 547

Proposal 12-91, 12-92, 12-94
Log 887, 1362, 3049
ROP, p. 675, 676

Comment 12-67
Log 545
ROC, p. 386

Analysis and Effect

This change was the result of action that combined several proposals addressing similar issues regarding audio cable installation and abandoned audio distribution cables' removal or identification requirements. Abandoned audio cables must be handled in the same manner as abandoned remote-control signaling cables, class 2 fire alarm cables, fiber optic cables, communications circuit cables, CATV cables, and network broadband communication cables; they must either be removed or identified with a "sufficiently durable" tag that is suitable and for the environment in which it is installed. Audio cables are now included with the other limited-energy cables that have specific rules for use and identification or removal of accessible portions of abandoned cables.

> ### Change at a Glance
> Audio cables are permitted to be supported with cable ties, and the installation must meet the requirements of Sections 300.4 and 300.11. Accessible portions of abandoned audio cable shall be removed unless identified with a durable tag indicating its intended future use.

More and more audio cables are being installed, and new technologies result in many of the older existing audio cables being abandoned. Cable ties have been included as an acceptable means of support for audio cable as a result of action on Proposal 12-92 (Log No. 1362).

Code Language
640.6
Mechanical Execution of Work

(A) Neat and Workmanlike Manner. Audio signal processing, amplification, and reproduction equipment, cables, and circuits shall be installed in a neat and workmanlike manner.

(B) Installations of Audio Distribution Cables. Cables installed exposed on the surface of ceilings and sidewalls shall be supported in such a manner that the audio distribution cables will not be damaged by normal building use. Such cables shall be secured by straps, staples, cable ties, hangers or similar fittings designed and installed so as not to damage the cable. The installation shall also comply with 300.4 and 300.11(A).

(C) Abandoned Audio Distribution Cables. The accessible portion of abandoned audio distribution cables shall be removed.

(D) Installed Audio Distribution Cable Identified for Future Use.

(1) Cables identified for future use shall be marked with a tag of sufficient durability to withstand the environment involved.

(2) Cable tags shall have the following information:
  (1) Date cable was identified for future use
  (2) Date of intended use
  (3) Information relating to the intended future use of cable

Summary of Change

This section has been revised to reference all of 300.4, and it was expanded into a list format in accordance with the *NEC Style Manual*. New subdivisions (C) and (D) provide information about abandoned cable removal and identification.

6

645.2

Information Technology Equipment
NEC, p. 550

Proposal 12-106
Log 2687
ROP, p. 678

Comment
None

Change at a Glance

The term *abandoned supply circuits and interconnecting cables* clearly defines the cables required to be removed by new Section 645.5(F).

Analysis and Effect

This change results in a new Section 645.2 containing a newly defined term, *abandoned supply circuits and interconnecting cables*. Substantiation with the proposal identified the need for a defined term that can be applied to information technology rooms. These rooms and their uses are dynamic and constantly changing wiring configurations as new and advancing technologies and equipment are incorporated into their use. The new definition includes and describes not only abandoned limited energy computer interconnecting cables, but also abandoned supply power branch-circuit wiring. The new definition is necessary because of the new requirements for removal of these abandoned circuits and cables required by 645.5(F).

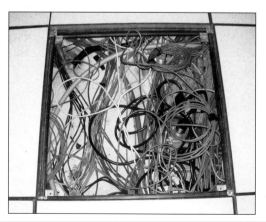

Code Language
645.2

Definitions
Abandoned Supply Circuits and Interconnecting Cables. Installed supply circuits and interconnecting cables that are not terminated at equipment and not identified for future use with a tag.

Summary of Change

A new Section 645.2 has been added to Article 645, and definition of the term *abandoned supply circuits and interconnecting cables* has been included.

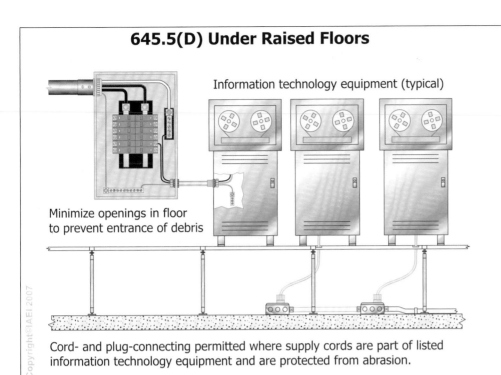

645.5(D) Under Raised Floors

Information technology equipment (typical)

Minimize openings in floor to prevent entrance of debris

Copyright IAEI 2007

Cord- and plug-connecting permitted where supply cords are part of listed information technology equipment and are protected from abrasion.

Under Raised Floors
NEC, p. 551

Proposal 12-114
Log 2339
ROP, p. 681

Comment 12-82, 12-83, 12-84
Log 688, 789, 1985
ROC, p. 390

Analysis and Effect

This revision recognizes common wiring methods used for connection of information technology equipment using cord- and plug- connection. This change eliminates confusion in the industry about whether cord- and plug-connections from listed information technology equipment supply cords are permitted under the raised floor. Section 645.5(B) permits cord- and plug-connections to data processing equipment from branch-circuit wiring. This clarifies that cord connections are allowed in these specific applications and the change permits listed cords under a raised floor where the length of the supply cord and attachment plug cap does not exceed 15 feet. The cord is also required to be protected from physical damage where run on the surface of the floor. Use of these cord allowances for wiring under raised floors in information technology rooms is dependent upon all of the requirements in 645.4(1) through (5) being satisfied. The revisions to this section provide clarity and improve usability and also are consistent with current industry practices that require use of cord- and plug-connected information technology equipment under prescribed conditions.

Change at a Glance

Code rules have been changed to permit increased use of cord- and plug- connections under raised floors for equipment used in information and technology equipment rooms, if all requirements in the section are met.

Code Language
645.5(D)

Under Raised Floors

Power cables, communications cables, connecting cables, interconnecting cables, cord-and-plug connections, and receptacles associated with the information technology equipment shall be permitted under a raised floor, provided the following conditions are met:

(1) unchanged

(2) unchanged

(3) Supply cords of listed information technology equipment in accordance with 645.5(B).

(After new item 3, all items are renumbered.)

(4) renumbered-text unchanged
Revise and renumber as follows

(5) Openings in raised floors for cords and cables protect cords and cables against abrasion and minimize the entrance of debris beneath the floor.

(6) renumbered-text unchanged

Summary of Change

The phrase "cord- and plug-connections" has been added to the section, item (3) is new, and the section was partially renumbered.

645.5(D) (6)c

Under Raised Floors
NEC, p. 551

Proposal 12-112
Log 2379
ROP, p. 680

Comment
None

Change at a Glance

A new table providing the types of cable permitted to be installed under raised floors of information technology rooms has been added to the *Code*. Plenum cables, riser cables, and general purpose cables are included.

Table 645.5

Table 645.5 Cable Types Permitted Under Raised Floors

Article	Plenum	Riser	General Purpose
336			TC
725	CL2P & CL3P	CL2R & CL3R	Cl2, Cl3 & PLTC
727			ITC
760	NPLFP & FPLP	NPLFR & FPLR	NPLF & FPL
770	OFNP & OFCP	OFNR & OFCR	OFN & OFC
800	CMP	CMR	CM & CMG
820	CATV	CATVR	CATV

Reproduction of *NEC* Table 645.5

Analysis and Effect

Section 645.5(D) addresses the types of power wiring cables, connecting cables, interconnecting cables, and receptacles associated with information technology equipment. The revisions to this section clarify and improve usability of the requirements related to limited energy cables permitted under raised floors in information technology rooms. The types of cables permitted to be used in these applications, and previously itemized within the text of 645.5(D)(6)c, have been placed in a new Table 645.5. Placing requirements in tabular form generally results in enhanced usability and clarity and is consistent with the provisions contained in Section 3.3.1 of the *NEC Style Manual*. The new table provides the type of cable covered by each article and the type of designations permitted for these various systems when they are installed under raised floors of information technology rooms. There is a column each for plenum cables, riser cables, and general purpose cables. The cables permitted for use in these applications are listed under each category. All conditions provided in 645.4(1) through (5) must be met before the requirements or provisions of Article 645 may be applied to information technology rooms.

Code Language
645.5(D)(6)c

Under Raised Floors

c. Cable type designations shown in Table 645.5 shall be permitted. Green, or green with one or more yellow stripes, insulated single-conductor cables, 4 AWG and larger, marked "for use in cable trays" or "for CT use" shall be permitted for equipment grounding.

Summary of Change

Section 645.5(D)(6)c has been revised to remove all cable type designations from the text and place them in a new Table 645.5 titled "Cable Types Permitted Under Raised Floors."

Analysis of Changes *NEC*-2008

645.5(F) and (G)

(F) Accessible portions of abandoned supply circuits and interconnecting cables shall be removed unless contained in a metal raceway or identified for future use with a tag.

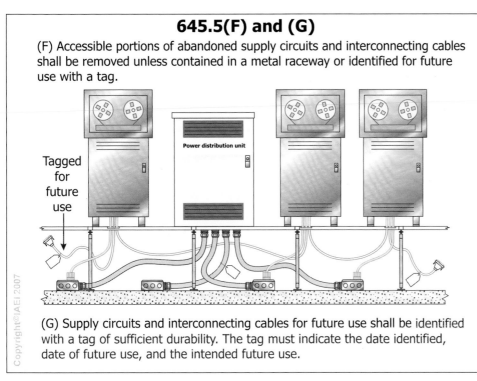

(G) Supply circuits and interconnecting cables for future use shall be identified with a tag of sufficient durability. The tag must indicate the date identified, date of future use, and the intended future use.

Abandoned Supply Circuits and Interconnecting Cables
NEC, p. 551

Proposal 12-116
Log 2649
ROP, p. 682

Comment 12-80, 12-85
Log 546, 84
ROC, p. 389, 391

Analysis and Effect

This change results in the creation of two new subdivisions (F) and (G) in Section 645.5. The significance of this revision is that the requirements for removing abandoned cables extends not only to the abandoned computer interconnecting cables, but also to any abandoned power supply circuit wiring. The wiring and configurations in information technology rooms are continuously changing, which often results in many abandoned cables and circuits that clutter the area below a raised platform or floor in these rooms. This revision provides users with a requirement to remove any supply circuit wiring and computer interconnecting cables that qualify by definition in 645.2 as abandoned supply circuits and interconnecting cables. The provisions of 645.5(G) provide more specific criteria that must be included on any tagged supply circuit wiring or interconnecting cable, regarding its intended future use and including the date of the intended use and what the use will be. This identification is required to be provided with a tag that is suitable and durable for the environment in which it is installed.

Change at a Glance

Abandoned supply circuit and interconnecting cables in IT rooms are required to be in metal raceways, removed, or tagged with an tag that is "sufficiently durable" and which identifies them for future use.

Code Language
645.5(F)

Abandoned Supply Circuits and Interconnecting Cables
The accessible portion of abandoned supply circuits and interconnecting cables shall be removed unless contained in a metal raceway.

(G)

Installed Supply Circuits and Interconnecting Cables Identified for Future Use
(1) Supply circuits and interconnecting cables identified for future use shall be marked with a tag of sufficient durability to withstand the environment involved.
(2) Supply circuit tags and interconnecting cable tags shall have the following information:
    a. Date identified for future use
    b. Date of intended use
    c. Information relating to the intended future use

Summary of Change
List item (6) has been removed from 645.5(D)(6) and relocated to 645.5(F), and two new subdivisions (F) and (G) have been added to Section 645.5 addressing abandoned supply circuit and interconnecting cables.

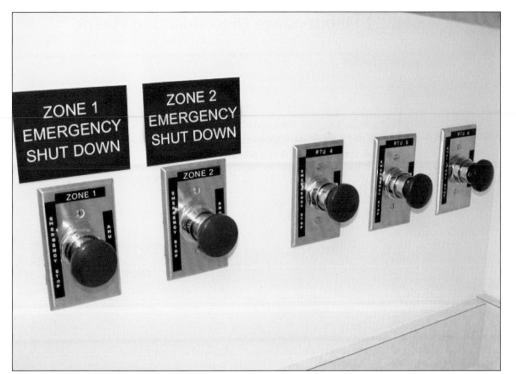

Disconnecting Means
NEC, p. 552

Proposal 12-120
Log 1714
ROP, p. 683

Comment 12-87
Log 790
ROC, p. 391

Analysis and Effect

This revision provides for alternative designs that allow for shutting down IT rooms by zones, in addition to disconnecting the entire room. These alternative designs are required to be approved by the authority having jurisdiction. Zoned shutdown is already widely used in telecommunications facilities and usually involves review and approval of the AHJ, special signs, posted instructions, and clear identification of the zones, or other specific requirements that provide approving authorities with evidence that an equivalent level of safety is provided. Some facilities use special floor markings to guide fire fighters to the affected zone. The provisions of this section still allow for single disconnecting means for power and air to the entire room if necessary. Technology today has the ability to control electricity and cooling with extreme precision. The requirements in NFPA 75 and *NEC* Article 645 were originally created for the protection of mission-critical operations, and the disconnecting means have evolved to meet current industry design needs. The revision actually improves safety because it encourages the use of Article 645 for information technology room designs and provides a reasonable balance of safety and business continuity, because the zoned areas will reduce the possibilities of complete unintended IT shutdown. Multiple zoned areas also provide fire fighters a more precise direction to any affected zone.

Code Language
645.10

Disconnecting Means

An approved means shall be provided to disconnect power to all electronic equipment in the information technology equipment room or in designated zones within the room. There shall also be a similar approved means to disconnect the power to all dedicated HVAC systems serving the room or designated zones and shall cause all required fire/smoke dampers to close. The control for these disconnecting means shall be grouped and identified and shall be readily accessible at the principal exit doors. A single means to control both the electronic equipment and HVAC systems in the room or in a zone shall be permitted. Where a pushbutton is used as a means to disconnect power, pushing the button in shall disconnect the power. Where multiple zones are created, each zone shall have an approved means to confine fire or products of combustion to within the zone.

Summary of Change

The concept of approved designated zone shut down has been added to 645.10. A new last sentence has been added requiring zones to include an approved means to confine fire or products of combustion to within the zone.

Change at a Glance

Alternative designs which permit shutting down electrical power and HVAC systems in IT equipment rooms by zones (in addition to disconnecting the entire room) are now permitted.

680.12

Maintenance Disconnecting Means
NEC, p. 568

Proposal 17-79, 17-80
Log 900, 1635
ROP, p. 696

Comments 17-70, 17-71
Log 455, 1950
ROC, p. 395

Change at a Glance

The maintenance disconnect must simultaneously disconnect all ungrounded conductors supplying the equipment, and must be located a minimum of 1.5 m (5 ft) from the edge of the water. Disconnects that are integral to hot tub assemblies are not recognized by this requirement.

680.12 Maintenance Disconnecting Means

Disconnecting mean(s) must simultaneously disconnect all ungrounded conductors of the circuit.

Disconnecting mean(s) must be located a minimum of 1.5 m (5 ft) from inside wall of pool, spa, or hot tub unless separated by permanently installed barrier.

Copyright©IAEI 2007

Applies to pools, spas, and hot tubs

Analysis and Effect

Section 680.12 provides requirements for installing a maintenance disconnecting means for all utilization equipment associated with pools or similar bodies of water covered by Article 680, other than lighting. The revisions clarify that the ungrounded conductors must all be simultaneously disconnected. The revisions to the last sentence and the additional text clarify where the distances must be measured from when applying this rule to equipment in the field. In addition to clarifying the disconnecting means' operation characteristics and requirements for approval, this section now identifies the types of equipment covered by this section. Referencing pools, spas, and hot tubs within this rule removes any question about the types of equipment that are required to be provided with a maintenance disconnecting means. Section 680.41 addresses emergency switches for spas and hot tubs, which provide a different type of safety switch for different reasons; this section applies only to installations in other than single-family dwellings. This type of emergency disconnect could direct a control circuit or even operate the equipment disconnect functions pneumatically. The disconnect covered by the general requirements in 680.12 is intended for use by service personnel to ensure worker and personnel safety during repair and maintenance operations.

Code Language
680.12

Maintenance Disconnecting Means
One or more means to simultaneously disconnect all ungrounded conductors shall be provided for all utilization equipment other than lighting. Each means shall be readily accessible and within sight from its equipment and shall be located at least 1.5 m (5 ft) horizontally from the inside walls of the pool, spa, or hot tub unless separated from the open water by a permanently installed barrier that provides a 1.5 m (5 ft) reach path or greater. This horizontal distance is to be measured from the water's edge along the shortest path required to reach the disconnect.

Summary of Change

The first sentence has been revised by adding the word "simultaneously." The last two sentences have been revised to clarify separation between the disconnect and the water and to indicate how the measurement is to be taken.

Analysis of Changes *NEC*-2008

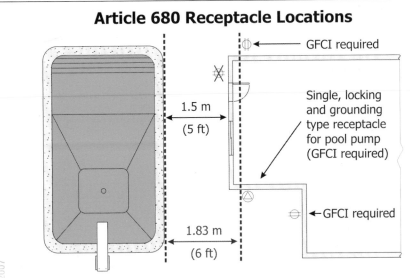

Article 680 Receptacle Locations

GFCI required

1.5 m
(5 ft)

Single, locking
and grounding
type receptacle
for pool pump
(GFCI required)

GFCI required

1.83 m
(6 ft)

Receptacle outlet locations requiring minimum distance from pool, spa, etc. of 1.5 m (5 ft) or 3.0 m (10 ft) have been changed to a consistent distance of 1.83 m (6 ft) in several sections of Article 680.

680.22, 680.34, 680.43, 680.62, and 680.71

Copyright©IAEI 2007

Swimming Pools, Fountains, and Similar Installations
NEC, p. 568, 575, 576, 579

Proposal 17-85a
Log 1707
ROP, p. 697

Comment
None

Analysis and Effect

The requirements of these sections within Article 680 address required receptacles and specify the locations for such receptacles. The revisions to these sections change the minimum or maximum distances mentioned from either 1.5 m (5 ft) or 3.0 m (10 ft) to a consistent 1.83 m (6 ft) distance. Action by CMP-17 on this proposal results in a consistent dimension that is sufficient in light of the expanded GFCI protection requirements added to Article 680 that afford equivalent protection as the minimum 3.0 m (10 ft) distance rules when ground-fault circuit-interrupter protection was not required in early editions of the *Code*. The change also correlates consistently with standard cord lengths for appliances and other utilization equipment, and with the 1.83 m (6 ft) dimensions in the receptacle GFCI rules in 210.8.

Summary of Change

The dimensions of 1.5 m (5 ft) and 3.0 m (10 ft) have been changed to 1.83 m (6 ft) within each of these sections.

Code Language
680.22(A)(1)

...shall be located at least 3.0 m (10 ft) from the inside walls of the pool, or not less than 1.83 m (6 ft) from the inside walls of the pool if they meet all of the following...

680.22(A)(2)

Other receptacles shall be not less than 1.83 m (6 ft) from the inside walls of a pool.

680.22(A)(3)

...a general-purpose branch circuit shall be located not less than 1.83 m (6 ft) from, and not more than 6.0 m (20 ft) from the inside wall...

680.34

Receptacles shall not be located less than 1.83 m (6 ft) from the inside walls of...

680.43(A)

...receptacle on a general-purpose branch circuit shall be located not less than 1.83 m (6 ft) from, and not exceeding 3.0 m (10 ft) from...

Change at a Glance

Receptacles shall not be located less than 1.83 m (6 ft) from the inside walls of any pool or other body of water specifically identified in each of these sections, which is more consistent with other 6 feet away GFCI requirements in the *Code*.

680.43(A)(1)

Receptacles shall be located at least 1.83 m (6 ft) measured horizontally...

680.62(E)

All receptacles within 1.83 m (6 ft) of a therapeutic tub shall be protected by a ground-fault circuit interrupter.

680.71

...All 125-volt, single-phase receptacles not exceeding 30 amperes and located within 1.83 m (6 ft) measured horizontally from the inside walls of a hydromassage tub shall be protected by a ground-fault circuit interrupter.

680.22(B)

GFCI Protection
NEC, p. 569

Proposal 17-85
Log 3493
ROP, p. 697

Comment 17-75
Log 1663
ROC, p. 396

Change at a Glance

All 15- or 20-ampere, 125- or 240-volt, single-phase outlets supplying pool pump motors require GFCI protection whether supplied by a receptacle and cord connection or hard wired to the branch-circuit outlet.

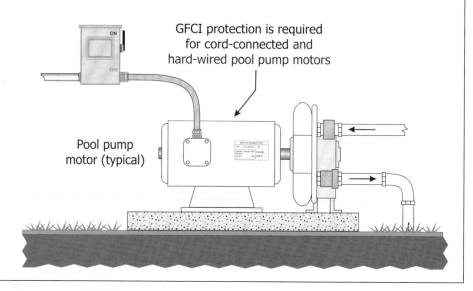

680.22(B) GFCI Protection

All 15 or 20-ampere, 125- <u>or</u> 240-volt, single-phase outlets supplying pool pump motors require GFCI protection whether supplied by a receptacle and cord connection or hard-wired to the branch-circuit outlet.

GFCI protection is required for cord-connected and hard-wired pool pump motors

Pool pump motor (typical)

Copyright©IAEI 2007

Analysis and Effect

Action by CMP-17 on Comment 17-75 reversed the initial rejection of Proposal 17-85. The influencing factor in the reversal was a compilation of data from the Consumer Product Safety Commission National Injury Information Clearinghouse that was analyzed by a task group of members of CMP-17. The revision results in the expansion of the GFCI requirements to pool pump motors that are supplied by a cord- and plug-connection to receptacles and by those that are wired solidly into the branch circuit. This requirement is limited to single-phase pool pump motors rated at 15 or 20 amperes, and 125 or 240 volts, single-phase.

This expansion of ground-fault protection for pool pump motors in these voltage and ampere configurations increase safety and provide consistency between requirements for cord- and plug-connected pool pump motors and for those that are connected directly to the branch-circuit outlet.

Code Language
680.22(B)

GFCI Protection

Outlets supplying pool pump motors from branch circuits with short-circuit and ground-fault protection rated 15 or 20 amperes, 125 volt or 240 volt, single phase, whether by receptacle or direct connection, shall be provided with ground-fault circuit-interrupter protection for personnel.

Re-identify existing (B) as (C) and text is unchanged.

Summary of Change

The last sentence of 680.22(A)(5) was relocated to a new 680.22(B) and existing 680.22(B) has been re-identified as 680.22(C). Section 680.22(A)(6) Measurements, was renumbered as 680.22(A)(5). This section has been revised to expand the GFCI protection requirements for pool pump motors directly connected to the branch-circuit outlets.

Other Outlets
NEC, p. 569

Proposal 17-96
Log 389
ROP, p. 699

Comment 17-81
Log 394
ROC, p. 397

Analysis and Effect

Panel 17 responded favorably to incorporating distance requirements for outlets containing circuits or systems that are other than for power and lighting use. Substantiation in the proposal indicated safety concerns and potential hazards could exist when these types of equipment are installed in close proximity to the pool. The revision to this section results in requirements to maintain a distance of 3.0 m (10 ft) for such outlets. The new fine print note following this requirement provides users with a non-inclusive list of circuit or system outlets that fall under this rule. The *Code* was previously silent on this issue. This change provides clear minimum distance requirements for outlets installed for these types of equipment and circuits.

Change at a Glance

Outlets for limited-energy systems — such as fire alarm, signaling, remote-control, communications systems, and so forth — must not be installed less than 3.0 m (10 ft) from the inside walls of a pool.

Code Language
680.22(E)
Other Outlets

Other outlets shall not be less than 3.0 m (10 ft) from the inside walls of the pool. Measurements shall be determined in accordance with 680.22(A)(5).

FPN: Other outlets may include, but are not limited to, remote-control, signaling, fire alarm, and communications circuits.

Summary of Change

A new subdivision (E) has been added to Section 680.22. A new fine print note has also been added following the new subdivision (E).

680.25(A)

Wiring Methods
NEC, p. 572

Proposal 17-113
Log 901
ROP, p. 705

Comment 17-90
Log 1661
ROC, p. 399

Change at a Glance

Aluminum conduit is not permitted to be installed in the pool area where it is subject to corrosion.

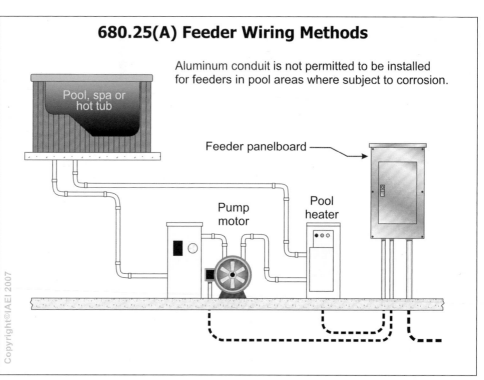

680.25(A) Feeder Wiring Methods

Aluminum conduit is not permitted to be installed for feeders in pool areas where subject to corrosion.

Pool, spa or hot tub

Feeder panelboard

Pump motor

Pool heater

Copyright©IAEI 2007

Analysis and Effect

Section 680.25(A) provides a limited list of acceptable wiring methods that can be used for feeders supplying pool equipment. This section includes conduit types that offer some inherent degree of protection from physical damage due to their construction characteristics. Electrical metallic tubing (EMT) and electrical nonmetallic tubing (ENT) are also permitted as feeder wiring, but under the restrictions that the ENT be installed within or on a building and the EMT be installed within the building. The revision to this section removes the question about using aluminum conduit for this application. Since corrosion of the feeder wiring method is one of the principal concerns addressed in this rule, the new last sentence provides a restriction on the use of aluminum conduit for these feeders where subject damage from the effects of corrosion.

Code Language
680.25(A)
Wiring Methods
Feeders shall be installed in rigid metal conduit, intermediate metal conduit...electrical nonmetallic tubing shall be permitted where installed on or within a building. Aluminum conduits shall not be permitted in the pool area where subject to corrosion.

Summary of Change

A new last sentence has been added to 680.25(A).

Equipotential Bonding
NEC, p. 573, 574

Proposal 17-114a
Log CP1708
ROP, p. 705

Comment 17-92
Log 950
ROC, p. 400

Analysis and Effect

Section 680.26 was significantly revised in *NEC*-2005. Those revisions included new requirements for constructing an equipotential bonding grid where there were limited conductive elements inherent to the pool construction that could serve as the bonding grid. Where pool installations did not include a conductive surface around the perimeter of the pool, the bonding grid was to be constructed by one of the alternative methods provided in *NEC*-2005, 680.26(C)(3). This new provision presented unique challenges with nonconductive pool shells, and, more specifically, with those pool installations where there were no conductive surfaces or components, such as a concrete deck or paved surface surrounding the pool perimeter in which to provide an equipotential bonding grid. A clarification had to be made by CMP-17 through Tentative Interim Amendment (TIA) 05-2 issued on 08-18-2005, which helped users better understand what was meant by the concept of the equipotential bonding grid having to follow the contour of the pool. The TIA provided needed clarification about the grid following the complete contour of the pool, where it is constructed in the earth using a conductive shell such as a poured-in-placed concrete pool structure. If encapsulated reinforcing steel is used in this type of pool design, a complete equipotential bonding grid must be installed using alternative methods. The bonding grid in this case has to follow the perimeter contour in addition to the depth contour in the earth to establish a complete equipotential bonding grid. If the pool is a nonconductive shell such as a molded fiberglass shell installed in the earth, the equipotential bonding grid is required to follow the perimeter contour only, rather than all dimensional contours. The revision and expansion of this section were necessitated by various pool construction methods that do not provide conductive elements from which an effective equipotential bonding grid can be built. In these cases, one must be constructed and installed to reduce the voltage gradients in the pool area.

> ### Change at a Glance
>
> This section provides the minimum requirements for establishing an equipotential bonding grid for various types of pool construction. Specific direction allows for alternative methods of constructing a common and equipotential bonding grid.

CMP-17 continued the work in this *Code* section after the TIA was issued, and developed a panel proposal for the *NEC*-2008 (Proposal 17-114a) to complete the work started in *NEC*-2005 development process. The restructuring of this section provides a more logical layout of the specific equipotential bonding requirements for swimming pools. If a pool is constructed of encapsulated rebar, an equipotential bonding grid in accordance with 680.26(B)(1)(b) has to be provided for the entire

contour of the pool. As revised, Section 680.26(B)(2)(b) provides the alternative means that must be used to establish the bonding required for perimeter surfaces, which now includes both paved and unpaved surfaces. This grid must be made by installing at least one 8 AWG solid copper conductor. If splices are necessary for the conductor, they are required to be made using a listed means. This conductor must follow the contour of the pool perimeter and be installed within 450 to 600 mm (18 to 24 in.) from the inside walls of the pool. This conductor must also be secured within or under the perimeter surface 100 to 150 mm (4 to 6 in.) below the subgrade. The references to *rebar*

have been removed from 680.26(B)(1)(a) to clarify that welded wire mesh is included under the term *structural reinforcing steel*. Where wire mesh or structural reinforcing is part of the equipotential bonding grid, it is required be bonded together using steel tie wires. Although this section has been extensively reorganized, expanded, and revised, the functional aspects and equipotential bonding have been preserved and improved by including more detailed and prescriptive bonding methods in this section of the *Code*. These revisions do not change any of the current requirements for establishing an equipotential bonding grid for pool installations. Instead, they clarify what this bonding is intended to accomplish while providing users with methods that must be used to establish an equipotential bonding grid when conductive elements are present for such use, and also when they are not present or integral to the construction or installation of a swimming pool.

Code Language
680.26

Equipotential Bonding.

(A) Performance. The equipotential bonding required by this section shall be installed to reduce voltage gradients in the pool area.

(B) Bonded Parts
(1) Conductive Pool Shells
    (a) *Structural Reinforcing Steel*
    (b) *Copper Conductor Grid*
(2) Perimeter Surfaces
    (a) *Structural Reinforcing Steel*
    (b) *Alternative Means*
(1) At least one…
(2) The conductors shall…
(3) Only listed…
(4) The required conductor shall be 450 to 600 mm (18 in. to 24 in.)…
(5) The required conductor shall be secured…
(3) Metallic Components
(4) Underwater Lighting
(5) Metal Fittings
(6) Electrical Equipment
    (a) *Double-Insulated Water Pump Motors*
    (b) *Pool Water Heaters*
(7) Metal Wiring Methods and Equipment

Note: See actual *NEC* Section 680.26 for full text.

Summary of Change

This entire section has been reorganized to provide a more logical order and layout of the requirements for swimming pool equipotential and to incorporate the requirements formerly found in 680.26(C), (D), and (E).

680.26(B)(1)(b) Copper Conductor Grid

The copper conductor grid shall be constructed of minimum 8 AWG solid copper conductors bonded to each other at crossing points.

The grid shall conform to the contours of the pool shell and the pool deck.

The grid shall be arranged in a minimum 12" x 12" network (pattern) of conductors uniformly spaced with a tolerance of 100 mm (4 in.).

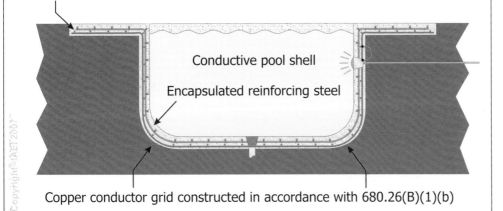

Copper conductor grid constructed in accordance with 680.26(B)(1)(b)

680.26(B)(2)(b) Perimeter Surfaces

Where structural reinforcing steel is not available or encapsulated, at least one 8 AWG solid copper conductor secured within or under the perimeter surface and installed 450 – 600 mm (18 to 24 in.) measured horizontally from the inside walls of the pool shall be utilized.

Where installed beneath the final grade material, the bonding conductor shall be buried 100 – 150 mm (4 to 6 in.) below the subgrade.

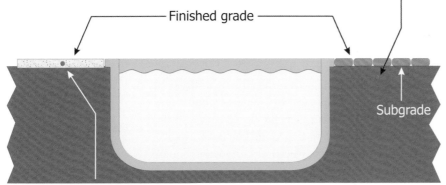

A single 8 AWG solid copper conductor, wire mesh, or rebar in the concrete is permitted as the bonding grid.

680.26(C)

Pool Water
NEC, p. 574

Proposal 17-122
Log 1894
ROP, p. 710

Comment 17-98
Log 802
ROC, p. 402

Change at a Glance

Pool water is required to be bonded to the equipotential bonding grid. This change introduces a new requirement for purposefully establishing a connection (bond) between the pool water and the constructed equipotential bonding grid, where other sufficient bonding means does not exist between the water and the grid.

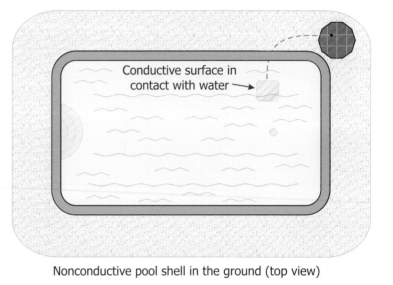

680.26(C) Bonding of Pool Water

An intentional bond of a minimum conductive surface area of 5806 mm² (9 in.²) shall be installed in contact with the pool water.

Conductive surface in contact with water →

Copyright©IAEI 2007

Nonconductive pool shell in the ground (top view)

Analysis and Effect

This new section incorporates a requirement to establish a sure connection (bonding) between the equipotential bonding grid and the pool water. The substantiation provided with Proposal 17-122 included information about testing performed by the National Electric Energy Testing Research and Application Center (NEET-RAC), which identified that shock hazard potentials increase where the chemically treated pool water is not in contact with the equipotential bonding grid of the pool. Where the pool water is isolated by an insulated pool shell and there are no conductive elements in contact with the pool water, reports indicate that potential shock hazards are increased for persons that can form a bridge between the isolated water and electrically conductive parts within the vicinity of the pool water. This new section requires connection be established between the pool water and the equipotential bonding grid. For pool installations that include electrical conductive equipment such as underwater luminaires, where the dimensions of the conductive surfaces of such equipment are at least 5806 mm² (9 in.²) of surface area, additional bonding means for the water is not required, because the water bonding connection is already established by the bonding requirements in 680.26(A) and (B). However, where no electrically conductive parts or equipment are in contact with the pool water, a conductive element that provides at least

5806 mm² (9 in.²) of surface contact area with the water shall be provided and it must be connected to the equipotential bonding grid. Section 680.26(B) requires conductive parts of equipotential bonding grids to be bonded together using a minimum 8 AWG solid copper conductor.

Code Language
680.26(C)
Pool Water

An intentional bond of a minimum conductive surface of 5806 mm² (9 in.²) shall be installed in contact with the pool water. This bond shall be permitted to consist of parts that are required to be bonded in 680.26(B).

Summary of Change

A new subdivision (C) has been added to 680.26, and the provisions of existing subdivisions (C), (D), and (E) have been incorporated into 680.26(B).

Analysis of Changes *NEC*-2008

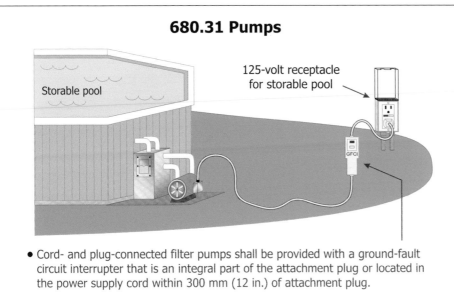

680.31 Pumps

Storable pool

125-volt receptacle
for storable pool

GFCI

- Cord- and plug-connected filter pumps shall be provided with a ground-fault circuit interrupter that is an integral part of the attachment plug or located in the power supply cord within 300 mm (12 in.) of attachment plug.

- All 125-volt receptacles located within 6.0 m (20 ft) of the inside walls of a storable pool shall be protected by ground-fault circuit-interrupter protection

Copyright IAEI 2007

Pumps
NEC, p. 575

Proposal 17-135
Log 3640
ROP, p. 714

Comment
None

Analysis and Effect

This revision accepts a new requirement for ground-fault circuit-interrupter protection to be provided as an integral part of a cord assembly for a storable pool pump motor. Proposal 17-132a and Comment 17-177a in the 2004 Report on Proposals and Report on Comments introduced this new requirement and it was acted on favorably by CMP-17 during the 2005 *NEC* development process. However, it introduced new material and, as a result, it was held by the Technical Correlating Committee until the 2008 *NEC* cycle. Action by CMP-17 on Proposal 17-135 completes the revision to this section as originally accepted by the panel in the 2005 *NEC* development process. This change adjusts manufacturing processes for storable pool pump motor manufacturers to include ground-fault circuit-interrupter protection as either an integral part of the attachment plug or in the cord assembly located not more than 300 mm (12 in.) from the attachment plug. The original substantiation for the proposal indicated that because of the excessive length of these pool pump motor cords, they are often subject to connection at receptacles that are not protected by ground-fault circuit interrupters. This revision increases public safety where storable pools are installed and used by including ground-fault protection integral to the equipment.

Code Language
680.31
Pumps

A cord-connected pool filter pump shall incorporate an approved system of double insulation or its equivalent and shall be provided with means for grounding only the internal and nonaccessible non–current-carrying metal parts of the appliance.

The means for grounding shall be an equipment grounding conductor run with the power-supply conductors in the flexible cord that is properly terminated in a grounding-type attachment plug having a fixed grounding contact member.

Cord-connected pool filter pumps shall be provided with a ground-fault circuit interrupter that is an integral part of the attachment plug or located in the power supply cord within 300 mm (12 in.) of the attachment plug.

Change at a Glance

Cord-connected pump motors for storable pools are required to be provided with ground-fault circuit-interrupter protection that is an integral part of the cord assembly, and to be located within 12 inches of the attachment plug. The revision affects storable pool pump motor manufacturers.

Summary of Change

A new last sentence has been added to Section 680.31.

680.52(B)
(2)(b)

Junction Boxes and Other Enclosures
NEC, p. 578

Proposal 17-157
Log 934
ROP, p. 719

Comment 17-104
Log 539
ROC, p. 403

Change at a Glance

Junction boxes for luminaires and equipment in fountains are permitted to be supported by the conduit only where the requirements in 314.23(E) and (F) are met. A minimum of two threaded metal conduit entries are required or additional supports are required.

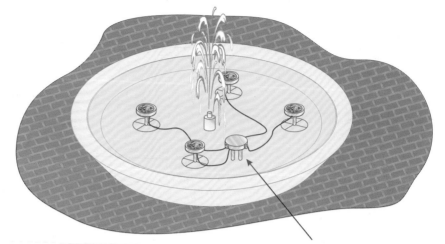

680.52(B)(2)(b) Underwater Junction Boxes

- Junction boxes for luminaires and other equipment in fountains are permitted to be supported by conduit only when 314.23(E) or (F) are satisfied

- Minumum of (2) threaded metal conduit entries are required or additional supports are required

Copyright©IAEI 2007

Analysis and Effect

This requirement in Part V of Article 680 applies to securing and supporting underwater junction boxes in fountains for luminaires or other equipment. This section previously recognized only one metallic conduit for support of a fountain underwater junction box; but under this revision, a minimum of two metallic conduits will be required where the conduit provides the only support for the box in accordance with 314.23(E) or (F). This revision promotes consistency between the box support provisions contained in 314.23 which recognize two conduits as a sole means of support for boxes. The requirements for supporting fountain junction boxes supplied by nonmetallic conduits are not affected by this change. The fine print note referencing 314.23 is no longer necessary since direct references to 314.23 are now included in the rule.

Code Language
680.52(B)(2)

Installation
(a) Unchanged

(b) Underwater enclosures shall be firmly attached to the supports or directly to the fountain surface and bonded as required. Where the junction box is supported only by conduits in accordance with 314.23(E) and (F), the conduits shall be of copper, brass, stainless steel, or other approved corrosion-resistant metal. Where the box is fed by nonmetallic conduit, it shall have additional supports and fasteners of copper, brass, or other approved corrosion-resistant material.

Summary of Change

References to Sections 314.23(E) and (F) have been incorporated into this rule and the FPN has been removed.

346

Protection
NEC, p. 580

Proposal 17-165
Log 2547
ROP, p. 720

Comment 17-106
Log 1660
ROC, p. 404

Analysis and Effect

This change gives clear direction on the branch circuit requirements necessary for hydromassage bathtub installations. As revised, this rule will require at least one individual branch circuit for the tub and its associated equipment. Substantiation in the proposal indicated that some instances of connecting this type of equipment to general-purpose branch circuits were identified. This type of equipment is usually certified or listed by a qualified electrical testing laboratory and includes a specific requirement to provide an individual branch circuit. In accordance with 110.3(B), this is a requirement of the *Code*. The revision provides a specific requirement for an individual branch circuit in addition to any similar requirement in the installation instructions provided with the equipment. Some hydromassage bathtubs include a water heater in addition to a circulating and air pump motor. These units typically require multiple individual branch circuits, usually one circuit for the heater and another for the motor. The revision includes a plural form of *branch circuit* to recognize at least one individual branch circuit is necessary for the installation but a listing requirement and installation instructions may well require more than one branch circuit. This revision ensures that this type of load will be connected to a supply branch circuit with adequate capacity as a minimum requirement of the *NEC* in addition to any listing requirements.

Change at a Glance

Hydromassage bathtubs and their associated equipment must be supplied by at least one separate individual branch circuit.

Code Language
680.71
Protection

Hydromassage bathtubs and their associated electrical components shall be on an individual branch circuit(s) and protected by a readily accessible ground-fault circuit interrupter. All 125-volt, single-phase receptacles not exceeding 30 amperes and located within 1.83 m (6 ft) measured horizontally of the inside walls of a hydromassage tub shall be protected by a ground-fault circuit interrupter(s).

Summary of Change

The words "on an individual branch circuit(s) and" have been added to the first sentence of this section.

680.74

Bonding
NEC, p. 580

Proposal 17-166
Log 347
ROP, p. 720

Comment 17-110
Log 215
ROC, p. 404

Change at a Glance

Bonding jumpers for hydromassage bath tub installations are required for equipotential bonding and are not required to be routed to any remote panelboard, service equipment, or grounding electrode.

Analysis and Effect

This section requires metal water piping systems and any metal parts in contact with the circulating water to be bonded together and to the circulating pump motor where it is not double insulated. The revision to this section clarifies that the bonding required for hydromassage bathtub installations is for establishing an equipotential between all conductive parts or piping associated with the tub. The new last sentence clearly parallels the information in 680.26(B), indicating bonding jumpers required for hydromassage bath tubs that do not have to be run to a branch-circuit panelboard, service equipment, or grounding electrode. The branch circuit supplying the hydromassage bathtub includes an equipment grounding conductor for establishing a connection to ground (earth) and for facilitating operation of the branch-circuit overcurrent protective device in the event of a ground fault in the circuit or equipment. The bonding required by 680.74 serves to ensure that electrical continuity and conductivity are established between conductive parts, equipment, and piping at the tub location. The revision provides clarity and improves usability while, at the same time, it promotes more consistent and uniform enforcement of the requirements in this section.

Code Language
680.74
Bonding

All metal piping systems and all grounded metal parts in contact with the circulating water shall be bonded together using a solid copper bonding jumper, insulated, covered, or bare, not smaller than 8 AWG. The bonding jumper shall be connected to the terminal on the circulating pump motor that is intended for this purpose. The bonding jumper shall not be required to be connected to a double insulated circulating pump motor. The 8 AWG or larger solid copper bonding jumper shall be required for equipotential bonding in the area of the hydromassage bathtub and shall not be required to be extended or attached to any remote panelboard, service equipment, or any electrode.

Summary of Change

A new last sentence was added to clarify the installation requirements for the bonding jumper covered by this requirement.

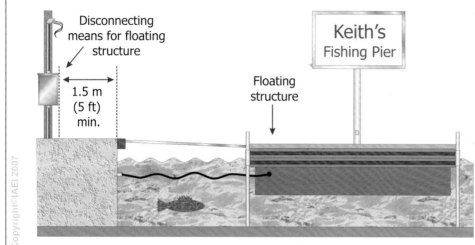

682.14(A) Type of Disconnecting Means

Disconnecting means for a floating structure or submersible electrical equipment is permitted to consist of circuit breakers, switches, or both that simultaneously open all ungrounded circuit conductors, and is properly identified as to the structure or equipment it controls.

Disconnecting means for floating structure

1.5 m (5 ft) min.

Keith's Fishing Pier

Floating structure

Copyright©IAEI 2007

Disconnecting Means
NEC, p. 581

Proposal 17-177
Log 902
ROP, p. 723

Comment 17-112
Log 435
ROC, p. 404

Analysis and Effect

Section 682.14 addresses disconnecting means types and locations for floating structures or submersible electrical equipment installed in natural and artificially made bodies of water. The revision to this section clarifies the operational characteristics of the disconnecting means; it must open all ungrounded (hot) conductors at the same time. The concept of simultaneous disconnection of all ungrounded conductors of a circuit is consistent through numerous sections in the *Code*. This change correlates with those other rules and, at the same time, it clarifies which conductors must be opened when the disconnecting means is operated. This clarification removes any question about the type of disconnect that must be used to meet the requirements in 682.14 and ensures that safety is achieved by interruption of all ungrounded conductors connected to the load side of the switch or circuit breaker.

Change at a Glance

The disconnecting means addressed in this rule must disconnect all ungrounded conductors of the circuit at the same time.

Code Language
682.14

Disconnecting Means for Floating Structures or Submersible Electrical Equipment

(A)
Type
The disconnecting means shall be permitted to consist of a circuit breaker, switch, or both, and shall be properly identified as to which structure or equipment it controls.

Summary of Change

The words "that simultaneously opens all ungrounded circuit conductors" have been added to this section.

> * This change was placed on hold for the *NEC*-2011 by the TCC for new material being introduced in a comment that had not had adequate public review.

690.4(D)

Equipment
NEC, p. 584

Proposal 13-21
Log 2083
ROP, p. 733

Comment
None

690.4(D) Equipment

Required to be listed and identified for the application:

Inverters
Motor generators
Photovoltaic modules
Photovoltaic panels
AC photovoltaic modules
Source-circuit combiners
Charge controllers

Copyright © IAEI 2007

Analysis and Effect

The new requirement for listing of inverters, motor generators, photovoltaic modules, photovoltaic panels, ac photovoltaic modules, source-circuit combiners, and charge controllers will aid electrical inspectors and installers in determining whether photovoltaic power equipment has been tested and listed for the specific use intended by a nationally recognized electrical testing laboratory that is approved for that function by the inspection jurisdiction.

Change at a Glance

PV equipment must now be listed as well as identified.

Code Language
690.4(D)

Equipment

Inverters, motor generators, photovoltaic modules, photovoltaic panels, ac photovoltaic modules, source-circuit combiners, and charge controllers intended for use in photovoltaic power systems shall be identified and listed for the application.

Summary of Change

The words "shall be identified and listed for the application" have been added to 690.4(D).

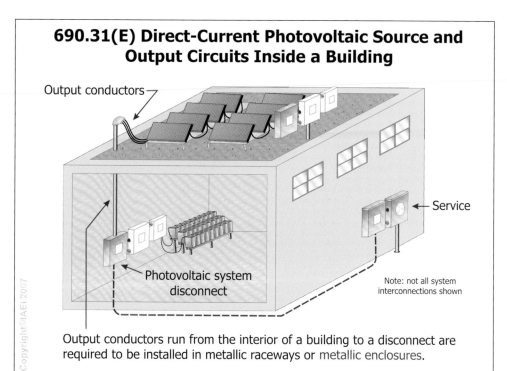

690.31(E) Direct-Current Photovoltaic Source and Output Circuits Inside a Building

Output conductors

Photovoltaic system disconnect

Service

Note: not all system interconnections shown

Copyright©IAEI 2007

Output conductors run from the interior of a building to a disconnect are required to be installed in metallic raceways or metallic enclosures.

690.31(E)

Direct-Current Photovoltaic Source and Output Circuits Inside a Building
NEC, p. 589

Proposal 13-39
Log 2089
ROP, p. 738

Comment
None

Analysis and Effect

Proposals and comments that would have permitted metallic cable assemblies, such as Type MC cable, were rejected by the code-making panel, and "metallic enclosures" were accepted as a new wiring method. Metallic raceways continue to be required to enclose photovoltaic systems or circuit conductors within buildings. It is now clear that metallic raceways and enclosures are required wiring methods for inside a building for photovoltaic system conductors. Metal-sheathed cables, or nonmetallic raceways, for example, are wiring methods that are not permitted for dc circuits within a structure. These types of wiring methods would be permitted to be used outdoors in wet locations for PV systems, if all other *Code* requirements were met. It is understood that safety concerns with dc circuits operating at higher voltage and amperage, that possible hazards arising from physical damage were considerations in the decision.

Change at a Glance

DC circuits installed in buildings require containment in metallic enclosures or metallic raceways.

Code Language 690.31(E)

Direct-Current Photovoltaic Source and Output Circuits Inside a Building

Where direct-current photovoltaic source or output circuits of a utility-interactive inverter from a building-integrated or other photovoltaic system are run inside a building or structure, they shall be contained in metal raceways, or metal enclosures, from the point of penetration of the surface of the building or structure to the first readily accessible disconnecting means. The disconnecting means shall comply with 690.14(A) through (D).

Summary of Change

The word "metallic" has been added in front of the word "enclosures."

690.31(F)

Flexible, Fine-Stranded Cables
NEC, p. 589

Proposal 13-40
Log 2061
ROP, p. 739

Comment 13-49
Log 1724
ROC, p. 411

Change at a Glance

Only terminals, lugs, devices, or connectors identified and listed for use with flexible, fine-stranded cables shall be used on these types of cables.

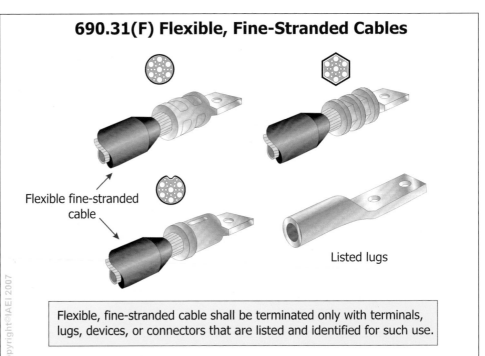

690.31(F) Flexible, Fine-Stranded Cables

Flexible fine-stranded cable

Listed lugs

Flexible, fine-stranded cable shall be terminated only with terminals, lugs, devices, or connectors that are listed and identified for such use.

Analysis and Effect

UL Standard 486 A and B require that connectors, lugs, and terminals intended for use with fine-stranded cables be marked for the use. Very few connectors and terminals have been listed and marked for use with fine stranded cables; the vast majority is not suitable for this use. Many installers are unaware of this problem, and failures in these types of connectors have been reported in photovoltaic and other electrical systems, including UPS equipment supporting computer-data processing equipment. The limited distribution of the proper connectors, ignorance of the problem and associated failures, and lack of awareness of the standard have resulted in these non-marked connectors being installed and used improperly with flexible, fine-stranded cables. Information provided in the comment stage indicated PV industry support of the change, and further stated, "the use of fine-stranded, flexible cables is not required in any commonly used PV system where *NEC*-compliant, listed electrical equipment is used. When such cables have been used, they have been improperly terminated…" Further comments indicated, "the proper ferrules and crimping tools, while readily available from multiple sources in Europe are not commonly or readily available in the U.S. Neither the typical electrical supply house nor big-box building centers carry them or the required crimping tools." All panel members voting unanimously agreed. This change delineates the termination requirements

and concerns for fine-stranded cables, and the importance of using proper termination methods and tools when installing these types of connectors in PV type installations.

Code Language
690.31(F)

Flexible, Fine-Stranded Cables
Flexible, fine-stranded cables shall be terminated only with terminals, lugs, devices, or connectors that are identified and listed for such use.

Summary of Change

New Subdivision 690.31(F) covering flexible, fine-stranded cables has been added.

Courtesy of John Wiles

690.33(C), 690.33(E)

Connectors
NEC, p. 590

Proposal 13-41, 13-42
Log 2071, 2090
ROP, p. 739

Comment 13-51
Log 2505
ROC, p. 411

Analysis and Effect

Circuits operating above 50 volts (either dc maximum systems voltages or ac nominal voltages) pose shock hazards when the energized conductors are exposed (see Section 250.20). Comments submitted with the proposal indicated that connectors are permitted in PV systems, used commonly in PV source circuits where the voltages typically range from 27 volts to 600 volts, and may be opened by simply pulling them apart, especially those of the latching type. Although these existing connectors are manufactured as "touch safe," they are not to be opened under load; if inadvertently opened, the resulting arc (particularly on dc circuits) may disable the "touch-safe" feature by carbonizing the insulation. The carbonized connector would then have a conductive tip, be energized, and represent a shock hazard. Where installed in readily accessible locations, these connectors should require a tool to open. The tool may be a connector-specific opening device or merely the blade of a screwdriver or other pointed instrument. In some cases, the connector may consist of a latching connector with a locking shell that prevents the connector from being pulled apart. The change of 690.33(E) now requires a warning label on these connectors. Panel action on Proposal 13-37changed the voltage from 50 to 30 to make it consistent with Table 11(B), Note 4 for accessible Class II circuits in wet locations, and accepted the changes to 690.33(C) and (E) in order to provide standards which will improve electrical safety in these installations.

Code Language
690.33(C)
Type

The connectors shall be of the latching or locking type. Connectors that are readily accessible and that are used in circuits operating at over 30 volts, nominal, maximum system voltage for dc circuits, or 30 volts for ac circuits, shall require a tool for opening.

690.33(E)
Interruption of Circuit

Connectors shall be either (1) or (2):
(1) Be rated for interrupting current without hazard to the operator.
(2) Be a type that requires the use of a tool to open and marked "Do Not Disconnect Under Load" or "Not for Current Interrupting."

Summary of Change

New second sentences have been added to subdivisions (C) and (E) of Section 690.33.

Change at a Glance

PV system connectors now require a tool to open, and are required to be marked "Do Not Disconnect Under Load" or "Not for Current Interrupting."

6

690.45(B), FPN

Size of Equipment
Grounding Conductors
NEC, p. 591

Proposal 13-22
Log 2060
ROP, p. 733

Comment 13-29
Log 287
ROC, p. 407

Change at a Glance

Equipment grounding conductors for photovoltaic systems without GFP and installed on non-dwelling units must have an ampacity of at least two (2) times the temperature and conduit fill corrected circuit conductor ampacity.

Analysis and Effect

Section 690.45 provides the minimum sizing requirements for equipment grounding conductors for photovoltaic systems. Exception No. 2 to 690.5 correlates with 690.45, which now includes a sizing requirement in excess of current EGC sizing requirements contained in 690.45 and 250.122 for specific reasons related to the performance of photovoltaic equipment. Substantiation indicated that the amount of short-circuit current produced from solar photovoltaic equipment is slightly higher than the normal output current levels. In ground-fault conditions, solar photovoltaic equipment is not able to supply the high levels of short-circuit or ground-fault currents necessary to activate quickly the overcurrent devices as in typical AC systems. Protection for equipment grounding conductors in photovoltaic systems that are not provided with ground-fault protection is related to size and withstand capability of the equipment grounding conductor, rather than to overcurrent device operation. This explanatory information is provided in a new FPN following the new equipment grounding conductor sizing provisions. The FPN describes the unique conditions that warrant increased equipment grounding conductor sizes where ground-fault protection is not provided.

Summary of Change

A new subdivision and FPN have been added to the section.

Code Language
690.45

Size of Equipment Grounding Conductor
Equipment grounding conductors for photovoltaic source and photovoltaic output circuits shall be sized in accordance with 690.45(A) or (B).

(A) General. Equipment grounding conductors in photovoltaic source and photovoltaic output circuits shall be sized in accordance with Table 250.122. When no overcurrent protective device is used in the circuit, an assumed overcurrent device rated at the photovoltaic rated short-circuit current shall be used in Table 250.122. Increases in equipment grounding conductor size to address voltage drop considerations shall not be required. The equipment grounding conductors shall be no smaller than 14 AWG.

(B) Ground-Fault Protection Not Provided. For other than dwelling units where ground-fault protection is not provided in accordance with 690.5(A) through (C), each equipment grounding conductor shall have an ampacity of at least two (2) times the temperature and conduit fill corrected circuit conductor ampacity.

FPN: The short-circuit current of photovoltaic modules and photovoltaic sources is just slightly above the full-load normal output rating. In ground-fault conditions, these sources are not able to supply the high levels of short-circuit or ground-fault currents necessary to quickly activate overcurrent devices as in typical AC systems. Protection for equipment grounding conductors in photovoltaic systems that are not provided with ground-fault protection is related to size and withstand capability of the equipment grounding conductor, rather than overcurrent device operation.

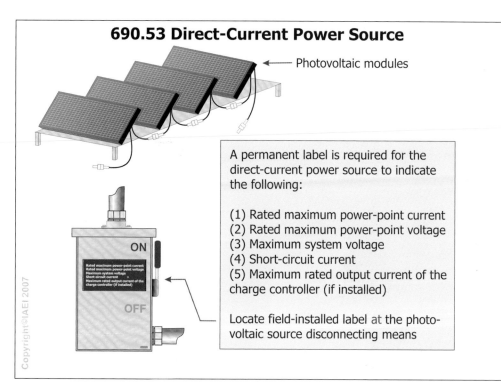

690.53 Direct-Current Power Source

Photovoltaic modules

A permanent label is required for the direct-current power source to indicate the following:

(1) Rated maximum power-point current
(2) Rated maximum power-point voltage
(3) Maximum system voltage
(4) Short-circuit current
(5) Maximum rated output current of the charge controller (if installed)

Locate field-installed label at the photovoltaic source disconnecting means

690.53

Direct-Current
Photovoltaic Power
Source
NEC, p. 592

Proposal 13-54
Log 546
ROP, p. 744

Comment 13-71
Log 93
ROC, p. 415

Analysis and Effect

Electrical workers are exposed to hazards when working on equipment while it is energized and/or when they are unfamiliar with electrical equipment and systems. Photovoltaic electrical equipment and systems are special equipment and expose electrical workers to hazards. The safety objective of the change is to inform workers of the amount of electrical power available from the particular photovoltaic power source and to raise awareness so that proper safety precautions may be taken before work begins.

Change at a Glance

DC power sources must be permanently labeled, and the specific information required has been clarified.

Code Language

Direct-Current Photovoltaic Power Source

A permanent label for the direct-current photovoltaic power source indicating items (1) through (5) shall be provided by the installer at the photovoltaic disconnecting means:

(1) Rated maximum power-point current
(2) Rated maximum power-point voltage
(3) Maximum system voltage
FPN to (3) See 690.7(A) for maximum photovoltaic system voltage.
(4) Short-circuit current.
FPN to (4): See 690.8(A) for calculation of maximum circuit current.
(5) Maximum rated output current of the charge controller (if installed)

Summary of Change

Text added to clarify marking requirements. List items (1) and (2) have been revised; fine print notes (FPN) have been added to items (3) and (4), and item (5) is new.

6

690.74

Battery Interconnections
NEC, p. 595

Proposal 13-70
Log 2062
ROP, p. 749

Comment
None

Analysis and Effect

Photovoltaic installations with batteries frequently use flexible, fine-stranded cables for ease of installation and interconnection of batteries. The flexibility of the cables is convenient and works well for the application; however, there are often problems and failures at connections and terminals because the fine-stranded cables are not properly terminated, and not all of the strands in the cable may fit properly into the lug or termination. When this occurs, loose connections and terminations, overheating and failing are common. Often cables are installed with terminals that are not listed for use with the cable. UL Standard 486 A and B require that connectors, lugs, and terminals intended for use with flexible, fine-stranded cables be marked for use with these types of cables. Very few connectors and terminals have been listed for this use, and are appropriately marked. Many installers are unaware that a standard exists for these types of connections and that widespread failures have resulted from the improper termination of fine-stranded conductors. (There are similar concerns when fine-stranded cables are used to connect uninterruptible power supplies (UPS) equipment, for example). This new *Code* language describes the requirement and raises the awareness of installers and inspectors to the types of failures that can occur when fine-stranded cables are not properly terminated.

Change at a Glance

Fine-stranded cables used for battery terminals, devices, and connections require lugs and terminals listed and marked for the use.

Code Language
690.74
Battery Interconnections
Flexible cables... (This paragraph unchanged – see *Code* text)

Flexible, fine-stranded cables shall only be used with terminals, lugs, devices, and connectors that are listed and marked for such use.

Summary of Change
A new paragraph has been added to Section 690.74

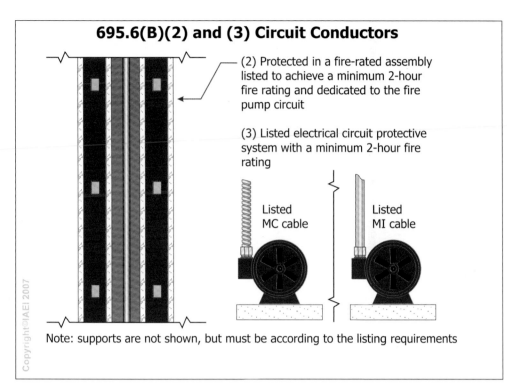

695.6(B)(2) and (3) Circuit Conductors

(2) Protected in a fire-rated assembly listed to achieve a minimum 2-hour fire rating and dedicated to the fire pump circuit

(3) Listed electrical circuit protective system with a minimum 2-hour fire rating

Listed MC cable

Listed MI cable

Note: supports are not shown, but must be according to the listing requirements

Copyright©IAEI 2007

695.6(B) (2) & (3)

Circuit Conductors

NEC, p. 601

Proposal 13-99, 13-100, 13-101
Log 3018, 3017, 2986
ROP, p. 764, 765

Comment 13-139
Log 1990
ROC, p. 441

Analysis and Effect

This revision entails listed fire-rated assemblies constructed in the field to meet the requirements in 695.6(B)(2), and increases the minimum fire rating in (2) and (3) from 1-hour to 2-hour. The revision aligns the fire-rating requirements for fire-pump circuit conductors with the fire-rating survivability requirements for notification circuits and interconnecting wiring to the fire command center provided in NFPA 72. The 2-hour ratings can be achieved by either constructing a 2-hour fire-rated enclosure that is listed to provide that fire rating, or by installing a listed 2-hour rated electrical circuit protective system. A typical 2-hour listed enclosure would be two layers of 5/8" drywall on each side of metal studding. For proper construction of a 2-hour listed assembly, see the UL Fire Resistance Directory. Substantiation in the proposal identified certain conditions where automatic sprinkler systems are permitted by the AHJ as another alternative. Substantiation in Comment 13-139 indicated that NFPA 20-2007 requirements for fire ratings as provided in Table 5.121.1.1.2 for equipment protection entails a 2-hour fire rating, unless both the pump room/house and building(s) exposing pump rooms or house are

Change at a Glance

Fire-rated assemblies covered in (2) are required to be listed and to achieve a minimum 2-hour fire rating, and listed electrical circuit protective systems covered by (3) are required to achieve a minimum 2-hour rating.

fully sprinkled. In some cases, the fire pump may be required to operate even after the fire department has arrived to provide supplemental pressure. In these cases, the fire pump is installed in the sprinkler system; therefore, the fire pump circuit should require a minimum 2-hour fire rating for protection of the circuit conductors. A new fine print note following list item (3) references where to obtain important information about listed electrical protective systems. The FPN refers users to the UL Guide Information for electrical circuit protective systems in (FHIT), which clarifies installation requirements where minimum fire ratings are necessary. Fire ratings apply to the entire system, including any components in the fire zone. These components could be, but are not limited to pull boxes, vertical supports, pulling lubricants or grounding conductors. Individual components and materials are designated for use with specific systems, and are not to be interchanged.

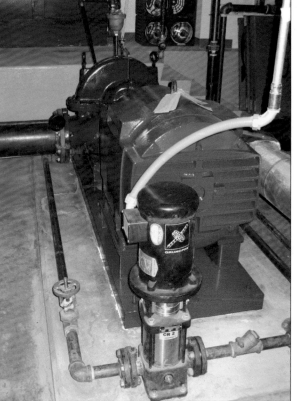

Code Language
695.6(B)
Circuit Conductors

(2) Be protected by a fire-rated assembly listed to achieve a minimum fire rating of 2 hours and dedicated to the fire pump circuit(s).

(3) Be a listed electrical circuit protective system with a minimum 2-hour fire rating

FPN: UL guide information for electrical circuit protective systems (FHIT) contains information on proper installation requirements to maintain the fire rating.

Summary of Change

List item (2) has been revised to require a listed fire-rated assembly; and the minimum fire rating has been increased from a 1-hour to a 2-hour fire rating. List item (3) has been revised by changing the 1-hour fire rating to a 2-hour fire rating for listed electrical circuit protective systems. A new fine print note refers users to the UL guide information (FHIT).

Chapter 7

Selected Changes

Article 700

7

700.6(C)

Automatic Transfer Switches
NEC, 604

Proposal 13-117
Log 2369
ROP, p. 768

Comment
None

Change at a Glance

Transfer switches installed for emergency systems must be listed for emergency system use.

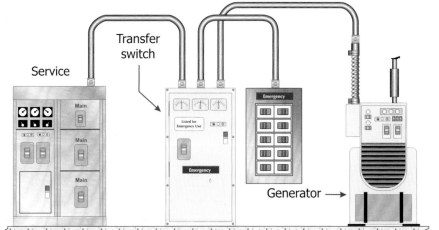

700.6(C) Automatic Transfer Switches

Automatic transfer switches shall be electrically operated and mechanically held.

Automatic transfer switches are required to be listed for emergency use.

Analysis and Effect

This revision introduces a listing requirement in Article 700 for automatic transfer switches used in emergency systems. In Section 700.3, all equipment used on emergency systems is required to be approved. This is a general requirement provided in Section 110.2 of the *Code. Approved* is defined in Article 100 as "acceptable to the authority having jurisdiction." In carrying out the responsibilities for approvals of electrical installations, the authority having jurisdiction generally utilizes listing or labeling as a basis for approvals of equipment. Substantiation with the proposal indicated that transfer switch equipment that has not been evaluated (tested) for closing into a fault might not be adequately protected by the alternate source line-side overcurrent protective device. Generally, this transfer switch performance must be established by high current laboratory testing at facilities capable of such testing and evaluations. The recognized national standard for testing automatic transfer switch equipment is ANSI/UL 1008. This listing requirement in 700.6(C) would apply specifically to automatic transfer switches; it is not intended to rule out other types of transfer equipment identified for emergency system use and acceptable to the AHJ under 700.6(A). The new listing requirement would not apply to systems rated above 600 volts, but would apply to 600 volts and below where UL 1008, Standard for Transfer Switch Equipment, provides ANSI testing specifications.

Code Language
700.6(C)
Automatic Transfer Switches
Automatic transfer switches shall be electrically operated and mechanically held. Automatic transfer switches, rated 600 VAC and below, shall be listed for emergency system use.

Summary of Change
Section 700.6(C) has been revised by adding a new sentence: "Automatic transfer switches, rated 600 VAC and below, shall be listed for emergency system use."

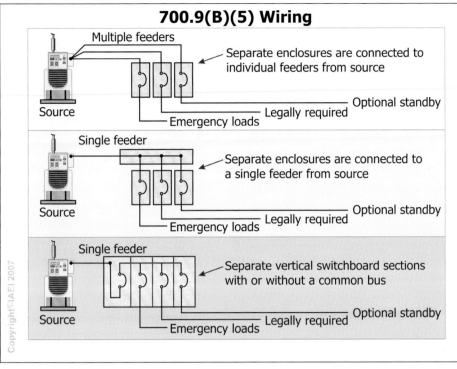

700.9(B)(5) Wiring

Multiple feeders

Separate enclosures are connected to individual feeders from source

Source

Optional standby
Legally required
Emergency loads

Single feeder

Separate enclosures are connected to a single feeder from source

Source

Optional standby
Legally required
Emergency loads

Single feeder

Separate vertical switchboard sections with or without a common bus

Source

Optional standby
Legally required
Emergency loads

Copyright©IAEI 2007

700.9 (B)(5)

Emergency System Wiring
NEC, p. 604

Proposal 13-118
Log 833
ROP, p. 768

Comment 13-156
Log 110
ROC, p. 444

Analysis and Effect

Section 700.9(B) relates to separation between emergency circuits from other than emergency loads, unless in accordance with the allowances provided in this section. Action by CMP-13 resulted in a new list item (5), which clarifies that from the source to the loads or from the source distribution overcurrent protection to the loads, separation is required unless modified by any of the provisions in items (1) – (5). The revision further clarifies that it is permitted to supply any combination of emergency, legally required, or optional loads from a single feeder or from multiple feeders or from separate vertical sections of a switchboard that are supplied by either a common bus or individually. Separate individual enclosures supplied by a common single feeder from the source, or separate enclosures supplied by separate individual feeders from the source are permitted. Separation requirements start from the distribution point (switchboard or separate enclosures). The use of an overcurrent protective device at the standby source or for the equipment is related to reliability and design. While the new requirements in (5)(b) maintain the highest degree of reliability, the exception to (5)(b) will also permit the use of an overcurrent device at the source or for the equipment. Selective coordination of the overcurrent protection at the source or for the equipment with the downstream overcurrent protection requirement will maintain the highest degree of reliability possible, while allowing protection for conductors and equipment. The revised text in the main paragraph clarifies that circuits supplying emergency loads are not to be combined in panelboard enclosures with circuits supplying other loads.

Code Language

700.9(B)(5)

Emergency System Wiring

Wiring from an emergency source to supply any combination of emergency, legally required, or optional loads in accordance with (a), (b) and (c):

(a) From separate vertical switchboard sections, with or without a common bus, or from individual disconnects mounted in separate enclosures.

(b) The common bus or separate sections of the switchboard or the individual enclosures shall be permitted to be supplied by single or multiple feeders without overcurrent protection at the source.

Exception to (5)(b): Overcurrent protection shall be permitted at the source or for the equipment, provided the overcurrent protection is selectively coordinated with the downstream overcurrent protection.

(c) Legally required and optional standby circuits shall not originate from the same vertical switchboard section, panelboard enclosure, or individual disconnect enclosure as emergency circuits.

Summary of Change

A new item (5) has been incorporated into Section 700.9(B)(5).

Change at a Glance

A single source can supply emergency, legally required standby and optional standby systems using a single feeder with separation requirements starting at a switchboard equipped with barriers, separate enclosures, or with separate feeders connected to the source output terminals.

7

700.9(D) (1)(2) FPN

Feeder-Circuit Wiring
NEC, p. 605

Proposal 13-125
Log 2985
ROP, p. 770

Comment 13-163
Log 1989
ROC, p. 447

Change at a Glance

Installation requirements for establishing and maintaining minimum fire ratings when installing a listed electrical protective system is provided in UL Guide category (FHIT).

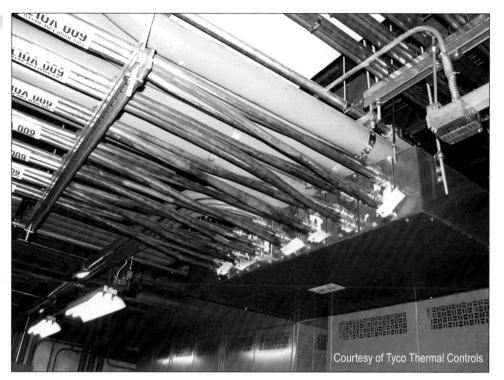

Courtesy of Tyco Thermal Controls

Analysis and Effect

Section 700.9(D)(1)(2) requires a listed electrical circuit protective system and refers users to the appropriate UL documentation that includes essential information about installing these systems to achieve the minimum 1-hour fire-rating, which applies to the entire system, including any components in the fire zone. These components could be, but are not limited to, pull boxes, vertical supports, pulling lubricants, or grounding conductors. Individual components and materials are designated for use with specific systems, not for interchange between systems. The new fine print note following list item (2) provides an important reference about where to obtain information about listed electrical circuit protective systems. The FPN refers users to the UL Guide Information for electrical circuit protective systems, category (FHIT), which contains useful information to clarify installation requirements where minimum fire ratings are necessary. Suitable wiring methods must be selected to achieve the 1-hour rating; and even more important, they must be installed properly to achieve the desired fire-ratings.

Code Language
700.9(D)(1)(2)
Feeder-Circuit Wiring

FPN: UL guide information for electrical circuit protection systems (FHIT) contains information on proper installation requirements to maintain the fire rating.

Summary of Change

A new fine print note has been added to 700.9(D)(1)(2) and refers users to UL Guide Information category (FHIT).

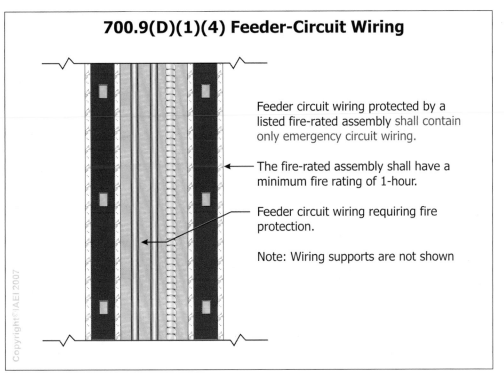

700.9(D)(1)(4) Feeder-Circuit Wiring

Feeder circuit wiring protected by a listed fire-rated assembly shall contain only emergency circuit wiring.

The fire-rated assembly shall have a minimum fire rating of 1-hour.

Feeder circuit wiring requiring fire protection.

Note: Wiring supports are not shown

Copyright©IAEI 2007

700.9(D)(1)(4)

Feeder-Circuit Wiring
NEC, p. 605

Proposal 13-124
Log 3022
ROP, p. 770

Comment 13-165
Log 111
ROC, p. 447

Analysis and Effect

The revision to this requirement clarifies that where a listed fire-rated assembly (such as a drywall shaft or soffit) is constructed around emergency feeders, it must not contain any wiring other than emergency circuit wiring. The fire-rated assembly is required to contain only the emergency feeder(s). Substantiation with the proposal identified conditions in the field where both normal and emergency wiring were sharing the same fire-rated assembly. This revision provides users with a clear requirement for the fire-rated construction to contain only the emergency feeder wiring required to be protected and to maintain physical separation of other general wiring circuits not being contained within the same fire-rated assembly. The revision to the second sentence clarifies that the assembly must be a listed assembly with a minimum 1-hour fire rating as compared to an assembly that achieves a 1-hour fire rating. Proper construction of a listed assembly is described in the UL Fire Resistance Directory. The wording as revised is clear relative to the original objective of this requirement.

Change at a Glance

The fire-rated assembly must be a listed 1-hour fire-rated construction specified in 700.9(D)(1)(4) and may contain only emergency circuit wiring.

Code Language
700.9(D)(1)(4)

Feeder-Circuit Wiring

(4) Be protected by a listed fire-rated assembly that has a minimum fire rating of 1-hour and contains only emergency wiring circuits.

Summary of Change

The words "and contains only emergency wiring circuits" have been added. The previous wording has been altered some, but has the same meaning.

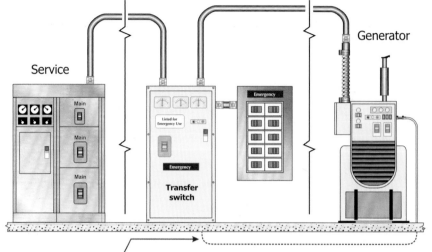

700.9(D)(3) Generator Control Wiring

Generator control circuit conductors between the transfer equipment and the generator shall be kept entirely independent of all other wiring.

Service

Generator

Main

Main

Main

Listed for Emergency Use

Emergency

Emergency

Transfer switch

Copyright©IAEI 2007

Generator control circuit wiring is required to comply with the fire-rating or other circuit integrity provisions in 700.9(D)(1).

700.9 (D)(3)

Generator Control Wiring
NEC, p. 605

Proposal 13-126
Log 3015
ROP, p. 770

Comment
None

Change at a Glance

Emergency generator control circuit wiring (including the start circuit) between the transfer equipment and the generator must be kept independent of other wiring and meet the minimum 1-hour fire rating protection requirements by utilizing one of the methods provided in 700.9(D)(1).

Analysis and Effect

This revision addresses critical control circuit wiring of emergency generator systems that are required to remain operational. This section addresses survivability of essential wiring that is part of an emergency system. Substantiation with the proposal clearly indicated that the generator start circuit is a critical component of the emergency system and should have the same protection as the feeder-circuit wiring. This revision provides a new separation requirement for generator control circuit wiring and adds a fire-rating protection requirement of not less than 1 hour in accordance with 700.9(D)(1), which provides acceptable methods of achieving a minimum 1-hour fire rating. This new requirement also is consistent with similar existing requirements for generator systems that serve as the alternate power source for a fire pump as provided in 695.14(F) to ensure the survivability of the starting circuit and other control circuit wiring for the generator.

Code Language
700.9(D)(3)
Generator Control Wiring
Control conductors installed between the transfer equipment and the emergency generator shall be kept entirely independent of all other wiring and shall meet the conditions of 700.9(D)(1).

Summary of Change

A new item (3) covering generator control wiring protection has been added to 700.9(D).

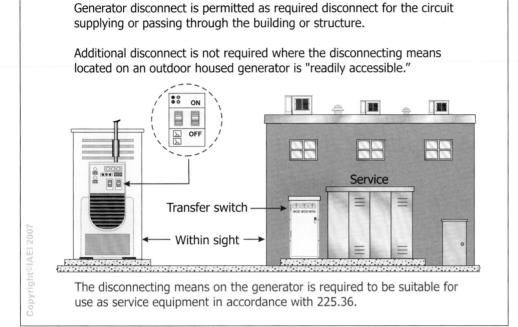

700.12(B)(6) Outdoor Generator Sets

Generator disconnect is permitted as required disconnect for the circuit supplying or passing through the building or structure.

Additional disconnect is not required where the disconnecting means located on an outdoor housed generator is "readily accessible."

ON

OFF

Transfer switch

Within sight

Service

The disconnecting means on the generator is required to be suitable for use as service equipment in accordance with 225.36.

Copyright©IAEI 2007

Outdoor Generator Sets
NEC, p. 606

Proposal 13-131
Log 1283
ROP, p. 771

Comment 13-169
Log 2117
ROC, p. 448

Analysis and Effect

This revision clarifies that the disconnecting means part of the generator assembly is required be rated as suitable for use as service equipment where installed to meet the requirements in 700.12(B)(6). As described in Article 100, conductors supplying a building or other structure from a generator are *feeder conductors*. Where a generator is outdoors, the conductors supplied by the generator are *outside-feeder conductors;* therefore, they are included in the scope of Article 225. Section 225.31 requires that a disconnecting means be provided to disconnect all conductors that supply or pass through a building or structure, and 225.36 requires this disconnecting means to be suitable for use as service equipment. Section 700.12(B)(6) amends the requirements of 225.32 and allows the disconnect that is equipped with a outdoor housed generator as long as it is readily accessible and located within sight of the building or structure served. The provisions of 700.12(B)(6) do not remove the requirements of 225.36 that the building or structure disconnecting means is to be suitable for use as service equipment. This revision correlates with 225.36 and clarifies that the disconnecting means equipped with an emergency generator installed in an outdoor enclosure and intended as the feeder disconnecting means required by 225.31, as allowed by 700.12(B)(6), is required to be suitable for use as service equipment. The same change also occurs in 701.11(B) and 702.11 covering disconnecting means for outdoor generators used with legally required standby systems and optional standby systems.

Code Language
700.12(B)(6)

Outdoor Generator Sets

Where an outdoor housed generator set is equipped with a readily accessible disconnecting means located within sight of the building or structure supplied, an additional disconnecting means shall not be required where ungrounded conductors serve or pass through the building or structure. The disconnecting means shall meet the requirements of 225.36.

Summary of Change

A new last sentence referencing 225.36 has been added to Section 700.12(B)(6).

Change at a Glance

The disconnecting means equipped as part of an outdoor generator set and intended to meet the provisions in 700.12(B)(6) is required to be suitable for use as service equipment in accordance with the requirements of 225.36.

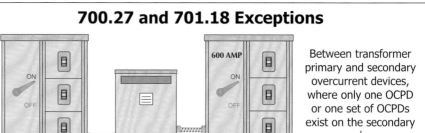

700.27 and 701.18 Exceptions

Between transformer primary and secondary overcurrent devices, where only one OCPD or one set of OCPDs exist on the secondary

600 AMP

225 AMP

Between overcurrent devices of the same size (ampere rating) that are in series

400 AMP   400 AMP

Copyright©IAEI 2007

Selective coordination between overcurrent devices is not required under either of these specific conditions in the exception.

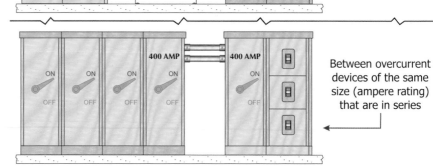

700.27, 701.18 Exceptions

Emergency Systems
Coordination
NEC, p. 608, 611

Proposal 13-135, 13-161
Log 3428, 2516
ROP, p. 772, 780

Comment 13-185, 13-238
Log 1278, 1500
ROC, p. 451, 465

Change at a Glance

Selective coordination of overcurrent devices is not required between transformer primary and secondary overcurrent protection devices or between overcurrent devices of the same rating that are in series with each other.

Analysis and Effect

CMP-13 received numerous proposals and comments related to the *Code* requirements for selective coordination of overcurrent devices for emergency and legally required electrical power systems. The general requirements for selective coordination for these systems have been retained as in *NEC-* 2005, with two new exceptions. Selective coordination is not required between transformer primary and secondary overcurrent protective devices, or where only one overcurrent protective device or set of overcurrent protective devices exist(s) on the transformer secondary, or between overcurrent protective devices of the same size (ampere rating) in series. CMP-13 explained their actions on the subject, "The overriding theme of Articles 700 and 701 is to keep the power on throughout an emergency situation for life safety. Selective coordination increases the reliability of the emergency system. Selective coordination is essential for the continuity of service required in emergency and legally required standby circuits." Action by CMP-13 resulted in exceptions recognizing two conditions where selective coordination is not necessary or practical. The new exceptions were added after comments clearly substantiated the need to provide relief for selective coordination issues in certain series feeders and circuits.

Code Language

700.27

Coordination

Exception: Selective coordination shall not be required in (1) or (2):
(1) Between transformer primary and secondary overcurrent protective devices, where only one overcurrent protective device or set of overcurrent protective devices exists on the transformer secondary,
(2) Between overcurrent protective devices of the same size (ampere rating) in series

701.18

Coordination

Exception: Selective coordination shall not be required in (1) or (2):
(1) Between transformer primary and secondary overcurrent protective devices , where only one overcurrent protective device or set of overcurrent protective devices exists on the transformer secondary,
(2) Between overcurrent protective devices of the same size (ampere rating) in series.

Summary of Change

New exceptions have been added to selective coordination requirements in 700.27 and 701.18.

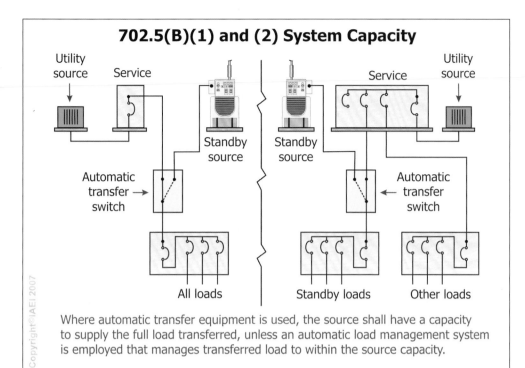

702.5(B)(1) and (2) System Capacity

Where automatic transfer equipment is used, the source shall have a capacity to supply the full load transferred, unless an automatic load management system is employed that manages transferred load to within the source capacity.

702.5

Capacity and Rating
NEC, p. 611

Proposal 13-168
Log 2741
ROP, p. 782

Comment 13-255
Log 114
ROC, p. 470

Analysis and Effect

Recent natural disasters and events have resulted in the increase in generator installations for commercial and industrial applications and, specifically, for residential applications. These revisions provide clear direction about the capacity requirements of an optional standby source that uses automatic transfer. Substantiation with the proposal indicated that automatic transfer equipment is being installed with generators that have a capacity much less than the total load (often an entire panelboard) being transferred. There have been significant inconsistencies in interpretation of the minimum requirements that apply to automatic transfer switches applied in these situations. The revisions now require the standby source to have a minimum capacity to supply the full load that is transferred by an automatic transfer switch, unless there is a load management system employed that controls the amount of connected load on the standby power source. This revision provides needed clarification that should result in designs and installations of optional standby systems that provide sufficient source capacity that is directly related to the type of transfer equipment selected and load management system employed.

Change at a Glance

Where optional standby sources are installed using automatic transfer equipment, the source must be able to carry the entire load served, unless automatic load management systems are installed.

Code Language
702.5

Capacity and Rating

(A) Available Short-Circuit Current. Optional standby system equipment shall be suitable for the maximum available short-circuit current at its terminals.

(B) System Capacity. The calculations of load on the standby source shall be made in accordance with Article 220 or by another approved method.

(1) Manual Transfer Equipment. Where manual transfer equipment is used, an optional standby system shall have adequate capacity and rating for the supply of all equipment intended to be operated at one time. The user of the optional standby system shall be permitted to select the load connected to the system.

(2) Automatic Transfer Equipment. Where automatic transfer equipment is used, an optional standby system shall comply with (2)(a) or (2)(b).

(a) Full Load. The standby source shall be capable of supplying the full load that is transferred by the automatic transfer equipment.

(b) Load Management. Where a system is employed that will automatically manage the connected load, the standby source shall have a capacity sufficient to supply the maximum load that will be connected by the load management system.

Summary of Change

This section has been revised and reorganized to provide a logical layout and clarify the requirements. The revisions include rearranging the requirements into a list format that conforms to Section 2.1.5.1 of the *NEC Style Manual*.

7

Article 708

Critical Operations Power Systems (COPS)
NEC, 616–621

Proposal 20-1
Log 3497
ROP, p. 615

Comments 20-1a, 20-1b,
20-2, 20-6a, 20-8a, 20-9a,
20-11, 20-12
Log CC2000, CC2001, 2109,
CC2003, CC2004, CC2210,
CC2012, CC2348
ROC, p. 347, 349, 350

Change at a Glance

New Article 708 provides requirements for installation, operation, supervision, and maintenance of critical operations power systems.

Analysis and Effect

Emergency systems generally help people evacuate occupancies during power failures or power interruption caused by localized building events. Optional standby systems provide the convenience of power during such interruption of power, but are not a requirement of the *Code*. An increased sense of awareness and urgency resulted from the horrific events of 911 and in the wake of hurricane Katrina. The NEC Technical Correlating Committee had the task of reassessing the adequacy of the existing *NEC* requirements for emergency and standby systems. This resulted in the formation of a special assigned Task Group on Emergency and Standby Systems for Homeland Security. Action by the TCC resulted in the formation of CMP-20 to conduct this review of the existing *NEC* rules for these types of power systems and to handle the resulting *Code* proposals that address these concerns. The NFPA Electrical Engineering Division proactively assembled a group containing representatives from various industries and occupations to address these issues and ultimately draft a proposed article for *NEC*-2008. This group consisted of inspectors, the U.S. Army Corps of Engineers, manufacturers, labor, utilities, and others. Work was already underway in developing a proposed new article in the summer of 2005, long before hurricane Katrina. The findings and work of this assigned task group resulted in the new Article 708 (Article 585 was used during the Proposal and Comment meetings) titled "Critical Operations Power Systems." The focus of the requirements in this article targets electrical power continuity for systems and circuits that are vital to national security, the economy, or public health and safety. Examples of facilities that are designated as mission critical, but not limited to these, are data processing centers, 911 operations centers, hospitals, transportation and municipal infrastructure, police, fire, and civil defense stations, telecommunications centers, cellular telephone towers, air traffic control towers, water pumping stations, and petrochemical plants.

An important aspect of this new article is how qualifying facilities are determined or designated as mission critical. As outlined in the scope of the article, these requirements apply to facilities that are intended to supply, distribute and control electrical power that is essential for continuity of vital operations. Critical operations power systems (COPS) are classified as such by municipal, state, federal, or other governmental agency having jurisdiction, or by facility engineering documentation establishing the necessity for such power continuity. Those operational facilities or part of a facility deemed as critical fall under the requirements of this new article. Some of the rules in this article call for hardened electrical circuit wiring, specific power sources and source location designs, overcurrent protection operational characteristics and locations, and system performance and analysis.

There are building systems necessary for continued operation such as HVAC systems, fire alarm systems, communications and signaling systems that are necessary to the operation of mission critical facilities. Action by CMP-20 on Comment 20-2 resulted in those additional systems being included as critical operations systems where so designated as critical operations areas (DCOA). The events of 911, hurricane Katrina and other concerns raised awareness and appreciation for mission critical facilities in operation in today's world. This article is an effective set of electrical rules for facilities that must remain operational during and after these types of natural and manmade events. The *NEC* does its part by including applicable requirements in Article 708 for facilities where effective strategies for maintaining continuity of services are necessary for critical operations.

Summary of Change
New Article 708 has been added to the *NEC* that provides requirements for facilities that are designated as mission critical. The new article includes four parts, and information has been provided in the annex about maintenance and testing requirements for SCADA systems associated with critical operations power systems for facilities.

Article 725

Class 1, Class 2, and Class 3 Remote-Control, Signaling and Power-Limited Circuits
NEC, 622–631

Proposal 3-137
Log 843
ROP, p. 793

Comment
None

Change at a Glance

Article 725 was renumbered and reorganized to improve usability and consistency with *Code* format.

Analysis and Effect

Article 725 was reorganized and re-numbered to provide a logical layout that is sequentially consistent with Article 760. This re-numbering resulted from a comment held from the 2005 *NEC* cycle, which proposed identical section numbers for Articles 725, 760, 770, 800, 820 and 830. Panel 3 held this comment for Articles 725 and 760 only, because even though all the articles cover similar installations, they are not the same and exact correlation with 770, 800, 820 and 830 was not feasible. The renumbering leaves room between sections for future additions or reconfigurations. The renumbering of Articles 725 and 760 is not identical since the articles differ in specific requirements and numbering arrangements.

Summary of Change

The article was reorganized to provide a more logical order and sequential numbering scheme consistent with Articles 760, 770, 800, 820, and 830.

Code Language
Article 725

Class 1, Class 2, and Class 3 Remote-Control, Signaling, and Power-Limited Circuits

I. General

725.1 Scope.

725.2 Definitions.

725.3 Other Articles.

725.21 Access to Electrical Equipment Behind Panels Designed to Allow Access.

725.24 Mechanical Execution of Work.

725.25 Abandoned Cables

725.30 Class 1, Class 2, and Class 3 Circuit Identification.

725.31 Safety-Control Equipment.

725.35 Class 1, Class 2, and Class 3 Circuit Requirements.

II. Class 1 Circuits.

725.41 Class 1 Circuit Classifications and Power Source Requirements.

725.43 Class 1 Circuit Overcurrent Protection.

725.45 Class 1 Circuit Overcurrent Device Location

725.46 Class 1 Circuit Wiring Methods.

725.48 Conductors of Different Circuits in the Same Cable, Cable Tray, Enclosure, or Raceway.

725.49 Class 1 Circuit Conductors.

725.51 Number of Conductors in Cable Trays and Raceway, and Derating.

725.52 Circuits Extending Beyond One Building.

III. Class 2 and Class 3 Circuits (in part)

IV. Listing Requirements (in part)

725.179 Listing and Marking of Class 2, Class 3, and Type PLTC Cables.

See *NEC*-2008 for full text.

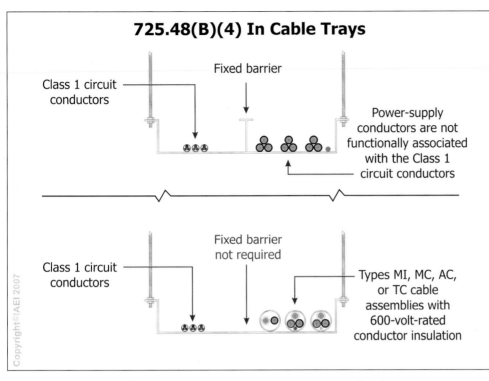

725.48(B)(4) In Cable Trays

Class 1 circuit conductors

Fixed barrier

Power-supply conductors are not functionally associated with the Class 1 circuit conductors

Class 1 circuit conductors

Fixed barrier not required

Types MI, MC, AC, or TC cable assemblies with 600-volt-rated conductor insulation

Copyright©IAEI 2007

In Cable Trays
NEC, p. 624

Proposal 3-160
Log 821
ROP, p. 833

Comment 3-112
Log 622
ROC, p. 481

Analysis and Effect

This change was the result of a comment held from the 2005 *NEC* cycle; and it was developed by a task group before the start of the 2008 cycle. The original proposal for *NEC*-2005 wanted to eliminate the requirement for a fixed barrier between power conductors and Class 1 conductors in a cable tray. The task group and the panel did not accept elimination of the barrier, but instead they developed and accepted a modified version of that concept and added new provisions for multiconductor cable assemblies that provide the required inherent separation. If the Class 1 wiring is enclosed in a Type TC, AC, MC or MI cable, the panel agreed that there would be enough mechanical strength and electrical separation from the power conductors to be acceptable without an additional barrier. This application is limited, but it would apply especially in industrial locations where cable tray is most often used as a wiring method support. The application is also limited to cable trays containing power conductors operating at no more that 600 volts. The conductors for the Class 1 circuit(s) also have to be rated at 600 volts. In addition, action by CMP-3 on Comment 3-112 (Log No. 622) improved clarity and usability of this section by restructuring the requirements into a logical order and list format.

> ### Change at a Glance
>
> Separate multiconductor cables such as Types AC, MC, MI, and TC are permitted in the same cable tray with Class 1 circuit conductors without the use of a fixed barrier in the tray.

Code Language
725.48(B)(4)

In Cable Trays

Installations in cable trays shall comply with 725.48(B)(4)(1) or 725.48(B)(4)(2).

(1) Class 1 circuit conductors and power-supply conductors not functionally associated with the Class I circuit conductors shall be separated by a solid fixed barrier of a material compatible with the cable tray.

(2) Class 1 circuit conductors and power-supply conductors not functionally associated with the Class I circuit conductors shall be permitted to be installed in a cable tray without barriers where all of the conductors are installed with separate multiconductor Type AC, Type MC, Type MI, or Type TC cables and all of the conductors in the cables are insulated at 600 volts.

Summary of Change

This section has been revised and put into a list format conforming to the *NEC Style Manual*, and the requirements for barriers and separation have been clarified.

7

725.130(B)
Exc. No. 3

Class 2 and Class 3 Wiring Methods
NEC, p. 626

Proposal 3-196
Log 3288
ROP, p. 846

Comment
None

Change at a Glance

Bare Class 2 conductors are permitted where they are installed as part of a listed intrusion protection system.

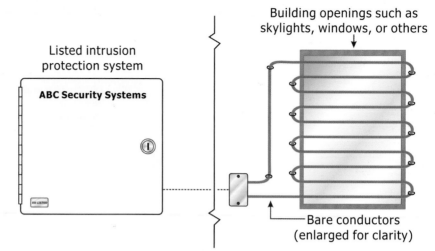

725.130(B) Exception No. 3

Building openings such as skylights, windows, or others

Listed intrusion protection system

ABC Security Systems

XX LISTED

Bare conductors (enlarged for clarity)

Copyright©IAEI 2007

Bare Class 2 conductors are permitted where they are part of a listed intrusion protection system.

Installed in accordance with the installation instructions [110.3(B)]

Analysis and Effect

A new Exception No. 3 was added to 725.130(B) to recognize a practice used by security system installers called "lacing." This bare conductor, commonly a 26 AWG, is stretched over an opening that is to be protected and if the conductor is broken by an intrusion, the alarm system is activated. The conductor is bare so that it is harder for the intruder to see and possibly bypass. During the 1999 *Code* cycle, a proposal was accepted to require minimum insulation of 150 volts on all Class 2 conductors, which would outlaw the practice. This new exception again allows this practice of lacing, but only where the bare Class 2 conductors are installed as part of a listed intrusion protection system and according to the instructions included in the listing and labeling of the system.

Code Language
725.130(B)

Class 2 and Class 3 Wiring Methods
Exception No. 3: Bare Class 2 conductors shall be permitted as part of a listed intrusion protection system where installed in accordance with the listing instructions for the system.

Summary of Change

A new Exception No. 3 has been added to 725.130(B).

Courtesy of Underwriters Laboratories Inc.

Photo courtesy of UL

Construction
NEC, p. 632

Proposal 3-210
Log 1420
ROP, p. 849

Comment
None

Analysis and Effect

A new FPN was added to Section 727.6 to reference the UL Flame Exposure, Vertical Tray Flame Test found in UL 1685-2000 Standard for Safety for Vertical-Tray Fire-Propagation and Smoke-Release Test for Electrical and Optical-Fiber Cables. The testing and meeting or exceeding the standard is a requirement for listing and labeling of most all types of cable type wiring methods, particularly those installed and used within buildings or structures. This change promotes consistency in the *Code*, and makes it clear to which standard instrumentation tray cables must be listed.

Companion proposals were accepted for Sections 725.82(C), 725.8(E) 725.82(H), 760.82(E) and (F) FPNs to update to the newer version of the standard.

Change at a Glance

A brief reference and explanation of required testing for physical damage, smoke release, and fire spread in order for Type ITC cables to be listed as "resistant to the spread of fire" has been added.

Code Language
727.6
Construction

FPN: One method of defining *resistant to the spread of fire* is that the cables do not spread fire to the top of the tray in the "UL Flame Exposure, Vertical Tray Flame Test" in UL 1685-2000, *Standard for Safety for Vertical-Tray Fire-Propagation and Smoke-Release Test for Electrical and Optical-Fiber Cables.* The smoke measurements in the test method are not applicable.

Another method of defining *resistant to the spread of fire* is for the damage (char length) not to exceed 1.5 m (4 ft 11 in.) when performing the CSA "Vertical Flame Test — Cables in Cable Trays," as described in CSA C22.2 No. 0.3-M- 2001, *Test Methods for Electrical Wires and Cables.*

Summary of Change

A new fine print note has been added to Section 727.6. (Revisions have occurred in Articles 725 and 760 to update the standard references only. UL 1581 now references UL 1685 for the text of the test method. The test method remains the same as before.)

Article 760

Fire Alarm Systems
NEC, 632–640

Proposal 3-211
Log 842
ROP, p. 849

Comment
None

Change at a Glance

Article 760 was renumbered and reorganized to improve usability and consistency with *Code* format.

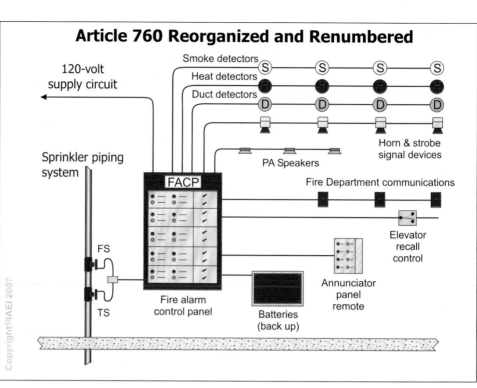

Article 760 Reorganized and Renumbered

120-volt supply circuit

Smoke detectors
Heat detectors
Duct detectors

PA Speakers

Horn & strobe signal devices

Sprinkler piping system

Fire Department communications

FACP

Elevator recall control

FS

TS

Fire alarm control panel

Batteries (back up)

Annunciator panel remote

Copyright©IAEI 2007

Analysis and Effect

The renumbering and reorganization of Article 760 resulted from a comment held from the 2005 *NEC* cycle, which proposed identical section numbers for Articles 725, 760, 770, 800, 820 and 830. Action by CMP-3 in the 2005 *NEC* development process held this comment for Articles 725 and 760, because even though all the articles cover similar installations, they are not the same and exact correlation with 770, 800, 820 and 830 was not feasible. The renumbering leaves room between sections for future additions or reconfigurations. The renumbering of Articles 760 and 725 is not identical since the articles differ in various specific requirements and numbering arrangements.

Summary of Change

Article was reorganized to provide a more logical order and a sequential numbering scheme consistent with Articles 725, 770, 800, 820, and 830.

Code Language

Article 760
Fire Alarm Systems
I. General
    760.1 Scope.
    760.2 Definitions.
    760.3 Other Articles.
    760.21 Access to Electrical Equipment Behind Panels Designed to Allow Access.
    760.24 Mechanical Execution of Work.
    760.25 Abandoned Cables.
    760.30 Fire Alarm Circuit Identification.
    760.32 Fire Alarm Circuits Extending Beyond One Building.
    760.35 Fire Alarm Circuit Requirements.
II. Non–Power-Limited Fire Alarm (NPLFA) Circuits
    760.41 NPLFA Circuit Power Source Requirements.
    760.43 NPLFA Circuit Overcurrent Protection.
    760.45 NPLFA Circuit Overcurrent Device Location.
    760.46 NPLFA Circuit Wiring.
    760.48 Conductors of Different Circuits in Same Cable, Enclosure, or Raceway.
    760.49 NPLFA Circuit Conductors.
    760.51 Number of Conductors in Cable Trays and Raceways, and Derating.
    760.53 Multiconductor NPLFA Cables.
III. Power-Limited Fire Alarm (PLFA) Circuits (in part)
IV. Listing Requirements (in part)

760.3(G) Installation of Conductors with Other Systems

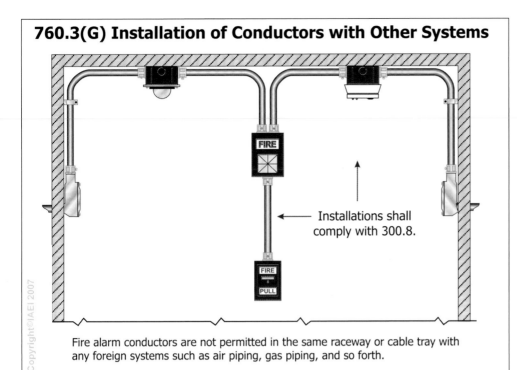

Fire alarm conductors are not permitted in the same raceway or cable tray with any foreign systems such as air piping, gas piping, and so forth.

Installations shall comply with 300.8.

Copyright©IAEI 2007

Installation of Conductors with Other Systems
NEC, p. 633

Proposal 3-221
Log 2184
ROP, p. 851

Comment
None

Analysis and Effect

Section 300.8 prohibits installation of any piping, tubing, or equal for steam, water, gas, air, drainage, or any other system foreign to an electrical system in the same raceway or cable tray with electrical circuit conductors. In previous editions of the *NEC*, there was no correlation to 300.8 from Article 760. This revision provides the necessary reference that will prohibit conductors of fire alarm systems from being installed in the same raceway or cable tray that is used for any of these aforementioned systems that are not electrical. The new prohibition in 760.3(G) restricts combining these systems in such a manner that the functionality of the system could be compromised because of possible physical damage. The reference to 300.8 closes this gap and provides the necessary restriction.

Change at a Glance

Fire alarm conductors are not permitted to be installed in the same raceway or cable tray that contains piping, tubing, or the equivalent for systems foreign to electrical wiring systems, such as steam, air, gas, and so forth.

Code Language
760.3(G)

Installation of Conductors with Other Systems

Installations shall comply with 300.8.

Summary of Change

A new subdivision (G) has been added to Section 760.3 covering installations with other systems.

Articles 760, 760.41(B) and 760.121(B)

Branch Circuit
NEC, p. 632, 634, 635

Proposal 3-211, 3-239, 3-245
Log 842, 1909, 1910
ROP, p. 849, 856, 857

Comment
None

Change at a Glance

Individual branch circuits are required for supplying the power source of NPLFA circuits and PLFA circuits.

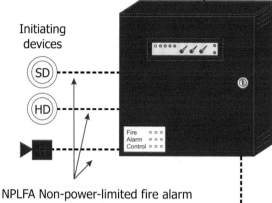

760.41(B) Branch Circuit

Power source circuits are not permitted to be supplied through GFCI or AFCI devices

Branch circuit(s) (power source) supplying NPLFA fire alarm system

Required to be supplied by an individual branch circuit

Initiating devices

SD

HD

Fire Alarm Control

NPLFA Non-power-limited fire alarm signaling and initiating circuits

Modem connection

Copyright©IAEI 2007

Analysis and Effect

Article 760 has been renumbered and restructured to address usability; this is the result of the work of an assigned task group formed to address held 2005 *NEC* Comment 3-108 (Log No. 995), which proposed a new parallel numbering system for Articles 725 and 760. The requirements for power sources for both power-limited and non-power-limited fire alarm circuits have been relocated to Sections 760.41 and 760.121 respectively, as a result of this reorganization in *NEC*-2008. A new subdivision (B) has been added to each of these sections. An additional sentence in each of these sections is a technical revision that brings the requirements into alignment with NFPA 72, 4.4.1.4.1, which requires a dedicated branch circuit to supply the fire alarm power supply. The addition to the *NEC* clearly requires an individual branch circuit for the fire alarm supply. Use of the term *individual branch circuit* is intended to make the language consistent with the *NEC* definitions. These new subdivisions continue to restrict ground-fault circuit interrupters and arc-fault circuit interrupters from being applied in the branch circuits (power sources) supplying fire alarm systems.

Code Language

760.41(B)
Branch Circuit
An individual branch circuit shall be required for the supply of the power source. This branch circuit shall not be supplied through ground-fault circuit interrupters or arc-fault circuit interrupters.

760.121(B)
Branch Circuit
An individual branch circuit shall be required for the supply of the power source. This branch circuit shall not be supplied through ground-fault circuit interrupters or arc-fault circuit interrupters.

Summary of Change

Article 760 has been reorganized and restructured to provide a more logical layout and a more consistent sequential numbering scheme. *NEC*-2005 Sections 760.21 and 760.41 have been renumbered as 760.41 and 760.121 respectively. In addition to the restructuring of the article, a new subdivision (B) has been included in Sections 760.41 and 121, addressing requirements for individual branch circuits.

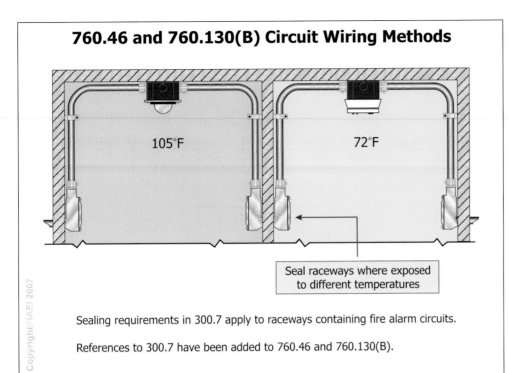

760.46 and 760.130(B) Circuit Wiring Methods

105°F

72°F

Seal raceways where exposed
to different temperatures

Sealing requirements in 300.7 apply to raceways containing fire alarm circuits.

References to 300.7 have been added to 760.46 and 760.130(B).

Copyright©IAEI 2007

Fire Alarms Systems
NEC, p. 634, 636

Proposal 3-240, 3-246
Log 1201, 1200
ROP, p. 856, 858

Comment 3-159
Log 1940
ROC, p. 494

Analysis and Effect

The rules in 300.7 for sealing raceways exposed to different temperatures have been included for conduits containing fire alarm circuit conductors. The reference to 300.7 has been added to 760.46 covering NPLFA wiring methods, and to 760.130(B) covering PLFA wiring methods. This new reference to Section 300.7 will require raceways used for fire alarm systems to be sealed against moisture where the raceways go through different temperatures, such as from outdoors to indoors. Condensation inside the raceway caused by these temperature differentials could possibly run onto alarm equipment and affect its operation. Since Section 300.7 applies to raceway installations, those fire alarm circuits installed using cable wiring methods in accordance with 760.46 or 760.130(B) would require sealing where the cable wiring method was installed within a raceway that is exposed to different temperatures.

Change at a Glance

Sealing requirements in 300.7 apply to raceways containing fire alarm circuits where the raceways are exposed to different temperatures, such as from inside to outside.

Code Language

760.46

NPLFA Circuit Wiring Methods
Installation of non–power-limited fire alarm circuits shall be in accordance with 110.3(B), 300.7, 300.11, 300.15, 300.17, and other appropriate articles of Chapter 3.

Exception No. 1: As provided in 760.48 through 760.53.

Exception No. 2: Where other articles of this Code require other methods.

760.130(B)

PLFA Wiring Methods and Materials
Power-limited fire alarm conductors and cables described in 760.179 shall be installed as detailed in 760.130(B)(1), (B)(2), or (B)(3) of this section and 300.7. Devices shall be installed in accordance with 110.3(B), 300.11(A), and 300.15.

Summary of Change

References to Section 300.7 have been added to Sections 760.46 and 760.130(B).

760.139 Installation of Conductors of Different PLFA Circuits, Class 2, Class 3, and Communications Circuits in the Same Cable, Enclosure, <u>Cable Tray</u> or Raceway

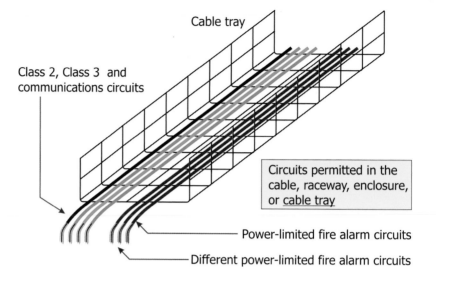

Cable tray

Class 2, Class 3 and communications circuits

Circuits permitted in the cable, raceway, enclosure, or cable tray

Power-limited fire alarm circuits

Different power-limited fire alarm circuits

Copyright©IAEI 2007

760.139

Installation of Conductors of Different PLFA Circuits, Class 2, Class 3, and Communications Circuits in the Same Cable, Enclosure, Cable Tray, or Raceway.
NEC, p. 638

Proposal 3-248
Log 1289
ROP, p. 858

Comment
None

Analysis and Effect

PLFA cables with different PLFA circuits and other circuits identified by this section were previously recognized only for the same cable, raceway or enclosure. This revision expands this allowance to cable trays. Cable tray is permitted for combining power-limited fire alarm circuits with other PLFA circuits, Class 2 circuits, network-powered broadband communications circuits and audio systems circuits. A reference to cable trays added in the title of this section and each of the subsections clarifies that cable trays can contain both fire alarm conductors and some other types of low-voltage conductors just the same as any raceway can contain these combinations.

Change at a Glance

Combinations of different PLFA circuits, and combinations of PLFA circuits with Class 2 circuits, PLFA circuits with network-powered broadband communications cables, and PLFA circuits with audio system circuits are permitted in a cable tray.

Summary of Change

The words "cable tray" have been incorporated into the title of Section 760.139 and subdivisions (A), (B), (C), and (D).

Code Language
760.139

Installation of Conductors of Different PLFA Circuits, Class 2, Class 3, and Communications Circuits in the Same Cable, Enclosure, Cable Tray, or Raceway

(A) Two or More PLFA Circuits. Cable and conductors of two or more power-limited fire alarm circuits, communications circuits, or Class 3 circuits shall be permitted within the same cable, enclosure, cable tray, or raceway.

(B) Class 2 Circuits with PLFA Circuits. Conductors of one or more Class 2 circuits shall be permitted within the same cable, enclosure, cable tray, or raceway with conductors of power-limited fire alarm circuits, provided that the insulation of the Class 2 circuit conductors in the cable, enclosure, or raceway is at least that required by the power-limited fire alarm circuits.

(C) Low-Power Network-Powered Broadband Communications Cables and PLFA Cables. Low-power network-powered broadband communications circuits shall be permitted in the same enclosure, cable tray, or raceway with PLFA cables.

(D) Audio System Circuits and PLFA Circuits. Audio system circuits described in 640.9(C) and installed using Class 2 or Class 3 wiring methods in compliance with 725.133 and 725.154 shall not be permitted to be installed in the same cable, cable tray, or raceway with power-limited conductors or cables.

760.176 Listing and Marking of NPLFA Cables

Fire alarm cables used in wet locations must be listed for wet location use or have a moisture impervious metal sheath.

Requirement applies to NPLFA cables [760.176] and PLFA cables [760.179].

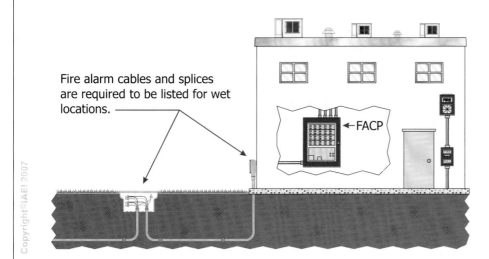

Fire alarm cables and splices are required to be listed for wet locations.

← FACP

Copyright©IAEI 2007

Listing and Marking of
NPLFA and PLFA Cables
NEC, p. 639, 640

Proposal 3-258, 3-264
Log 2978, 3057
ROP, p. 861, 863

Comment
None

Analysis and Effect

This new text will require that all power-limited fire alarm (PLFA) and non-power-limited fire alarm (NPLFA) cables that are installed in wet locations, whether indoors or outdoors, will have to be listed for use in these wet locations, or the cable will have to have a moisture-impervious sheath to prevent damage to the conductors. There is an existing optional listing for these types of cables. This revision provides users with direction regarding the use of suitable cable types where exposed to wet environments.

Change at a Glance

Fire alarm cables installed in wet locations must be listed for the application or have moisture impervious metal sheath.

Code Language
760.176
Listing and Marking of NPLFA Cables

Non–power-limited fire alarm cables installed as wiring within buildings shall be listed in accordance with 760.176(A) and (B) and as being resistant to the spread of fire in accordance with 760.176(C) through (F), and shall be marked in accordance with 760.176(G). Cable used in a wet location shall be listed for use in wet locations or have a moisture-impervious metal sheath.

760.179
Listing and Marking of PLFA Cables and Insulated Continuous Line-Type Fire Detectors

Type FPL cables installed as wiring within buildings shall be listed as being resistant to the spread of fire and other criteria in accordance with 760.179(A) through (H) and shall be marked in accordance with 760.179(I). Insulated continuous line-type fire detectors shall be listed in accordance with 760.179(J). Cable used in a wet location shall be listed for use in wet locations or have a moisture-impervious metal sheath.

Summary of Change

A new last sentence has been added to 760.176 and 760.179 addressing fire alarm cables installed in wet locations.

7

770.133(A)
Exc. No. 5

**Installation of Optical Fibers
and Electrical Conductors**
NEC, p. 644

**Proposal 16-65
Log 2627**
ROP, p. 888

Comment
None

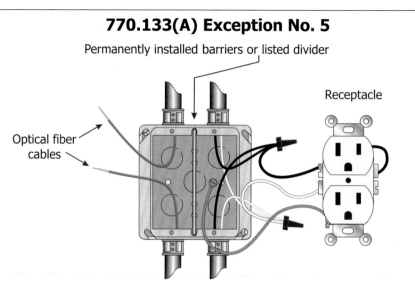

770.133(A) Exception No. 5

Permanently installed barriers or listed divider

Receptacle

Optical fiber
cables

Optical fiber cable is permitted in the same raceway, outlet box, or enclosure
as electric light, power, Class 1, non-power-limited fire alarm, and medium
power network-powered broadband communications circuits where separated
by a permanent barrier or listed divider.

Analysis and Effect

Section 770.133(A) generally restricts optical fiber cable from being installed within the same raceway, outlet box or enclosure. This is a new exception for 770.133(A) that would allow an optical fiber cable to share the same raceway, outlet box or enclosure as long as a barrier was in place. This language is similar to the language found in 800.133(A)(1)(c) Exception No. 1. Metal-clad optical fiber cable can become energized if it comes in contact with electrical conductors. This proposal defines the barrier as a permanent function of the enclosure, or one that may be a removable, or may be a field-installed listed divider. These barriers are used to divide the optical fiber cable from the power circuits.

Change at a Glance

Optical fiber cables may be placed in the same raceway or enclosure with power or communication circuits when separated by a permanent barrier or listed divider.

Code Language
770.133(A)

With Conductors for Electric Light, Power, Class 1, Non-Power-Limited Fire Alarm, or Medium Power Network-Powered Broadband Communications

Exception No. 5: Where all of the conductors of electric light, power, Class 1, nonpower-limited fire alarm, and medium-power network-powered broadband communications circuits are separated from all of the optical fiber cables by a permanent barrier or listed divider.

Summary of Change

A new exception to Section 770.133 has been added. This exception provides conditions for allowing optical fiber cables in the same enclosures with conductors of other systems.

770.154(F) Hazardous (Classified) Locations

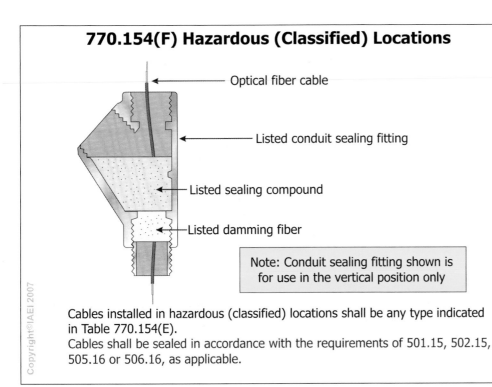

Optical fiber cable

Listed conduit sealing fitting

Listed sealing compound

Listed damming fiber

Note: Conduit sealing fitting shown is for use in the vertical position only

Cables installed in hazardous (classified) locations shall be any type indicated in Table 770.154(E).
Cables shall be sealed in accordance with the requirements of 501.15, 502.15, 505.16 or 506.16, as applicable.

Copyright©IAEI 2007

770.154 (F)

Hazardous (Classified) Locations
NEC, p. 645

Proposal 16-87
Log 2564
ROP, p. 897

Comment
None

REVISION!

Analysis and Effect

Substantiation included with the proposal indicated that the *Code* has not clearly addressed sealing requirements for optical fiber cables used in hazardous locations. It was pointed out that optical fiber cables could transfer flammable gases and vapors as easily as electrical cables used in similar applications. Optical fiber cables may be of the nonconductive, conductive, or composite type; it is possible for gasses and vapors, for instance, to travel from the classified (hazardous) location to a non-classified (hazardous) location through the interstices in the cables, particularly with composite type cables. The UL guide, *General Information for Electrical Equipment Directory* (UL White Book) provides information regarding these types of fittings in product category CYMX, and general information regarding equipment installed in Classes I, II, and III Divisions 1 and 2 hazardous locations in product category AAIZ.

It is now clear to designers, installers, and inspectors that optical fiber cables installed in these types of locations require sealing per the appropriate *Code* article(s) in chapter 5.

Change at a Glance

Cable seals are now required for optical fiber cables used in hazardous locations.

Code Language
770.154(F)

Hazardous (Classified) Locations
Cables installed in hazardous (classified) locations shall be any type indicated in Table 770.154(E). Cables shall be sealed in accordance with the requirements of 501.15, 502.15, 505.16 or 506.16, as applicable.

Summary of Change

A new second sentence was added.

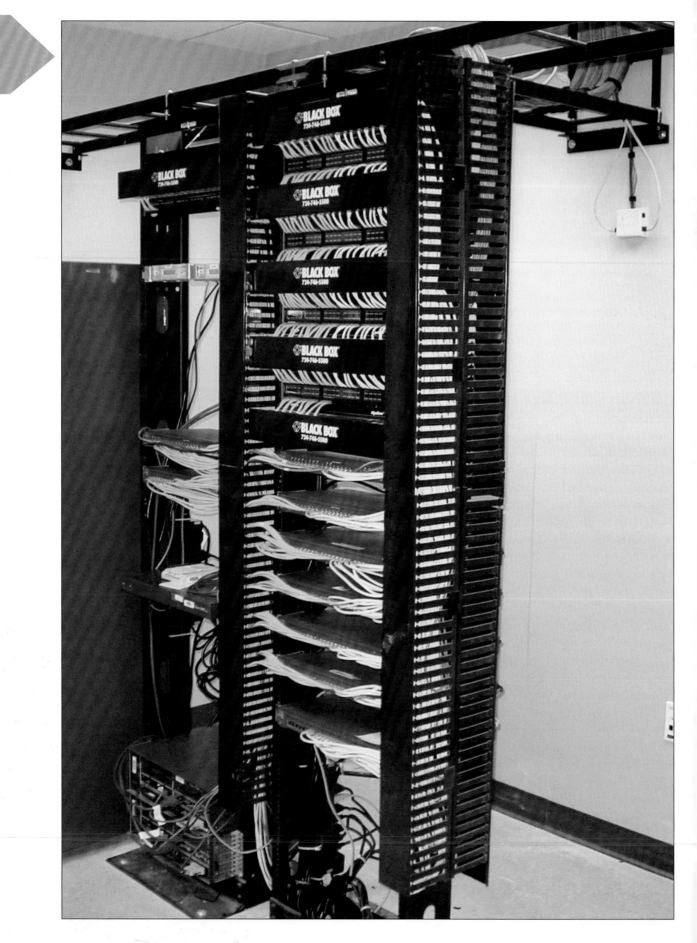

Chapter

8

Selected
Changes

Article 800

800.2

Communications Circuit
NEC, 648

Proposal 16-98
Log 651
ROP, p. 902

Comment 16-80
Log 1534
ROC, p. 523

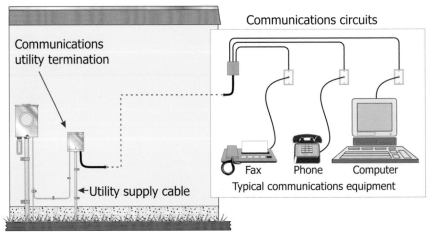

800.2 Communications Circuit

Communications circuits

Communications utility termination

Fax Phone Computer
Typical communications equipment

←Utility supply cable

Copyright©IAEI 2007

The circuit that extends voice , audio , video , data, interactive services, telegraph (except radio), outside wiring for fire alarm and burglar alarm from the communications utility to the customer's communications equipment up to and including terminal equipment such as a telephone, fax machine or answering machine.

Analysis and Effect

This definition describes a communication circuit and the typical connected equipment. The definition clarifies that the communications circuit begins at the point of demarcation (typically a telephone utility company punch-down block), and includes all cabling, equipment, supports, and so forth, up to and including the end-user equipment, such as a telephone or fax machine. Communication circuits are being installed in an ever-increasing number, and most installations are covered by *Code* rules. Where the *NEC* refers to a communication circuit in any of the rules, the defined term clarifies the limits of the application.

Change at a Glance

Communications circuit is defined; it extends from the utility to the final piece of user equipment.

Code Language
800.2
Communications Circuit
The circuit that extends voice, audio, video, data, interactive services, telegraph (except radio), outside wiring for fire alarm and burglar alarm from the communications utility to the customer's communications equipment up to and including terminal equipment such as a telephone, fax machine, or answering machine.

Summary of Change
A new definition has been added to Section 800.2.

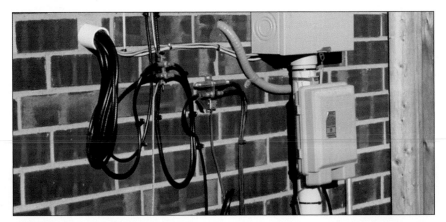

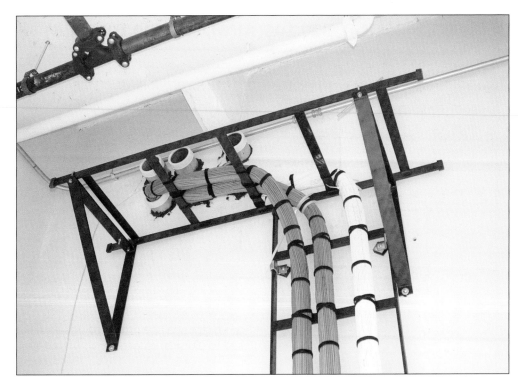

Mechanical Execution of Work
NEC, p. 649

Proposal 16-134, 16-137
Log 1385, 3053
ROP, p. 910, 911

Comment 16-107a, 16-108
Log CC1602, 171
ROC, p. 529

Analysis and Effect

Action by CMP-16 originally created a new requirement for all supporting hardware and fittings, including straps, staples, cable ties, hangers, or similar fittings, which support communications cables to be listed. The final result is that both listed and unlisted means of securement are acceptable.

Cable ties are included in the list of methods for communications cables. The submitter wished to bring consistency to the use of cable ties as a support method, as these devices have been permitted for cable support in some sections of chapter 3 since *NEC*-1993. It is now clear to installers, maintenance persons and inspectors that cable ties are permitted as a means of securing communication cables, if installed and used per the manufacturer's instructions included with the listing and labeling. Installers and users of these positioning devices must also be aware of building, fire, and mechanical code requirements prior to installation of communications cabling and equipment.

And finally, new information has been added to the fine print note following 800.24 that is related to updated ANSI and telecommunications industry installation standards, which may be referred to for workmanlike cable and telecommunications equipment installations in buildings.

Code Language

800.24
Mechanical Execution of Work

Communications circuits and equipment shall be installed in a neat and workmanlike manner. Cables installed exposed on the surface of ceilings and sidewalls shall be supported by the building structure in such a manner that the cable will not be damaged by normal building use. Such cables shall be secured by hardware, including straps, staples, cable ties, hangers, or similar fittings designed and installed so as not to damage the cable. The installation shall also conform with 300.4(D) and 300.11.

FPN: Accepted industry practices are described in ANSI/NECA/BICSI 568-2006, *Standard for Installing Commercial Building Telecommunications Cabling...*and other ANSI-approved installation standards.

Summary of Change

The words "cable ties" were added, and the updated FPN references the latest standard.

Change at a Glance

Cable ties are now recognized for securing communications cables.

800.100 (A)(6), 820.100 (A)(6), 830.100 (A)(6)

Physical Protection
NEC, p. 652, 664, 674

Proposal 16-166, 16-298, 16-392, 16-393
Log 858, 850, 377, 860
ROP, p. 918, 955, 983

Comment 16-127
Log 173
ROC, p. 534

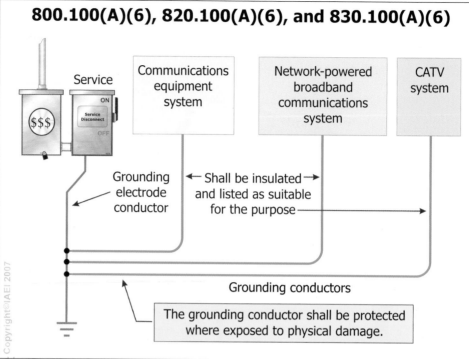

800.100(A)(6), 820.100(A)(6), and 830.100(A)(6)

Service

Communications equipment system

Network-powered broadband communications system

CATV system

Grounding electrode conductor

← Shall be insulated and listed as suitable for the purpose →

Grounding conductors

The grounding conductor shall be protected where exposed to physical damage.

Copyright©IAEI 2007

Analysis and Effect

Grounding and bonding of communications systems to the building or structure electrical system and connecting them to earth is a critical component of electrical safety, as is assuring that the grounding conductor(s) for all communications systems are protected from physical damage so that the bonding and earthing connections are maintained. *Code* language in these sections has been changed to promote consistency, to be less subjective, and to provide a clearer and more enforceable requirement. These three improvements were companion proposals to the one also found in 810.21(D).

Change at a Glance

Grounding conductors for communications systems shall be protected from physical damage.

Code Language

(A)(6)
Physical Protection

The grounding conductor shall be protected where exposed to physical damage. Where the grounding conductor is run in a metal raceway, both ends of the raceway shall be bonded to the grounding conductor or the same terminal or electrode to which the grounding conductor is connected.

Summary of Change

Words that stated "where necessary" were removed, because they were considered ambiguous, and "shall be protected where exposed to physical damage" were added.

Analysis of Changes *NEC*-2008

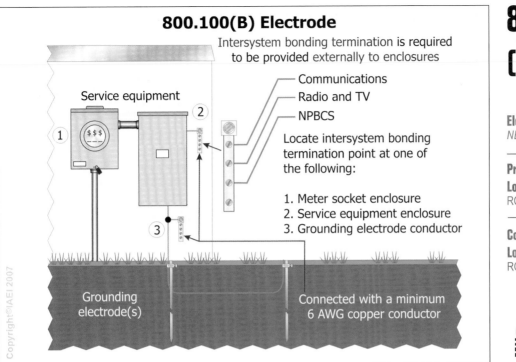

800.100(B) Electrode

Intersystem bonding termination is required to be provided externally to enclosures

Service equipment

(1) $$$

(2)

(3)

Communications
Radio and TV
NPBCS

Locate intersystem bonding termination point at one of the following:

1. Meter socket enclosure
2. Service equipment enclosure
3. Grounding electrode conductor

Grounding electrode(s)

Connected with a minimum 6 AWG copper conductor

Copyright©IAEI 2007

800.100 (B)

Electrode
NEC, p. 652

Proposal 16-167
Log 1890
ROP, p. 918

Comment 16-128
Log 174
ROC, p. 534

Analysis and Effect

This is one of several proposals to improve the requirements related to intersystem bonding and grounding of communication systems (telecom, satellite, CATV, etc.) to each other, and to onsite electrical power systems. *Code* panel action created a dedicated and well-defined location for terminating the grounding and bonding conductors required in chapter 8 articles, and 770.93. The newly required termination point must have enough capacity (*NEC* 110.14) to terminate multiple communication system bonding conductors (telecom, satellite, CATV, etc.) on premises to the electrical system, and at one location. Intersystem grounding and bonding accomplished by the connection of communication system bonding conductors to the power system greatly improves electrical safety for people and property by stabilizing and equalizing voltages between these systems.

The submitter of the proposal pointed out that it is becoming more difficult to bond between communication and electrical systems because of the increased use of flush-mounted electrical meter bases and non-metallic conduits for service-entrance raceways. Often, in new construction, the grounding electrode, the grounding electrode conductor(s), and any metal service raceway(s) are all concealed behind walls and are not accessible to terminate a bonding conductor connection which is routed to the communication system(s). The new requirement clearly directs those who install, maintain, and inspect electrical communications and power systems to the requirement for and location of intersystem bonding. A new definition of *intersystem bonding termination* was included in Article 100 Definitions. Companion proposals regarding intersystem bonding terminations were accepted by the *Code* panel to revise Sections 810.21(F), 820.100(B), and 830.100(B) as well.

Change at a Glance

An intersystem bonding termination point is now specifically required at buildings or structures for bonding of all communications systems to the electrical system present at the site.

Code Language
800.100(B)
Electrode

The grounding conductor shall be connected in accordance with 800.100(B)(1), (B)(2), or (B)(3).

(1) In Buildings or Structures with an Intersystem Bonding Termination. If the building or structure served has an intersystem bonding termination, the grounding conductor shall be connected to the intersystem bonding termination.

(2) In Buildings or Structures with Grounding Means. If the building or structure served has no intersystem bonding termination, the grounding conductor shall be connected to the nearest accessible location on the following...

(3) In Buildings or Structures Without Intersystem Bonding Termination or Grounding Means. If the building or structure served has no intersystem bonding termination or grounding means, as described in 800.100(B)(2), the grounding conductor shall be connected to either of the following:
(1) To any one of the individual electrodes described in 250.52(A)(1), (A)(2), (A)(3), or (A)(4)
(2) If the building or structure served has no intersystem bonding termination or has no grounding means, as described in 800.100(B)(2), or (B)(3)(1), to any one of the individual electrodes described in 250.52(A)(7), and (A)(8) or to a ground rod or pipe not less than 1.5 m (5 ft) in length and 12.7 mm (1/2 in.) in diameter, driven, where practicable, into permanently damp earth and separated from lightning conductors as covered in 800.53 and at least 1.8 m (6 ft) from electrodes of other systems. Steam or hot water pipes or air terminal conductors (lightning-rod conductors) shall not be employed as electrodes for protectors.

Summary of Change
A new subdivision, Section 800.100(B), has been added, and wording has been revised in the existing text.

800.156 Dwelling Unit Communications Outlet

At least one communications outlet shall be provided in all new dwelling unit construction.

The wiring for this communication outlet shall be routed to the service provider demarcation point of the dwelling unit.

800.156

Dwelling Unit Communications Outlet
NEC, p. 655

Proposal 16-207
Log 2655
ROP, p. 931

Comment
None

Analysis and Effect

While it is a common practice to include communications systems wiring and outlets in dwellings, there have not been any mandatory requirements in the *Code* for such wiring or outlets. This new section requires at least one communications outlet and associated wiring to be installed in all new construction of dwelling units. It is very common to include several communications outlets in dwelling unit construction. Substantiation provided with the proposal indicated that at least one communications outlet in the home is needed for many reasons, but most important is for emergency services such as a simple call for police, fire or rescue squad. In addition to the problem it solves for communications needs for occupants of a dwelling, the proposal also targets safety of technicians and emergency responding personnel while enhancing the five key NFPA strategies to reduce fatal home fires. The new definition of *dwelling unit* in Article 100 clarifies where this requirement must be applied. Direction for installers included in this requirement calls for the rough wiring for this communications outlet to be routed to the service provider demarcation point of the dwelling unit.

Change at a Glance

For new dwelling units, a minimum of one communications outlet shall be installed within the dwelling and cabled to the service provider demarcation point.

Code Language
800.156

Dwelling Unit Communications Outlet

For new construction, a minimum of one communications outlet shall be installed within the dwelling and cabled to the service provider demarcation point.

Summary of Change

New Section 800.156 has been added to Article 800.

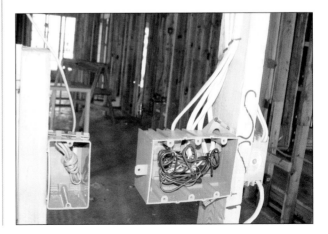

8

810.21(D)

Mechanical Protection
NEC, p. 660

Proposal 16-235
Log 857
ROP, p. 938

Comment
None

Analysis and Effect

Grounding and bonding of radio and telephone systems to the building or structure electrical system and connecting them to earth is a critical component of electrical safety, as is assuring that the grounding conductor(s) for all types of radio, telephone, and other communications systems are protected from physical damage so that the bonding and earthing connections are maintained. *Code* language in this section has been changed to promote consistency, to be less subjective, and to provide a clearer and more enforceable requirement.

The question often came up in the field — "How much is the grounding conductor to be increased proportionately in size for this instance, where it may be subject to physical damage?" This improvement settles that question, and is a companion proposal to the ones found in Sections 800.100(A)(6), 820.100(A)(6), and 830.100(A)(6).

Code Language
810.21(D)
Mechanical Protection
The grounding conductor shall be protected where exposed to physical damage. Where the grounding conductor is run in a metal raceway, both ends of the raceway shall be bonded to the grounding conductor or to the same terminal or electrode to which the grounding conductor is connected.

Summary of Change
The words "or the size of the grounding conductors shall be increased proportionally to compensate for the lack of protection" have been removed from the section.

Change at a Glance

No longer required to increase the size of the grounding conductor proportionately to compensate for the lack of protection when the grounding conductor is subject to physical damage and not protected from same.

810.21(F)(2)(6) Bonding Device

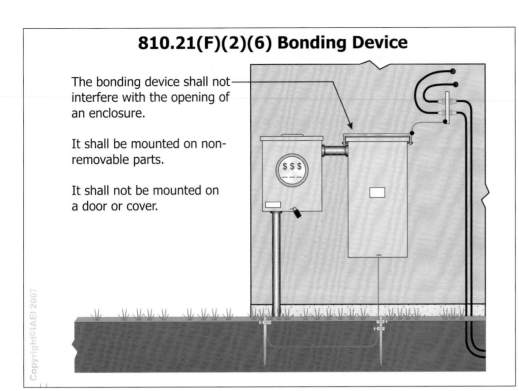

The bonding device shall not interfere with the opening of an enclosure.

It shall be mounted on non-removable parts.

It shall not be mounted on a door or cover.

Copyright©IAEI 2007

Grounding Conductors – Receiving Stations
NEC, p. 660

Proposal 16-237
Log 1992
ROP, p. 939

Comment 16-188
Log 183
ROC, p. 551

Analysis and Effect

Concerns were raised by the submitter of the proposal relating to what was considered poor grounding practices by some persons or entities that install and/or maintain CATV, telephone, satellite and other communication systems. Installation of termination devices that clamp to enclosure covers have resulted in interruption of grounding continuity. This may occur when access is needed into enclosures and these types of termination devices are either improperly installed or re-installed; or they are not replaced at all after access is gained and the enclosure is (hopefully) re-closed. Bonding of all radio, television, and other types of communication systems to the electrical system is essential for electrical safety at a building or structure.

This is a companion proposal to proposals to add this requirement to 800.100(B), 820.100(B), and 830.100(B).

Change at a Glance

Intersystem bonding device(s) shall be installed only on non-removable parts of a metal enclosure or raceway, and shall not interfere with the opening of the equipment enclosures.

Code Language
810.21

Grounding Conductors – Receiving Stations
(F)(2) In Building or Structures with Grounding Means.
(6) The grounding electrode conductor or the grounding electrode conductor metal enclosures.

A bonding device intended to provide a termination point for the grounding conductor (intersystem bonding) shall not interfere with the opening of an equipment enclosure. A bonding device shall be mounted on non-removable parts. A bonding device shall not be mounted on a door or cover even if the door or cover is non-removable.

Summary of Change

The connection requirements for grounding at receiving stations have been revised.

820.93(C) and (D) Locations

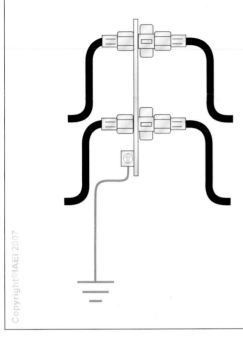

A listed primary protector is required on each community antenna and radio distribution CATV cable external to the premises.

The listed protector shall be located as close as practicable to the entrance point of the cable to the building.

The listed protector shall be located on either side of the grounding block, or integral to the grounding block.

The primary protector shall not be located in a hazardous location or in the vicinity of easily ignitible material.

Copyright©IAEI 2007

820.93 [C] & [D]

Location and Hazardous (Classified) Locations
NEC, p. 664

Proposal 16-289
Log 73
ROP, p. 953

Comment 16-225, 16-226, 16-227
Log 191, 192, 563
ROC, p. 560

Analysis and Effect

Due to changes in technology and improved communication services, this proposal was accepted to require listed primary protectors for outdoor CATV and radio distribution cables that enter buildings. VoIP (voice over internet protocol) services are being delivered by CATV (community antenna television) and radio distribution systems, both of which fall under Article 820. These systems provide internet services and may include the provision for telephone service as well. Information submitted with the proposal voiced concerns that primary protection should be required for VoIP systems because when one is using a telephone headset, a potential safety hazard exists from high voltage surges, such as lightning strikes, that could travel on phone lines and injure people using the phone. It was also pointed out that primary protection is already required for network-powered and communications circuits found in Articles 800 and 830. Article 820 systems were previously not required to have the protection.

In addition, information provided by the submitter indicated that it is possible for third parties to deliver VoIP over Article 820 systems without the knowledge or approval of the carrier. The point was made that primary protection should be required on all Article 820 systems, whether or not the carrier is providing VoIP services. It is now clear to installers and inspectors that for communication, CATV and radio distribution, and network-powered broadband systems, listed primary protectors will be required for outdoor cables that enter buildings. A new subdivision (D) was added to prohibit the primary protector or the equipment providing the primary protection from being located in a hazardous (classified) location as described in 500.5 or in the vicinity of easily ignitible materials.

> ### Change at a Glance
>
> Listed primary protectors are now required for outdoor CATV and radio distribution cables that enter buildings.

Code Language
820.93(C)
Location

Where installed, a listed primary protector shall be applied on each community antenna and radio distribution (CATV) cable external to the premises. The listed primary protector shall be located as close as practicable to the entrance point of the cable on either side or integral to the ground block.

(D)
Hazardous (Classified) Locations

Where a primary protector or equipment providing the primary protection function is used, it shall not be located in any hazardous (classified) location as defined in 500.5 or in the vicinity of easily ignitible material.

Exception: As permitted in 501.150, 502.150, and 503.150.

Summary of Change

New subdivisions have been added to Section 820.93.

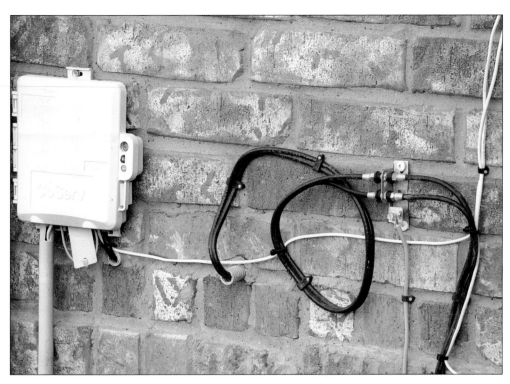

Cable Grounding
NEC, p. 664

Proposal 16 -295
Log 851
ROP, p. 954

Comment
None

Analysis and Effect

The words "as suitable for the purpose" have been deleted from the text, because listed insulated conductors are currently being used for this purpose, and there do not appear to be insulated conductors that are listed specifically for the purpose of accomplishing the grounding required by this section.

Along with the other requirements in Section 820.100(A), this change clarifies that insulated copper conductors which are 14 AWG and larger, installed (run) in a straight line, not over 6.0 m. (20 ft) in length (or less), and protected from physical damage are required to be connected to the intersystem bonding termination location in accordance with Section 800.100(B), in order to bond the CATV system to the building or structure electrical

Change at a Glance

The grounding (and bonding) conductor for CATV systems is required to be insulated and listed.

power system and all other communication systems for the structure.

Code Language
820.100

Cable Grounding
The shield of the coaxial cable shall be grounded as specified in 820.100(A) through (D).

(A) Grounding Conductor

(1) Insulation. The grounding conductor shall be insulated and shall be listed.

Summary of Change

The words "as suitable for the purpose" have been deleted from the text.

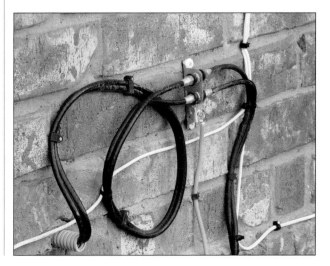

830.24

Mechanical Execution of Work
NEC, p. 669

Proposal 16-372
Log 1390
ROP, p. 977

Comment
None

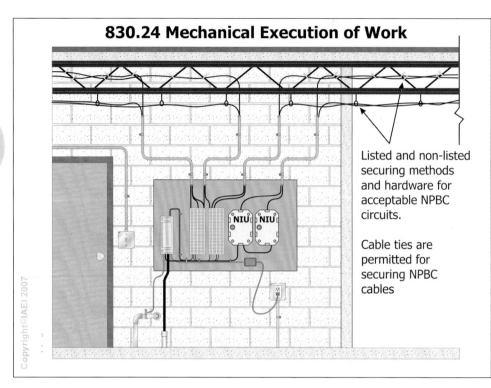

830.24 Mechanical Execution of Work

Listed and non-listed securing methods and hardware for acceptable NPBC circuits.

Cable ties are permitted for securing NPBC cables

Copyright©IAEI 2007

Change at a Glance

Cable ties are now recognized as a means of securement for NPBCS cables.

Analysis and Effect

Action by CMP-16 originally created a listing requirement for all supporting hardware and fittings, including straps, staples, cable ties, hangers, or similar fittings which support network-powered broadband communications. As an end result of the process, both listed and unlisted support and securement methods are acceptable. Though often used as a support method for network-powered broadband communication system cables, cable ties were not specifically mentioned in the *Code* but are now recognized in this section.

These support methods are called "positioning devices" in applicable product standards. Listed devices are evaluated using UL 1565, Standard for Positioning Devices. The scope of the standard states, "This standard applies to those metallic and nonmetallic devices used for positioning—which may include bundling and securing—or to a limited extent supporting cable, wire, conduit, or tubing of a wiring system in electrical installations to reduce the risk of fire, electric shock, or injury to persons." The Guide Information for product category ZODZ, Wire Positioning Devices, states, "The investigation of these products includes consideration of the rated mechanical strength, maximum operating temperature, smoke and heat generation, corrosion resistance and weatherability characteristics as appropriate for the product." In response to panel action, the comments raised concerns about the safety of cable ties installed and used in air handling spaces such as plenums, for their possible toxicity and fire resistance rating—as most cable ties commonly used are nonmetallic. Concerns were also raised with the mechanical strength of these devices, such as minimum loop tensile strength. The panel response was that these concerns are addressed in the product standards. Requirements for the distance of spacing between cable supports was not addressed, as they are in chapter 3 of the *Code*. CMP-16 clarified that securing an additional cable to an existing cable does not constitute support. Additional cables must be directly supported by the same structural member that supports the first cable. The requirements of 300.4(D) and 300.11(C) are applicable to network-powered broadband cables. The text clarifies for installers and inspectors that cable ties are permitted for use, and it gives further installation guidelines for supports per *NEC* 300.4(D) and 300.11. Similar provisions have been included in other limited-energy articles in chapters 7 and 8, recognizing cable ties as a means of securement and support.

Code Language

830.24

Mechanical Execution of Work

Network-powered broadband communications circuits and equipment shall be installed in a neat and workman-like manner. Cables installed exposed on the surface of ceilings and sidewalls shall be supported by the building structure in such a manner that the network-powered broadband communications cables will not be damaged by normal building use. Such cables shall be secured by hardware including straps, staples, cable ties, hangers, or similar fittings designed and installed so as not to damage the cable. The installation shall also conform to 300.4(D) and 300.11.

Summary of Change

"Cable ties" have been added to the text as a permitted support method.

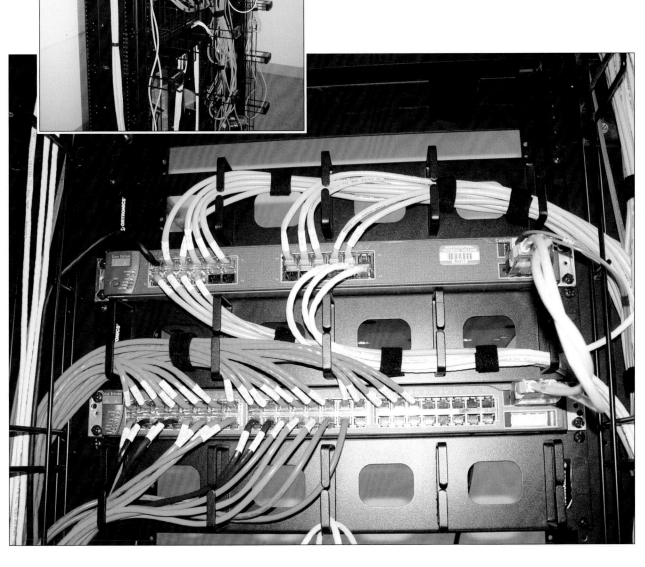

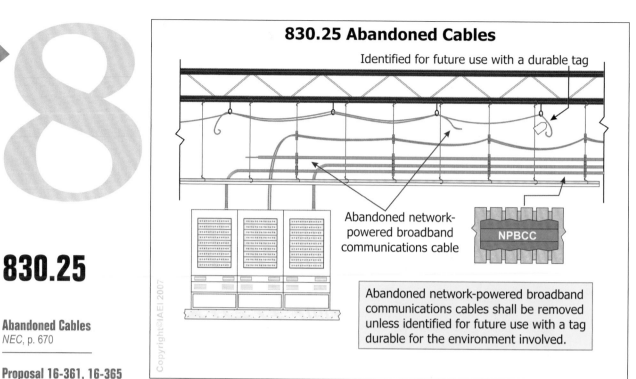

830.25 Abandoned Cables

Identified for future use with a durable tag

Abandoned network-powered broadband communications cable

NPBCC

Abandoned network-powered broadband communications cables shall be removed unless identified for future use with a tag durable for the environment involved.

Copyright©IAEI 2007

830.25

Abandoned Cables
NEC, p. 670

Proposal 16-361, 16-365
Log 787, 3315
ROP, p. 974, 975

Comment
None

Analysis and Effect

A requirement to remove abandoned cables has been relocated to 830.25. In *NEC*-2005, abandoned cables were defined in Section 830.2, and 830.3(A) required those in accessible areas to be removed. Particularly in older buildings, cables may have been installed unsupported and in a non-workmanlike manner. Abandoned cables provide material that may be fuel for a fire, and they raise safety issues for building occupants because of possible toxic gasses being released if the cable becomes engulfed in flames. Unlisted or unevaluated cables, in particular, can be a serious health or fire risk. Fire-rated walls, floors, or ceilings may have been breached or penetrated, with no understanding or regard for proper sealing to prevent the spread of fire or particles of combustion.

There are also issues related to the weight of the accumulated cable(s), with the possible failure of suspended ceiling systems or components, or building-related structural or other system failures. Abandoned cables also may restrict or hamper access for workers who install, repair, or maintain building systems. This change places the requirement to remove accessible abandoned cables near the requirements for the work to be installed in a neat and workmanlike manner. Persons who install and maintain these cables must be made aware of the *Code* requirements, and the reason behind them. Judgment as to which areas are considered accessible, and how far the removal of abandoned cables will go rests with the inspection authority.

Code Language
830.25
Abandoned Cables
The accessible portion of abandoned network-powered broadband cables shall be removed. Where cables are identified for future use with a tag, the tag shall be of sufficient durability to withstand the environment involved.

Summary of Change
The requirements to remove abandoned NPBC cables has been moved from 830.3(A) and added to new Section 830.25 and expanded.

Change at a Glance

It is now clear that accessible abandoned NPBC cables must be removed unless tagged for future use.

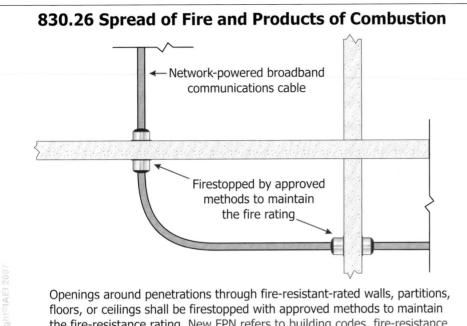

830.26 Spread of Fire and Products of Combustion

← Network-powered broadband communications cable

Firestopped by approved methods to maintain the fire rating

Openings around penetrations through fire-resistant-rated walls, partitions, floors, or ceilings shall be firestopped with approved methods to maintain the fire-resistance rating. New FPN refers to building codes, fire-resistance directories, and product listings.

Copyright©IAEI 2007

830.26

Spread of Fire or Products of Combustion
NEC, p. 670

Proposal 16-361, 16-365, 16-378
Log 787, 3315, 57
ROP, p. 975, 979

Comment
None

Analysis and Effect

Requirements for firestopping and otherwise sealing of fire penetrations have been relocated from Section 830.3(A) to 830.26. The CMP-16 Editorial Task Group submitted proposals in order to place requirements in more appropriate sections, to improve parallelism between *Code* articles under their purview, to make articles as self-sufficient as possible, and to improve the language in difficult to read sections. The requirements for sealing fire penetrations were relocated to improve usability for communications installers, many of whom, until recent years, were unaware of *Code* requirements for cable installations, including firestopping penetrations through fire-rated walls, ceilings, and floors.

Change at a Glance

Firestopping requirements for NPBC systems are now found in Section 830.26.

Summary of Change

Requirements to seal fire penetrations have been moved from 830.3(A) to 830.26.

Code Language

830.26

Spread of Fire or Products of Combustion

Installations of network-powered broadband cables in hollow spaces, vertical shafts, and ventilation or air-handling ducts shall be made so that the possible spread of fire or products of combustion will not be substantially increased. Openings around penetrations of network-powered broadband cables through fire-resistant–rated walls, partitions, floors, or ceilings shall be firestopped using approved methods to maintain the fire resistance rating.

FPN: Directories of electrical construction materials published by qualified testing laboratories contain many listing installation restrictions necessary to maintain the fire-resistive rating of assemblies where penetrations or openings are made. Building codes also contain restrictions on membrane penetrations on opposite sides of a fire-resistance–rated wall assembly. An example is the 600-mm (24-in.) minimum horizontal separation that usually applies between boxes installed on opposite sides of the wall. Assistance in complying with 830.26 can be found in building codes, fire resistance directories, and product listings.

Chapter

g

Selected
• • • • • • • •
Changes

Chapter 9

Table 1, Note 9

Percent of Cross Section of Conduit and Tubing for Conductors
NEC, 680

Proposal 8-200
Log 1840
ROP, p. 990

Comment 8-87
Log 525
ROC, p. 583

Chapter 9, Table 1, Note (9)

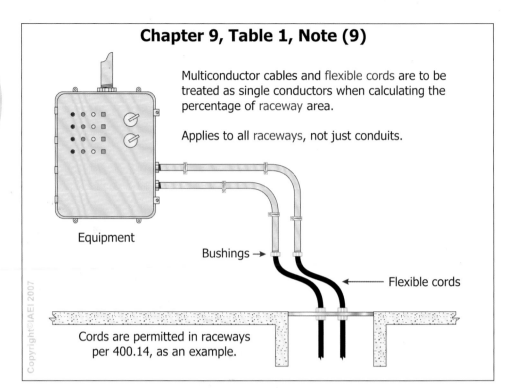

Multiconductor cables and flexible cords are to be treated as single conductors when calculating the percentage of raceway area.

Applies to all raceways, not just conduits.

Equipment

Bushings →

← Flexible cords

Cords are permitted in raceways per 400.14, as an example.

Copyright©IAEI 2007

Analysis and Effect

Action by CMP-8 resulted in the addition of flexible cords to note (9) to Table 1 in chapter 9. A few provisions within the *NEC* permit flexible cords to be installed in complete raceways, for example, 400.14 allows this for industrial installation under certain conditions. Previous editions of the *NEC* did not address conduit fill percentages where cords are installed within conduits or other raceways. This change clarifies that where other provisions of the *Code* permit flexible cords in raceways, the method of calculating the percentage of fill is the same as that required for multiconductor cables, and the flexible cords are treated as a single conductor in this sense. Note (9) to Table 1 has also been revised to apply to all raceways, not just to conduits.

Change at a Glance

Multiconductor cables and flexible cords are to be treated as single conductors when calculating the percentage of raceway area.

Code Language

Chapter 9, Table 1, Note (9)
Percent of Cross Section of Conduit and Tubing for Conductors
A multiconductor cable or flexible cord of two or more conductors shall be treated as a single conductor for calculating percentage conduit fill area. For cables or cords that have elliptical cross sections, the cross-sectional area calculation shall be based on using the major diameter of the ellipse as a circle diameter.

Summary of Change

The words "or flexible cords" have been incorporated into Note (9) to Table 1.

Chapter 9, Table 4 (in part)

Article 352 - Rigid PVC Conduit (PVC) Schedule 80
Articles 352 and 353 - Rigid PVC Conduit (PVC) Schedule 40, and HDPE Conduit (HDPE)
Article 352 - Type A, Rigid PVC Conduit (PVC)
Article 352 - Type EB, Rigid PVC Conduit (PVC)

The term *rigid nonmetallic conduit* changed to *rigid PVC conduit* Code-wide.

Table 4

Dimensions and Percent Area of Conduit and Tubing
NEC, 680–685

Proposal 8-204a
Log 1937
ROP, p. 990

Comment 8-88
Log 1383
ROC, p. 584

Analysis and Effect

Article 352 and the title of the article have been revised to remove references to *rigid nonmetallic conduit* (RNC) and to replace that term with *rigid PVC conduit* (PVC). The change resulted from action by CMP-8 on proposal 8-53. In the 2005 *NEC* development process, high-density polyethylene conduit Type HDPE was removed from Article 352 and placed in a new Article 353. CMP-8 acted favorably to Proposal 8-78 to include requirements for reinforced thermosetting resin conduit Type RTRC, another nonmetallic conduit that was not thoroughly addressed in previous editions of the *NEC*. Because Article 353 for HDPE was developed in *NEC*-2005, and Article 355 for RTRC was developed for *NEC*-2008, it logically follows that Article 352 is now providing only the requirements for rigid PVC conduit (PVC). Other types of nonmetallic conduits are covered within their respective articles. The new FPN following 352.1 refers users to Article 353 for HDPE and to Article 355 for RTRC. The changes to the titles of Table 4 correlate with the revisions in Article 352 and remove the references to rigid nonmetallic conduit.

Change at a Glance

Rigid nonmetallic conduit covered by Article 352 is now referred to as rigid PVC conduit (PVC).

Code Language

Table 4 Titles (in part):

Article 352 – Rigid PVC Conduit (PVC), Schedule 80

Articles 352 and 353 – Rigid PVC Conduit, Schedule 40, and HDPE Conduit (HDPE)

Article 352 – Type A, Rigid PVC Conduit (PVC)

Article 352 – Type EB, Rigid PVC Conduit (PVC)

Summary of Change

The titles to Table 4 covering rigid nonmetallic conduits (RNC) have been changed to reference rigid (PVC) conduit.

Chapter D

Selected Changes

Annex D

Example D3(a)

D

Example D3(a) Annex D

Industrial Feeders in a Common Raceways
NEC, 777

**Proposal 2-166, 2-275
Log 1319, 1322**
ROP, p. 95, 116

Comment
None

Change at a Glance

Neutral conductors are permitted to be sized at 100% of the continuous and non-continuous loads when not connected to an overcurrent device. The minimum size of the neutral conductor must be sufficient for the load (220.61) and must meet the minimum sizes required in 250.122 to protect against line-to-neutral short-circuit events as provided in the example.

Example D3(a) Annex D

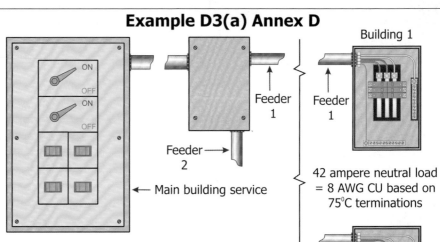

In a line-to-neutral short circuit, the 8 AWG would not be adequate based on a 150-amp overcurrent device on each feeder.

Therefore, a 6 AWG CU neutral conductor is required because that is minimum required EGC based on Table 250.122.

Feeder 1
Feeder 2
Main building service

Building 1
Feeder 1

42 ampere neutral load = 8 AWG CU based on 75°C terminations

Feeder 2
Building 2

Copyright IAEI 2007

Analysis and Effect

New exceptions to 210.19(A)(1) and 215.2(A)(1) allow the neutral conductors of branch circuits and feeders to be sized at 100% of the continuous and non-continuous connected loads. These exceptions apply when the neutral conductors do not terminate in an overcurrent device. The revision to Example D3(a) correlates with the new exceptions and provides important information about the minimum required sizes for grounded (neutral) conductors. In the neutral sizing exercise in the last paragraph of the example, an 8 AWG would be sufficient for a calculated load of 42 amperes. However, the feeders to the two separate buildings are each protected by a 150-ampere overcurrent device. In the case of a line-to-neutral short-circuit event, the neutral conductor would not be sufficient to facilitate a 150-ampere overcurrent device, therefore the neutral must be a minimum of 6 AWG in accordance with 250.122.

Summary of Change

The last paragraph of Example D3(a) in Annex D has been revised to correlate with new Exception No. 3 to 210.19(A)(1) and the new Exception to 215.2(A)(1).

Code Language

Annex D3(a)

Industrial Feeders in a Common Raceways

Example D3(a) [last paragraph only]
Because the neutral runs between the main switchboard and the building panelboard, likely terminating on a busbar at both locations, and not on overcurrent devices, the effects of continuous loading can be disregarded in evaluating its terminations (see 215.2(A)(1) Exception No. 2). That calculation is (11,600 VA ÷ 277 V) = 42 amperes, to be evaluated under the 75°C column of Table 310.16. The minimum size of the neutral might seem to be 8 AWG, but that size would not be sufficient to be depended upon in the event of a line-to-neutral short circuit [see 215.2(A)(1), second paragraph]. Therefore, since the minimum size equipment grounding conductor for a 150-ampere circuit, as covered in Table 250.122, is 6 AWG, that is the minimum neutral size required for this feeder.

Becoming a member of IAEI automatically links you to a network of experts in the electrical industry

Because of its reputation for fairness and code-compliance, IAEI has long been a strong leader in the industry and has played a cohesive role among testing agencies, standards organizations, manufacturers, distributors, and contractors.

Membership in IAEI gives you access to these leaders and experts.

IAEI makes the top experts available to speak on the latest code changes

Sign up online and become a member immediately, or return the application to:

P. O. Box 830848 • Richardson, TX 75083-0848

MEMBERSHIP APPLICATION *PLEASE PRINT*

Name - Last _____ First _____ M.I. _____

Title _____

Employer _____

Address of Applicant _____

City	State or Province	ZIP or Postal Code

Chapter, where you live or work, if known	(Division, where appropriate)

For Office Use	Section	Chapter No.	Division No.

If previous member, give last membership number and last year of membership.

_____

Endorsed by _____ Endorser's Membership Number

_____

Applicant's Signature

_____

(Area Code) Telephone Number

☐ MasterCard ☐ Visa ☐ AMEX ☐ Money Order
☐ Discover ☐ Diners Club ☐ Check

Name on Card _____

Charge Card Number _____ Expiration Date

☐ Inspector $90   ☐ Associate $90

Inspector Member MUST sign below:

I, _____
meet the qualification for inspector member as described below.

Inspector members must regularly make electrical inspections for preventing injury to persons or damage to property on behalf of a governmental agency, insurance agency, rating bureau, recognized testing laboratory or electric light and power company.

Contact IAEI customer service department for information on our other membership categories – Section, National and International Member; Sustaining Member (Bronze, Silver, Gold, or Platinum); and Inspection Agency Member.

Mail to: IAEI, P.O. Box 830848, Richardson, TX 75083-0848
For information call: (972) 235-1455 (8–5 CST) Analysis 08

Contributing Developer	Michael J. Johnston	
Contributors	Michael J. Johnston	Michael K. Weitzel
Technical Review	Michael J. Johnston L. Keith Lofland Jeff Sargent	James W. Carpenter Mark Earley Michael K. Weitzel
Illustration Concepts	Michael J. Johnston L. Keith Lofland	Michael K. Weitzel
Photographs by	Ardee Lighting Bill McGovern, City of Plano, TX Cantex Fote-duct Carlon, Lamson and Sessions Don Offerdahl Erico International Flowserve Corporation FRE Composites Fred Hartwell Georgia Power, Roger McDaniel IAEI Archives IdleAire Technologies Corporation Rick Maddox Thomas and Betts Michael K. Weitzel	Jim Conrad, Tyco Thermal Controls John Watson Keith Lofland Leviton Manufacturing Co., Inc., Ken Vannice Mark Hilbert Michael J. Johnston Pass and Seymour/Legrand Ron Janikowski Schneider Electric/Square D Company Southwire Company, Inc. Thomas Garvey Underwriters Laboratories, Inc. John Wiles ThyssenKrupp Access The Austin Co.
Technical Drawings	Michael J. Johnston	L. Keith Lofland
Design by	John Watson	
Graphic Production	John Watson	Laura Hildreth
Technical Editor	Michael J. Johnston	
Managing Editor	Kathryn P. Ingley	
Editor in Chief	James W. Carpenter	

IAEI representatives to 2008 NEC Code-Making Panels:

CMP-1   Lanny McMahill and Russ Helmick
CMP-2   Ray Weber and Bill McGovern
CMP-3   Richard Owen and Robert Walsh
CMP-4   James Rogers and Mark Hilbert
CMP-5   Michael Johnston and David Williams
CMP-6   Oran Post and John Stacey
CMP-7   Gaylen Rogers and James Hinrichs
CMP-8   David Humphrey and James Imlah
CMP-9   Robert McCullough and Donald Offerdahl
CMP-10 Gerald Williams and Robert Kauer

CMP-11 Robert Fahey and Thomas Moore
CMP-12 Ron Janikowski and Tim McClintock
CMP-13 Tarry Baker and Ron Chilton
CMP-14 Donald Cook and Larry Fuhrman
CMP-15 Eugene Moran and Marcus R. Sampson
CMP-16 Larry Chan and Robert McGann
CMP-17 Robert Milatovich and Jim Maldonado
CMP-18 Timothy Owens and Amos Lowrance
CMP-19 Monte R. Ewing and Joseph Bolesina
CMP-20 Tarry Baker and Timothy Owens

Composed at International Association of Electrical Inspectors in Adobe Garamond Pro, Gil Sans Standard, Helvetica, Folio and Times New Roman PS by Adobe® and Arial Narrow by TrueType®.

Printed by The Odee Company on 70# Book. Bound in 12 pt. Kallima Cover.

To order additional copies of this book, specify item 361014. Order online at IAEI.org or by phoning 800-786-4234.